D1158346

JOHN WILKINS
1614-1672

Portrait of John Wilkins
by Mary Beale (Wadham College)

JOHN WILKINS
1614-1672

An Intellectual
Biography

BARBARA J. SHAPIRO

UNIVERSITY OF CALIFORNIA PRESS

BERKELEY AND LOS ANGELES 1969

University of California Press
Berkeley and Los Angeles, California
University of California Press, Ltd.
London, England
Copyright © 1969 by
The Regents of the University of California
Library of Congress Catalog Card Number: 73-84042
Printed in the United States of America

For my Mother and Father

Preface

I am indebted to a number of persons and institutions for their help in completing this study. Mark Curtis first introduced me to the general problem of seventeenth-century English intellectual history and has subsequently given me much aid and encouragement. Myron Gilmore provided the necessary perspective of broader Renaissance studies and W. K. Jordan read the whole of an earlier version of the manuscript. The authorities of Wadham College, Oxford, Trinity College, Cambridge, the Royal Society, Dr. Williams Library, the Cheshire Record Office, the Borthwick Institute, Chester Cathedral, York Cathedral, the Guildhall Library, Lambeth Palace, the Public Record Office, and the University of Amsterdam graciously allowed me to work in their manuscript collections. The editors of *Past and Present* have permitted me to draw on an article of mine originally published there; and the Warden and Fellows of Wadham College have given permission to reproduce the portrait of Wilkins. The resources of the Huntington, William Andrews Clark, British Museum, Bodleian, and Harvard libraries proved essential. Pitzer College, the Claremont Colleges, provided funds to cover the costs of preparing the manuscript, and my husband provided editorial services without which there would have been nothing to prepare.

Contents

Introduction

As John Wilkins lay dying in the fall of 1672, a constant stream of friends and associates brought comfort and advice. Joseph Glanvill, like Wilkins a leading advocate of latitudinarian religion and the new philosophy, urged him to take "Oyster shells 4 red hot quenched in cyder a quart," and Jonathan Goddard, the physician, recommended "Blisters of cantharide apply'd to the neck or to the veins." Robert Hooke, already famous for his *Micrographia,* came almost every day. The naturalist John Ray hurried to London as soon as he heard of Wilkins's illness. His visitors reported that the Bishop of Chester regretted only that he would leave unfinished "his darling," as he called the artificial language he hoped to perfect, and that he appeared to take comfort from his past "healing Endeavours" in the church. Indeed, "He seem'd not to be much surprised, at the news of his Death, but say'd he was prepared for the great Experiment." *

Rather a strange turn of phrase for an Anglican bishop, and rather a strange collection of friends and last regrets. The Bishop of Chester, however, was no ordinary bishop. The mixed company of scientists, clergymen, and politicians who attended him in his dying days, apparently more curious about his "supression of the Urine" than the state of his soul, testifies to a life richly led both within and, more often, without the Anglican hierarchy. For Wilkins had been in turn or in tandem theologian, scientific experimenter, Warden of Wadham College, Oxford, science-fiction writer, linguist, encyclopedist, scientific entrepreneur and admin-

---

* All annotation will be found in the Notes section at the back of the book, pp. 251–320, where notes are keyed to the text by page and line number. Asterisks indicate the more important notes.

istrator, bishop, politician, and preacher. To say his fifty-eight years had been full ones would be to understate the case. It is not the fullness of his years, however, but their peculiar richness that makes John Wilkins a figure worthy of historical attention. Grant McColley once wrote that "When a complete biography is prepared, it will be found, I suspect, that John Wilkins was the most dynamic force in seventeenth-century England." His choice of words is apt. Not the greatest mind or the most influential scholar of the century, rarely a central figure in the political area, Wilkins nevertheless seems to have played a key role in each of the movements to reform and liberalize English intellectual life: first, the change from an authoritarian, dogmatic religious outlook to the more liberal, rationalistic credo of Restoration and eighteenth-century England; second, the scientific revolution that during the course of the century replaced the average man's traditional concept of the cosmos with that of Copernicus and to a more mechanistic concept of nature based on the findings of natural science; and third, though less important, the adaptation of simpler modes of intellectual communication.

Although not himself a major scientific innovator, Wilkins's popularizations of science were among the most widely read scientific works of the day in England. He was the nucleus of the group that for some years made Oxford the scientific center of the nation. And he was one of the principal founders and supporters of Oxford's successor as the national center of scientific learning, the Royal Society. In short, during and after the Civil War, Wilkins was England's single most influential and effective organizer and purveyor of the scientific culture.

He played a strikingly similar role in the movement to liberalize religious thought, practice, and regulation. Wilkins was the organizer of the best known, most vocal latitudinarian religious group in Restoration England, a key political negotiator in the efforts to achieve the comprehension of dissident groups in the Church of England, and one of the half dozen major literary exponents of "natural religion," a key doctrinal weapon in the fight to end decades of religious squabbling.

More than any other man, Wilkins was responsible for transforming the plain style of preaching from a Puritan protest into a national tradition. He brought this same concern for clarity to the scientific community, in part through his widely known works on a universal character and language.

Behind Wilkins's dynamism lay a remarkable ability to be in the right place at the right time, or perhaps to create the right place and time for furthering his religious and scholarly goals. As a young chaplain he was a retainer of the Pym group when it was seeking a compromise that would maintain the monarchy but reform the polity. During the Interregnum he moved from nobleman's retainer to Protector's brother-in-law, and became Warden of an Oxford college where he could shelter scientists from civil strife, no matter what their religious and political persuasions. At the Restoration, when the center of scientific activity returns to London, Wilkins is happily situated there to foster the Royal Society. Within a few years we find him, albeit still Cromwell's brother-in-law, increasingly influential in court circles and in possession of one of London's most important pulpits. Finally, when he lost his pulpit in the Great Fire, he finished his career as bishop of a diocese in which he could practice the latitudinarianism he had preached, with a seat in the House of Lords from which to fight for more liberal ecclesiastical laws. Moreover, at Oxford, in London, and as Bishop of Chester, and in spite of his personal ups and downs, Wilkins was generally in a position to reward, publicize, and support men who shared his scientific and religious views and organize them into groups whose collective intellectual impact far surpassed that of their individual efforts.

Wilkins owed his central role in part to personal charm and organizational skill. He seems to have had a unique talent for enlisting friendly cooperation among the best brains of his day in the face of bitter ideological, social, and political conflicts. But these personal qualities alone cannot explain his catalytic effect on the intellectual life of his time. More important were his firm grasp of the central problem of seventeenth-century English intellectual life—the achievement of a *modus vivendi* between knowledge and faith that would allow the tentative pragmatic tone of science to soften the dogmatism of English religious life—and his unremitting efforts to resolve that problem. Wilkins played a considerable part in fostering the mid-seventeenth-century alliance between the scientific movement, natural religion, and latitudinarianism. His main contribution to this alliance was probably methodological; he insisted on a nondogmatic approach toward both religious and scientific inquiry, and on the direct and simple presentation of the results of such inquiry.

As a central figure in this movement for intellectual reform, Wilkins quite naturally became a target of criticism. His popularizations of science were attacked both by scientific conservatives and by those who viewed the new science as a threat to classical learning and the authority of Scripture. His moderation and latitudinarianism inspired Puritan attacks during the Interregnum and High Church hostility during the Restoration. Hostility from both ends of the religious spectrum was further aggravated by the pattern of Wilkins's career. The moderate religious views that enabled him to comply with whatever religious establishment held sway and to accept office from whatever government was in power seemed like opportunism to those whose more extreme principles barred cooperation with their opponents. And once in office, his moderate views generally led him to protect the current losers in the religious struggle, which seemed like betrayal to the extremists in the party that had appointed him.

Because Wilkins was such a controversial figure, contemporary accounts of his religious and political views and activities rarely come from impartial observers. For instance, High Church commentators wrote in the context of Wilkins's attempts at toleration and comprehension during the Restoration; thus Anthony Wood, and Bishops Fell, Morley, Sheldon, Hackett, and Cosin derogate

Wilkins's abilities and motives. Restoration latitudinarians like John Tillotson, William Lloyd, Gilbert Burnet, and Peter Pett, most of whom belonged to Wilkins's personal circle, naturally defended him.* Much the same thing occurs in relation to Wilkins's scientific activities. Scientists like Robert Hooke, John Wallis, Seth Ward, Christopher Wren, and Huygens, most of whom were Wilkins's friends and many of whom benefited from his organizational abilities usually praised him, whereas Henry Stubbe, Alexander Ross, and others opposed to the new science naturally attacked Wilkins, as one of its leading spokesmen.

Thus there was considerable comment on Wilkins during his own lifetime, but much of it is unreliable. Interest in Wilkins's writings, particularly those concerning astronomy and the plurality of worlds and natural theology and latitudinarianism continued after his death. Indeed his ideas continued to be current during the early decades of the eighteenth century. Then, as what Wilkins had fought for became the accepted basis of English intellectual life, interest for the most part lapsed, and he was remembered only for his efforts to create a universal language and for his role in organizing the Royal Society.

In recent years, however, Wilkins has received considerable attention. Literary historians, interested in the transformation of prose style during the seventeenth century and in the general shift from poetry to prose as a means of conveying philosophical truth, have found Wilkins a key figure in these changes. Historians of science have also studied Wilkins, primarily in connection with the founding of the Royal Society. But perhaps most attention to Wilkins has come from historians seeking to show a causal relationship between Puritanism and science, an idea that has gained considerable currency since its original presentation in the mid-1930's by Robert K. Merton and Dorothy Stimson.*

Basically the hypothesis of an intimate relationship between Puritanism and the rise of science is an extension of the Weber-Tawney thesis to show that religious beliefs may affect not only economic but other nonspiritual endeavors as well. Perhaps the greatest difficulty in this theory lies in the definitions of Puritanism adopted by Merton and his followers. Merton's nearly all-inclusive definition fails to distinguish between the significant religious groups in seventeenth-century England. To hold that there is a close correlation between Puritanism and science, while including nearly the whole spectrum of English thought under the Puritan rubric, is simply to say that a correlation exists between Englishness and English science. This is true, but not very helpful. If it seems desirable to show the influence of Puritanism, viewed as a unique religious and social ethic, on science, it would seem necessary to define Puritanism in a way that reflects real historical divisions on religious questions. Furthermore, Merton's assumption that all the groups he calls Puritan shared one social ethic makes it difficult to explain a civil war between factions supposedly in essential agreement. Nor does the broadness of his Puritan category accord with his admission that only a small proportion of the population were in fact Puritans. These difficulties are further compounded by his treatment of Puritanism as a static phenomenon, which sometimes leads to the use of nineteenth-century statistics as indices of seventeenth-century conditions.

Miss Stimson, much more aware of the historical setting and development of religious thought, sought to show that moderate Puritans were at the core of the scientific movement. The coupling of "moderate" and "Puritan," however, creates both logical and historical difficulties. In contemporary usage "Puritan" was an expletive that either had no precise meaning or implied the very opposite of moderation. In that sense "moderate Puritan" is a contradiction in terms. Apart from contemporary usage there cannot, of course, be any "true" meaning for a word like Puritan, but only meanings more or less convenient for historical analysis. From this viewpoint Miss Stimson seems to be saying that those "Puritans" who were least differentiated from Anglicans were most involved in science. In effect, those men to whom it is least convenient and enlightening to apply the Puritan label are the ones who lead Miss Stimson to link Puritanism and science.

Miss Stimson further suggested that the right of private judgment and individual interpretation of the Bible was conducive to the scientific spirit. But scientists of the period tended to drift away from any rigid interpretation of the Bible and did not seek Biblical sanctions for church government or for scientific truth; they looked instead for solutions based on reason and experience, hardly the authorities to which Puritans looked for basic truth. In short, the alleged Puritan contribution to rationalism, empiricism, and utilitarianism is very much open to question. It seems likely that these elements were not fundamental to the Puritan movement and in fact entered Puritanism at a rather late stage in its development. It is more probable that the scientific spirit interacted with both Puritanism and Anglicanism during the course of the century. Indeed proponents of the Puritanism and science hypothesis often seem to succumb to the temptation of ascribing characteristics to Puritanism which it acquired during a later period or even as a result of its acceptance of science.

Christopher Hill, a more recent proponent of the ideas of Merton and Stimson, and one who cannot be accused of lacking historical sophistication, insists there is a "formidable amount of evidence" to support the Puritanism-science hypothesis. Like Merton, however, what he is essentially saying is that Englishmen contributed to English science, for he defines Puritanism basically in terms of "doctrine about religion and Church government, aiming at purifying the Church from the inside." Because the Laudians had been moving the church away from its traditional, Elizabethan form, every Englishman who was not a High Churchman favored reform at least in the sense of eliminating some of the Laudian innovations. Typically, Hill centers his discussion on the most Puritan Puritans, thus creating the impression that there was a distinct Puritan group distinguishable from a distinct Anglican group; but when it is convenient for his argument, he begins casting his net widely to include persons and ideas that are Puritan only in the vague "reform" sense, and ends by labeling as Puritan all sorts of men who were simply less High

Church than the Laudians, and intellectual movements in which a broad cross-section of non-Laudian Englishmen participated.

Merton, Stimson, and Hill all uncritically accept a traditional pair of categories, "Puritan" and "Anglican," a pairing that embodies and conceals both considerable vagueness and a major hiatus in historical research and analysis.* The customary equation of Laudianism and Anglicanism has an appealing simplicity, since the High Churchmen do form a relatively distinct group with a relatively distinct ideology. But the next step, which quite naturally follows the Puritan-Anglican dichotomy, is to regard all non-Catholic Englishmen except the Laudians as Puritans. Would it not be more accurate, or at least clearer, to speak of "all non-Laudian Protestants" when we really mean "all non-Laudian Protestants"?—the more so because to all but the most highly specialized historians, the word Puritan evokes a distinct group of English Protestants.

Even more important, the practice of dividing Englishmen into Puritans and Anglicans and equating Anglicanism with Laudianism obscures the existence of a broad middle category of divines, scholars, and politicians who sought mild reforms in the church and favored moderate means of accomplishing them. Some men in this group were Puritans in the sense of sharing the ideas "associated with men like Perkins, Bownde, Preston, Sibbes, Thomas Taylor, William Gouge, Thomas Goodwin, Richard Baxter." Others were Anglicans in the sense of maintaining their basic allegiance to the traditional forms of organization and ceremony in the Church of England. In short, it is possible to speak of moderate Anglicans and moderate Puritans.

It is possible, but is it wise? For attempts to distinguish between moderate Puritans and moderate Anglicans can lead only to protracted and largely pointless hairsplitting. Would it not be wiser, for certain purposes at least, to acknowledge the existence of a group of moderates who cannot be neatly split into Anglican and Puritan camps? I would submit that, once this acknowledgment is made, most of the debate over Puritanism and science will be cleared up, for we shall be able to see that nearly all of the seventeenth-century English scientists and scientific movements are to be found within this moderate category. It is particularly the absence of research on non-Laudian, moderate Anglicans, together with the work of Miss Stimson and others on moderate Puritans, that has obscured the fact that it is the moderation of Puritan moderates, not their Puritanism, that is the key link between science and religion. If we focus on "moderation and science," our attention will be drawn to the core of men and ideas that actually tied religion and science together. We will then be in a position to examine real historical phenomena, instead of simply continuing arguments over labels that are either too rigid, too vague, or too misleading to describe certain important intellectual currents of the seventeenth century.

It is in this light that we must treat Christopher Hill's accusation that the failure of many historians to accept the "convergence" of Puritanism and science is a form of historical nihilism, which rejects sociological interpretations and prefers to view society "in separate self-contained compartments" rather than "as a whole." It is precisely because Puritanism as a category of historical and sociological analysis is likely to misdirect our research and obscure our findings on the very question of the relationships between various aspects of social and intellectual life that it would be better to abandon the category.

Wilkins's activities and writing have frequently been offered as important evidence supporting the connection between Puritanism and science. Curiously enough, Wilkins provides an almost ideal illustration of the difficulties of that hypothesis. In his early life he was under the influence of his grandfather, John Dod—a Puritan to be sure, but one who in his later years emphasized that disputes over doctrine and ritual should be subordinated to church unity and the fostering of practical morality in daily life. Dod's teachings on these questions are practically indistinguishable from those of a group of moderate Anglican reformers, and it is these late teachings that are emphasized by Wilkins.

Wilkins's early patrons were Puritans, his later ones Anglicans. Even his earliest patrons were all members of the Pym group, which sought a series of moderate compromises to avoid civil war, and his later ones, Berkeley and Buckingham, were latitudinarians, active in the politics of religious compromise.

Wilkins himself changed religious allegiances as the regimes in London changed. He was intruded as a "Puritan" in Parliament's reform of Oxford, and then suspected, rightfully, of harboring Anglicans. He ended his career as a bishop in the Church of England, suspected, again rightly, of harboring nonconformists. Indeed his religious stance was so consistently moderate that he was always suspect to both Puritan and Anglican stalwarts. He devoted his later religious career to creating and fostering a latitudinarian movement and a theology of natural religion that would eliminate the issues dividing Anglicans and Puritans. Wilkins is a curiously anomalous figure on whom to base a theory linking Puritanism and science.

His scientific career, too, provides little support for the theory. The link between Wilkins's "Puritanism" and science is the new emphasis on science he fostered at Oxford by gathering a scientific circle about him during his Wardenship of Wadham. But it is by no means clear that the university had been markedly deficient in scientific instruction before Wilkins arrived. Moreover, there is little indication that the Puritan regimes actively sought to introduce more science into the university's curriculum. Third and most important, Wilkins succeeded as a scientific organizer at Oxford by making Wadham a haven for both Puritan and Anglican moderates who came to Oxford and engaged in scientific activities as an escape from the religious factionalism that had engendered and then been fostered by the Puritan revolution. It was this group, again with Wilkins as a central organizer, that under Anglican rule and with the patronage of Charles II became the Royal Society, an institution remarkable for the religious diversity of its membership and for its conscious effort to exclude divisive religious considerations from its scholarly program.

One of the central concerns of the Royal Society, and its predecessors in London and Oxford, was the communication of scientific knowledge. Wilkins himself worked for years on an international scientific language. Thus the English scientific movement conceived of itself as an integral part of the international scientific community, which, if we are to insist on connecting religion and science, we must call both Catholic and Protestant. It therefore seems more appropriate to describe the English scientific movement, and Wilkins's role in it, in terms of moderation, cosmopolitanism, and science, rather than in terms of Puritanism and science.

Any study of John Wilkins must necessarily combine biography and intellectual history, for the essential qualities of his thought often emerge more clearly from his actions than from his writings, and it is in what he did as much as in what he said that he made a significant contribution to English intellectual history. Some of the chapters that follow, therefore, are primarily concerned with the events of Wilkins's life, others with his writings, and a few with both.

I. Early Life and Education

The Wilkins family was a relatively old but not very prominent one in the city and environs of Oxford. On May 28, 1611, Walter Wilkins, a goldsmith, married Jane Dod, the daughter of the famous Puritan divine John Dod. Sometime after their marriage Wilkins and his bride seem to have gone to Northamptonshire, where it is probable that their first son, John Wilkins, was born in 1614. Walter Wilkins had returned to Oxford by 1615, and from 1615 to 1623 was active in the city's government.*

Four other children besides John were born to Jane and Walter Wilkins. A little of the later career of Timothy, the second son, can be traced because he was a drinking companion of Anthony Wood. Of Peter, Jane, and Martha we have little more than baptismal records. Walter Wilkins fell ill in 1623 and died two years later. Shortly thereafter his widow married Francis Pope of Oxford. The Popes had two children, a daughter who evidently did not survive childhood, and a son, Walter Pope, who at various times was very close to John. Wilkins's stepfather did not live long, and his mother died in 1633.

None of the Wilkins children seem to have had any inclination to join their father in goldsmithing, though smithing was a family tradition. John, however, may have picked up certain mechanical interests from his father. Walter Wilkins was known as a "very ingeniouse man [who] had a very Mechanicall head. He was very much for trying Experiments, and his head ran much upon the perpettuall motion."

Part of John's early education may have been undertaken by his grandfather. At the age of nine, however, he was in All Saints parish attending Edward Sylvester's school. Sylvester's grammar school was probably not unusual except that it did produce a fairly large number of prominent intellectuals. Sylvester was known as the university's "common drudge" for his services in writing or correcting the "Latin sermons of certain dull theologists thereof before they were to be delivered at St. Mary's." The school of this "noted Latinist and Grecian" probably emphasized grammar, and Wilkins no doubt learned his Latin thoroughly. It is often assumed that Wilkins's childhood training must have been highly Puritan in tone because of his grandfather's influence, but neither his grammar school education nor his home life with his father fell into any particularly Puritan mold.*

Wilkins entered the university in 1627 when he was thirteen, an early but not exceptional age. He first matriculated at New Inn Hall on May 4, but in October entered Magdalen Hall, receiving his Bachelor of Arts degree there in 1631. It has often been assumed that Wilkins was drawn to the Hall because of its Puritan associations, but his choice may simply have reflected family tradition.

Although his tutor would normally have been of the greatest importance in determining the direction of a student's education, there is no evidence that John Tombes, later famous for his opposition to infant baptism, particularly influenced Wilkins's religious outlook or scientific views. Nor is there anything to suggest that Tombes had any interest in the "new philosophy" so attractive to Wilkins in his university years. Tombes was an able Greek and Hebrew scholar with a "curious, searching piercing wit," himself educated at the Hall, and he no doubt continued Wilkins's education in the more traditional learning.

The decade Wilkins spent at Magdalen was a stormy one, both for Oxford as a whole and the Hall in particular. The university was engaged in the religious turmoil caused by the increasing power of the Laudians. The religious disputes at Oxford were, of course, part and parcel of the broader struggle over who would control Church and State. Control of the university was particularly important; not only did Oxford and Cambridge train the

English clergy, but they molded the minds of an increasing number of the sons of the aristocracy and gentry who would become the governing class. It was for this reason that Parliament was as eager to "depress the Arminian faction" at Oxford and Cambridge as elsewhere in the kingdom.

By the time Wilkins left Oxford in 1637, the Laudians had gained almost complete control. Magdalen Hall was known for its Puritanism in a period when Puritanism, or at least anti-Arminianism, was rapidly losing strength at both universities. It was one of the two Oxford colleges that remained faithful to pre-Laudian Calvinism, and John Wilkinson, an anti-Laudian, remained as head until 1631, when he was dismissed for "misgovernment and countenancing the factious parties." It was not only the Puritans who suffered from the Laudian ascendancy, but the more Calvinist Anglicans as well. At Oxford as elsewhere, when Anglicanism became increasingly identified with Laudianism, the moderates were pushed toward either Puritanism or silence. The conflicts at Oxford were continuous during the 1630's. The success of Laud may have contributed to Wilkins's decision to leave the university in 1637 and seek a clerical rather than academic career.

Wilkins had probably considered an academic career, for the intellectual life certainly appealed to him. He took a Master of Arts degree on July 11, 1634, and about that time became a tutor in Magdalen Hall. Magdalen had only a few members whom we know to have had scientific interests. Walter Charleton, Wilkins's tutee, was one. Others included Thomas Sydenham and Jonathan Goddard, who became one of the founders of the Royal Society. Whatever the scientific opportunities of Magdalen itself, Wilkins became seriously interested in scientific studies and the new philosophy while at the university. Two of his scientific treatises, *Discovery of a New World,* a defense of the new astronomy, and *Mathematical Magick,* a primer on mechanics, were largely composed in his "spare Hours in the University." Just when and how he became familiar with the new developments in astronomy and other scientific fields is not clear; experiments conducted by his father had probably stimulated his interest, but his scientific education itself was almost certainly a product of the university years.

Many scientists spent much of their life at the university. Mark Curtis has shown that even before Wilkins entered Oxford, the universities were "nurseries of the new philosophy rather than intellectual backwaters." While scientific investigation was to a considerable degree extracurricular, the university statutes provided that the study of arithmetic, geometry, astronomy, and natural philosophy must be included in the curriculum of all those who hoped to obtain degrees in the liberal arts. Tutors played a considerable role in diffusing the new knowledge. Although Wilkins probably received no particular help from Tombes in his scientific studies, at least one tutor at Magdalene Hall usually required his charges to study astronomy along with more traditional work in logic and divinity.*

The Savilian lectures in astronomy and geometry were almost certainly one of the important means by which Wilkins learned of the most advanced scientific views. Historians of science seem curiously uninterested in the influence of these new professorships on the academic community, even though it is often noted that famous mathematicians and astronomers held the posts. Henry Briggs who lectured on astronomy between 1620 and his death in 1630 taught his audience the Copernican hypothesis. And while John Bainbridge was not himself a Copernican, he was fully abreast of the most advanced scientific thought of the day.

While Gresham College has frequently been noticed as a center for advanced scientific work, many of the most talented Greshamites left London in order to become Savilian professors. Nor is there anything to suggest that men like Briggs felt that, in accepting these posts at Oxford, they were moving into a scientific backwater or that Oxford would prove hostile to their studies. The easy assumption that Gresham was scientifically progressive and the universities backward must certainly be revised in the light of the interchange of personnel and the willingness of the ablest mathematicians and astronomers to migrate to Oxford.* We know that in certain instances the Savilian lectures were extremely important in turning a young man's fancy to thoughts of Copernicus. Henry Gellibrand, later a Gresham professor, reported that after hearing one of the mathematics lectures by accident, he "immediately fell to the study of that noble science, and conquered it, before he took his master's degree" in 1623. John Greaves, himself a Savilian professor in later years, learned his mathematics and astronomy from Briggs, John Bainbridge, and Peter Turner, all Savilian professors. Others were no doubt similarly inspired.

Of course a scientific education also required independent reading. It is clear from Wilkins's *The Discovery of a New World,* published shortly after he left the university, that he was familiar with the most advanced work in astronomy. Scientific books were available to any who cared to purchase them, and Savile increased their availability by contributing his own valuable library to the Bodleian. The works of Copernicus, Kepler, and Galileo, along with those of lesser writers, were well known in university circles. By the time Wilkins entered Oxford, the Aristotelian-Ptolemaic cosmology was recognized as completely untenable by scientific writers. Given the high level of Wilkins's scientific publications immediately upon leaving the university and the facilities for scientific studies available there, it must be assumed that science was flourishing at Oxford and Wilkins took advantage of the opportunities he found there.

Shortly after Wilkins left Oxford, probably sometime early in 1637, he obtained his first clerical position. On June 2, 1637, he succeeded his grandfather John Dod as vicar of Fawsley, Northamptonshire, a preferment in the hands of the Knightley family. Dod, who had held the position since 1624, later resumed it and kept it until his death in 1645.* Wilkins's brief tenure may have been a device intended to circumvent the Laudian policy of limiting ordination to those about to receive a charge, Laud's purpose being to prevent young Puritan clerics from swelling the ranks of lecturers and private chaplains. By briefly giving up his post to Wilkins, Dod may have made it possible for his grandson to be properly ordained and then serve as private chaplain to Lord Saye and Sele, a close associate of Richard Knightley.

A vigorous Puritan movement had flourished in Northampton-shire prior to the outbreak of the war, but the country's Puritan-ism was now primarily anti-Laudian and was dominated by lay-men, particularly by large landholders like the Knightleys. From the Elizabethan period onward, the Knightleys had combined Puritanism with parliamentary opposition, first to the encroach-ments of James I, and then to those of Charles I.* By the time Wilkins joined his grandfather, Dod had abandoned not only his youthful Presbyterianism but his earlier views on prayers and ceremonies. Like most Puritans, he was dissatisfied with the rites of the Laudian church, and during his tenure at Hanwell in Ox-fordshire he had been frequently cited for disobedience. But at Fawsley he adopted a more moderate position. Although Dod continued to object to many ceremonial details, he had no "De-light in Contradiction" and could not find it "in his Heart to dis-turb the Peace of the Church for these Matters." He often told Wilkins that "when some thought their Dissents ground enough for a War, he declared himself against it, and confirmed others in their Allegiance." Unity of the Church became Dod's great desire, a desire deeply shared by his grandson. Dod was what the An-glican Thomas Fuller called a "Passive nonconformist," "not lov-ing [others] any the worse for difference in judgment about ceremonies, but all the better for their unity of affections in grace and goodness." Nor did Dod support violent attacks on epis-copacy. He hoped for a slightly modified Church of England. If such a modification could not be achieved without destroying the unity of the Church, it was not worth achieving. He did not even adopt the political views of his patron, Richard Knightley, but remained a Royalist of sorts. In the end it seems more useful to describe Dod as a moderate reformer, than to apply to him the Puritan-Anglican categories.

Unlike most Puritans, Dod did not emphasize the drama of spiritual war or the anatomy of sin, but focused, rather, on morality, often a frankly utilitarian morality, and on general rules of living. Yet he continued to be associated with the group of dedicated Puritan preachers whom William Haller called the "spiritual brotherhood." Wilkins must have met some of the "spiritual brotherhood" at Fawsley, and he certainly discussed their ideas with Dod. Wilkins recommends their writings as suitable reading for young clerics in his *Ecclesiastes,* published a few years later.

Although we cannot know precisely the extent of Dod's influence on his grandson, it seems clear that he played an important part in forming Wilkins's thought at least on certain religious questions. Perhaps it is in this sense that Dod "educated" Wilkins. Often we can trace in Wilkins the further liberalization of many of Dod's already liberal views. Dod's comprehensive view of the church, his dislike of conflict over questions of ritual, his emphasis on morality, and his generally charitable view of those who disagreed with him are all hallmarks of Wilkins's religious writings. It is almost as if there was, at the end of Dod's life, a turning back toward the national church, one that might comprehend differing views—in short a return to a position similar to that of Ussher and Fuller, among others. Wilkins extended this approach even further in the Anglican direction. Many of the specifically Puritan points of view were filtered out of Wilkins's thought, but an underlying sympathy with and understanding of Puritan goals remained. During the Civil War and Interregnum this broader, more tolerant school of thought, which might be designated Puritan-Anglican or Anglican-Puritan, was submerged, to resurface only at the time of the Restoration. Even then it was not strong enough to become the dominant approach to religious life. Thus its importance has been obscured by an essentially misleading Puritan versus Anglican tradition of historical interpretation.

Although Wilkins soon left the immediate company of the Knightleys and his grandfather at Fawsley, he continued to move in the same parliamentary circle, but now in the capacity of a private chaplain rather than a minister with parish duties. Most of the men with whom Wilkins would be associated, both during this period and in his later career, were anti-government and anti-Laudian. They were usually Puritans of an Erastian and anticlerical bent. As a group they probably wished to return to something like the semi-Calvinist broad church of Elizabeth. They wanted the local gentry and aristocracy, not the upstart Laud, to govern the Church. Politically they sided with Parliament against the King and favored a radical reduction in the King's prerogative powers. Though they were "old parliament men" to the core, they opposed the execution of the King and the resulting Commonwealth government, many of them leaving the political scene at its creation. Some, however, returned to politics and participated in the government of the Protectorate. Nearly all of them accepted the Restoration and some were prominent in promoting it. Few if any of these men had any intellectual or moral difficulties in adjusting to the Restoration. It was men of this political temperament whom Wilkins found most congenial politically.

Wilkins probably had met his next patron, Lord Saye, at Fawsley.* Lord Saye not only had participated in political meetings there, but since 1630 had been a trustee of the Knightleys' fund to augment the income of the Fawsley vicarage. The precise position of a young chaplain in the busy Fiennes establishment is difficult to determine. While Wilkins and Lord Saye may have struck a sympathetic chord, and thus been relatively close, it is more likely that he was a fairly minor member of the household. Whatever Wilkins's personal relationship with Saye, his position brought him into contact with political developments and with the men who would become the leaders of the Long Parliament.

Although Lord Saye's role in the parliamentary opposition to the Crown has never received the attention it deserves, it is clear

that his contemporaries regarded him as a major political figure
in the 1630's and 1640's. By the time Wilkins joined his household, Saye had long been a thorn in the side of the King and his
ministers. Throughout the late 1620's and 1630's, he was an important member of the alliance of Puritan clerics and parliamentary opposition that also included John Pym, Lord Brooke, Richard Knightley, and the Earl of Warwick. Saye's religious views,
like those of his associates, are difficult to classify. He was clearly
a Puritan and opposed to the Laudian innovations. Because he
did not support the Presbyterians, he is considered one of the two
Independent peers in the House of Lords, Lord Brooke being the
other. But unlike most Independents, he did not support the Commonwealth or even the Protectorate government. He combined
Puritanism with a strong strain of anti-clericalism and Erastian-
ism. In many ways Saye symbolizes the fusion of Erastian and
Independent ideas as a means of safeguarding the laity against the
pretensions of both the Laudian and the Presbyterian clergy.

Wilkins did not remain with Lord Saye for very long. By 1641
at the latest he was serving Lord George Berkeley as chaplain. For
Wilkins to become the chaplain of even a moderate Anglican and
Royalist, when such men were increasingly on the defensive,
hardly accords with the picture of Wilkins as a political opportun-
ist. It does suggest, however, that he was not strongly Puritan even
at this early stage in his career. Berkeley, too, is a confusing figure politically. He was a Royalist, although his movement toward Royalism occurred gradually. He initially supported the
parliamentary party and hoped the King would make concessions
to the Long Parliament. Although he particularly disliked the
divisiveness created by the wars, he continued to cooperate with
the parliamentary government until 1648, and even served on several parliamentary committees. Thus Berkeley, a moderate Anglican with Royalist leanings, was also something of a parliamentarian and could work with Puritans. During the Restoration,
Berkeley continued his participation in government, and was, if
anything, more active than he had been earlier.

Wilkins and Berkeley must have found one another compatible, for their relationship was to be renewed after the Restoration when Berkeley presented Wilkins with the living at Cranford, Middlesex. Though Berkeley was an Anglican, his views probably did not differ greatly from Wilkins's own. Both men wanted a less Laudian church, but neither wished reform at the risk of destroying the Church. Berkeley's selection of Thomas Fuller to fill the same rectory at Cranford in 1658 is suggestive, for Fuller, an admirer of Dod, was a sincere but moderate Anglican, willing to make concessions to preserve the Church. The "Anglicanism" of Fuller and Berkeley came strikingly close to Dod's "Puritanism."

During the 1640's Wilkins seems to have occasionally acted in an ecclesiastical capacity apart from his chaplain's duties. Influential preachers and theologians often served as preachers to the Inns of Court, and about 1645 Wilkins was engaged as preacher to Gray's Inn, another connection that was to be revived after the Restoration. Wilkins was to aid or perhaps even replace the Inn's somewhat dissatisfied chaplain, Isaac Reynolds, but since Reynolds did not officially leave Gray's Inn until 1670, Wilkins could not obtain a permanent foothold in this influential preaching post. Wilkins seems also to have been connected with the Savoy Chapel, for he is reported to have had Richard Gilpin as his assistant or reader there.

Wilkins left Berkeley's service to enter that of Charles Louis, Elector Palatine, soon after the Elector's return to England in August 1644. The Elector seems to have sought out Wilkins for his scientific interests, and Wilkins spent most of his leisure pursuing scientific activities. The family lived in a courtly rather than Puritan style even during their exile, and had absorbed the cosmopolitan Dutch culture. Charles Louis was a worldly man who enjoyed the theater, especially Shakespeare, and even prepared a Ben Jonson play for production. His experiences of religious intolerance had led him to distrust fanaticism and intolerant religious sects and to strive for religious reunion.

This rather egocentric but hard-working young man had visited England several times in an effort to recoup the lands he and his family had lost in the Thirty Years War. He made a point of being on good terms with the leading politicians and soon became involved in political intrigues, particularly those of the more Protestant critics of the King. It was natural for this group to take up the cause of the Palatinate, for the young Elector served as a symbol of the Protestant cause. His second sojourn in England began in 1641. By then the split between the court and the anti-court Puritan groups was more serious. Under these circumstances aid for the Palatinate, or even a pension for himself, might well have become a party issue, and thus difficult to obtain. He was, therefore, displeased with the increasing divisiveness in the House of Commons and the movement to eliminate the bishops. Nor did the Elector really trust his uncle the King. He said little openly, but he kept his own spies and cultivated relations with the parliamentary party. The Elector followed the court for a time, but gradually disassociated himself from the King and quietly left for the Netherlands in 1642. Two years later he suddenly returned. It was widely believed that a plan was afoot to place him on the throne in place of Charles I, in much the same way as William of Orange later replaced James II. Parliament voted the Elector a generous pension and gave him quarters in Whitehall, but it soon became less enthusiastic. Once settled at Whitehall, he was left pretty much to himself. Although he continued to play the game of high politics in various obscure ways, he began to devote more of his time as patron and companion to men of learning.

On one or more occasions Wilkins accompanied the Elector on visits to the staunchly Anglican and Royalist Dean Wren of Windsor, who shared the Elector's scientific interests. The Elector evidently visited Windsor regularly, sometimes remaining several weeks at a time. Yet it was Wilkins who introduced the Dean's son Christopher to the Elector, and encouraged him to present the Elector with several of his scientific papers. The young and extremely talented Wren became very attached to Wilkins and said of him, "He suffers me to be a most addicted Client of his." Early in his career, then, Wilkins befriended and encouraged talented young scientists.

By 1646 the Elector had ceased to be considered a possible candidate for the English throne, and from 1646 to 1648, as the Thirty Years War came to a close, he was increasingly preoccupied with negotiations involving the Palatinate. Shortly before his uncle Charles I was executed, Charles Louis was recognized as Elector of the Palatinate. Early in 1649 he renounced the parliamentary cause, denounced the Commonwealth government which he considered responsible for the death of his uncle, and ended his English exile. He spent the next thirty years trying to restore his wasted country.

Wilkins's association with the Elector gave him political experience that was especially useful after the Restoration; through the Elector he learned the ways of the court, mixed with important people, and made at least one trip to the Continent. According to Anthony Wood, Wilkins was a "piece of a traveller, having twice seen the Prince of Orange's court, at the Hague, in his journey to, and return from, Heidelburg, whither he went to wait upon the Prince Elector Palatine, whose chaplain he was in England." In 1649, after he had become Warden of Wadham, he still acted on the Elector's behalf. Wilkins's service with the Elector, and especially his visits to the Netherlands and the Palatinate, doubtless influenced the development of his thought. The contrast between flourishing, cosmopolitan Holland and the devastated Palatinate, with three-fourths of its population exterminated, would have provided stark confirmation for his already partially formed views on the destructive tendencies of religious fanaticism. Wilkins's career at Wadham, which followed immediately upon his travels, makes clear his firm preference for religious compromise over perfection if perfection involved persecution. Wilkins's views became increasingly Arminian after his travels. Samuel Hartlib and John Dury, who moved in the Elector's circle, were acquainted with the Remonstrant group, many of whom were interested in science and may have arranged introductions for Wilkins. Many of Wilkins's friends among the Cambridge Platonists, if not Wilkins himself, were acquainted with the Dutch Arminians and his later religious works were highly regarded by the liberal Dutch theologians. To his service with the Elector, then, Wilkins owed greater exposure to continental ideas and political maneuvering and first hand experience of the devastation wrought by the Thirty Years War.

Wilkins's earliest and most Puritan patrons, Richard Knightley and Lord Saye and Sele, did not share his interest in science. Lord Berkeley and the Elector, however, were both scientific amateurs.* Berkeley encouraged Wilkins to spend time at his scientific writings. He later became one of the original fellows of the Royal Society, and was elected to its Council in 1663. As we have seen, the Elector had considerable time on his hands during his English stay, and devoted much of it to the patronage of men of learning and the pursuit of his own scientific interests. The Elector and his chaplain were of the "same turn and temper." The Elector's interest in science may have stemmed from his study of mathematics and chemistry at the University of Leyden. Scientific study seems to have been a family habit, and it was not at all unusual for noblemen, especially exiled noblemen, to while away their enforced leisure with scientific experiments. The Elector became involved with, and probably even joined, the group of young scientists to which Wilkins belonged.

The patronage of Berkeley and particularly of the Elector allowed Wilkins considerable leisure to pursue his scientific interests. He was well aware that patronage was a necessity for anyone without a substantial independent income who wished to do scientific research. While in the service of the Elector he wrote, noting Alexander's support of Aristotle's scientific studies, "The reason why the world hath not many Aristotles is because it hath so few Alexanders." In the mid-seventeenth century there were no professional scientists; science was the leisure-time pursuit of clerics, physicians, academics, and men of independent means. While an established divine or physician might have little need of patronage, a young man in these professions was greatly aided by the support of a benefactor. Wilkins's early success in securing support for himself was followed later by notable success in finding support for other scientists, and even for whole projects and organizations.

By the time Wilkins arrived in London to serve Lord Berkeley, he was a fully grounded scientific scholar and the author of two well-known scientific books. In London he joined a group of young investigators who met weekly to discuss recent scientific developments and to carry out experiments. The meetings of the "1645 group" have been described by John Wallis, then a young cleric, and another member of the group:

Our business was (precluding matters of theology and state affairs), to discourse and consider of Philosophical Enquiries, and such as related thereunto: as Physick, Anatomy, Geometry, Navigation, Staticks, Magneticks, Chymicks, Mechanicks and natural Experiments: with the state of these studies, as then cultivated at home and abroad. We then discoursed of the circulation of the blood, the valves in the veins, the venae lactoae, the lymphatick vessels, the Copernical hypothesis, the nature of comets and new stars, the satellites of Jupiter, the oval shape (as it then appeared) of Saturn, the spots in the sun, and its turning on its own axis, the inequalities and selenography of the Moon, the several phases of Venus and Mercury, the improvement of telescopes, the grinding of glasses for that purpose, the weight of air, the possibility or impossibility of vacuities, and nature's abhorrence thereof, the Torricellian experiment in quicksilver, the descent of heavy bodies, and the degrees of acceleration therein, and divers other things of the like nature. Some of which were then but new discoveries, and things appertaining to what hath been called The New Philosophy.

Thus physiology, mathematics, and astronomy were the subjects of major concern, although there was no lack of interest in mechanical experiments. The group seems to have had a much stronger theoretical bent than its successors, the Oxford group and the Royal Society.* The deliberate avoidance of theology and state affairs, the strict focus on the "business of Philosophy," made it possible for Royalists, parliamentarians, Anglicans, and Puritans of several shades to pursue in harmony their common scientific interests.

The origins of the Royal Society have not yet been completely untangled. The traditional view followed the account of John Wallis, who suggested the Society could be traced to the 1645 group that included himself and Wilkins. The group split up in 1648 or 1649, with most of its members migrating with Wilkins to Oxford, but some remaining in London. Late in the 1650's the two parts merged again and shortly afterward became the Royal Society. So far as it goes, this account is correct. It now appears, however, that there were several roughly contemporary scientific groups, each with a different though occasionally overlapping membership and a somewhat different focus.* F. R. Johnson has traced the uninterrupted evolution of both Wallis's 1645 group and the Royal Society from previous scientific groups that met at Gresham College. The 1645 group often met in the rooms of the Gresham astronomy professor both before and after 1645. Johnson thus discounts the originality of the 1645 group. Although Johnson noted in passing that several Gresham Professors took Oxford chairs, he did not point out that this connection probably helped make the scientific group at Oxford a natural successor to the 1645 group. Several members of Wilkins's Oxford group became Gresham Professors during or after the Restoration, thus continuing the Oxford-Gresham connection.

Perhaps the greatest source of confusion about the 1645 group is its alleged connection with the Comenians, led by Samuel Hartlib, and with the "invisible college" mentioned by Boyle. The Comenians, inspired by the Moravian Amos Comenius, who in turn was greatly influenced by Francis Bacon, were dedicated to world reform. The members hoped that through pansophia, a combination of universal knowledge, universal education, and a universal language, society could be improved and universal peace established. All the arts and sciences were included in this universal knowledge. Educational reform was essential; teaching methods in particular had to be changed to focus on "things, not words." Hartlib was also the leading figure in the "Invisible College," which advocated the application of science to technology and agriculture in order to improve man's condition. Although for many years the "College" was assumed to be identical to the 1645 group, most scholars now agree that it was a separate group. Hartlib's correspondence suggests that it pursued pansophic and utopian goals. Only gradually did it turn to science, and particularly to chemistry. The 1645 group confined itself more strictly to science, as opposed to social and educational reform.

Although there is no evidence that Wilkins associated with the Comenians during the time the 1645 group operated in London, one cannot dismiss the possibility of such a connection. Wilkins must have been thrown into contact with Theodore Haak, who like himself was employed at least occasionally by the Elector. Wilkins came to London about the same time as Comenius himself. The Czech reformer and Hartlib were aided by John Pym and Lord Brooke, both close associates of Lord Saye and Knightley, and by mid-1649 Wilkins and Hartlib were exchanging scientific views. Wilkins shared the Comenians' interest in a universal language, but he may have acquired that interest directly from Bacon rather than through the Comenians.*

Like the search for progenitors of the 1645 group and the Royal Society, the related question of leadership within the scientific community has engendered scholarly debate. The two leading contenders appear to be Wilkins and Haak, though it is by no means certain that either of them can claim preeminence. Miss Stimson has supported Wilkins, citing his position as chaplain to the Elector and his authorship of two scientific books. Wilkins's main contribution, however, was to keep the group alive at Oxford and finally making it a permanent institution. And the only firm evidence that that contribution was primarily his is Wallis's comment that Wilkins and Dr. Goddard, through all the vicissitudes of the group, "continued those Meetings, (and had a great influence on them), from the Original, till the days of their death." * Even this statement, which distributes the honors evenly between Wilkins and Goddard, sheds no light on the period prior to 1645. If Johnson's theory of a longstanding group is correct, there is no reason to look for a particular leader in 1645, and efforts to discover one stem from a desire to find links between various groups, rather than from the evidence itself. It is unfortunate that Wilkins, who superintended the writing of Sprat's *History of the Royal Society,* did not give him more information.* Whatever the origins and character of the 1645 group, it is clear that when Wilkins went to Oxford the group lost its initial cohesion, and that for some years at least Wilkins became the central figure among the members at the university. If indeed Miss Purver's contentions that the 1645 group engaged in discussion and dissemination of current scientific discoveries rather than actual experimentation and that the Oxford group is to be viewed as the real progenitor of the Royal Society, then Wilkins, whose leadership of the Oxford group is undisputed can indeed be seen as the founder of the Royal Society.

In short, then, the 1630's and 1640's produced several intellectual groups that contributed to the founding of the Royal Society. Wilkins was associated with the key 1645 group, and became the leader of the Oxford wing after the group split. He also knew Hartlib, the key figure in the "Invisible College," and either through direct contact or by independent development from the same intellectual source became an exponent of some of the central and most constructive ideas of yet another group, the Comenians. He was, then, squarely in the mainstream of the intellectual community that later created the Royal Society.

Thus Wilkins early established a pattern of moderation that he adhered to throughout his life. This pattern has been taken for ambivalence or inconsistency by modern historians, as indeed it was by some contemporary critics of Wilkins's later years. At the time his early associations and habits of thought were established, however, they did not seem strange either to himself or to his fellows. The difficulty is inherent not in Wilkins's life or thought, but from seeking to apply certain conventional labels to them. Through his grandfather Wilkins was certainly exposed to Puritan tradition, but if he espoused a "Puritanism," it was one that insisted that the peace and good order of the Church should not be sacrificed to Puritan demands. At the university, Wilkins was a student of science, but one who routinely mixed scientific and religious discourse. As a young cleric, he served as a retainer to parliamentary leaders, but parliamentary leaders who wished to retain the monarchy. In all these spheres Wilkins was no rebel, but a man squarely within the main intellectual currents of his time. In short, Wilkins was a moderate, the kind of person whom we have all encountered, whom none of us find strange, and indeed with whom most of us identify. The moderate becomes a puzzle only when we try to fit him into neat historical or analytical categories that do not fit him precisely because the categories are constructed on the basis of extremes rather than the middle ground he occupies. In the England of the 1640's and 1650's, as revolution and religious controversy polarized philosophical, religious and political thought, such moderation might have appeared evasive and contradictory. Nevertheless, through all the bitter struggles that raged about him, Wilkins consistently maintained the allegiances of his early life: religious purity *and* religious unity, parliament *and* monarch, religion *and* science. These allegiances made it possible for him to foster creative intellectual undertakings amidst almost constant upheaval.

II. Early Scientific Writings

In the years between his departure from Oxford and his return as Warden of Wadham College, Wilkins published several books on religious matters and four of what may best be described as popular science. Because his major goal was the broad dissemination of scientific knowledge and method, he attempted not only to convey information but also to persuade his readers to pursue scientific studies. To a very great degree he felt it his primary duty to overcome such obstacles to the acceptance of the new scientific views as excessive reliance on traditional authorities and religious hostility to scientific findings. The relationship between religion and science, particularly Scripture and science, was for Wilkins the most essential problem requiring solution if science was to progress and religion to flourish.

All of Wilkins's scientific works are informed by a desire to spread scientific information to those who would not ordinarily come upon it or who were themselves incapable of dealing directly with scientific discourse due to a lack of education or the failure of their education to provide the proper mathematical, technical, and linguistic tools. In *The Discovery of a New World* (1638) and *A Discourse Concerning a New Planet* (1640), he sought to convey to the general public the findings of the new astronomy, and to show laymen that there was no reason, religious or otherwise, to reject such findings. In these two volumes he hoped to revise the traditional views of the structure of the universe and convince his readers that Copernicanism provided the best alternative to the older view. *Mathematical Magick* (1648) described the basic principles of mechanics and their application for a similar audience. *Mercury, or the Secret and Swift Mes-*

senger (1641) discussed the problems of language and communication, and is particularly relevant for its treatment of scientific communication.

The tasks Wilkins set himself were not especially difficult, for he was addressing a highly receptive audience. Not only was the average Englishman better educated than he had ever been before, and considerably better than he would be for several centuries thereafter, but he was an eager consumer of scientific books.* Wilkins directed his words at both the gentry in the countryside and the artisans and craftsmen in the towns. He obviously did not expect either the learned or the totally ignorant to bother with them. Science was to be a leisure-time occupation with some practical application. *Mathematical Magick,* for example, was designed to aid the gentry in draining mines and coal pits, in addition to presenting the theoretical basis and nature of mechanical devices and giving the common artificer the theoretical basis of his craft.

For Wilkins, his scientific associates, and hopefully for his audience, science was to be cultivated as one of the pleasures of the mind. Philosophical speculations, "ravish and sublime the Thoughts with clear Angelical Contentments." Wilkins urged those with the time and means not only to contemplate but also to participate in scientific activities. *Mathematical Magick* is sprinkled with expressions of hope that the reader will further pursue the various ideas and inventions the author has presented. One express purpose of the *Discovery* is to "rise up some more active Spirit to a Search after other hidden and unknown Truths." It was the study of astronomy, however, that Wilkins particularly wished to encourage. He offered a number of reasons why this neglected field should be explored. Some were religious: the study of astronomy would prove the existence of God and Providence, and the contemplation of nature would lead to a closer appreciation of God and a more religious life. The pleasure astronomical study would bring is also stressed. And finally, greater knowledge of astronomy would be extremely helpful to navigators.

Wilkins particularly deplored the esoteric aura that frequently surrounded scientific knowledge. The ancient Pythagorean and Platonist mathematicians were especially reprehensible, for they had deprived later generations of many "useful and excellent Inventions" that could have been derived from their mathematical principles. Because of the secretiveness of the ancient savants, posterity had lost "not only the Benefit of those particular Discoveries, but also the Proficiency of those Arts in General." Nor would Wilkins accept the idea that potentially dangerous knowledge be suppressed. All knowledge was potentially dangerous. After all "nothing hath more occasioned Troubles and Contention than the art of Writing." * Publicity, Wilkins was convinced, was absolutely essential for progress. But publicity alone was not enough. Clarity of exposition was just as important if scientific knowledge was to be really comprehended. Although he treated this problem at greater length in his religious writings, there is no doubt that he felt clarity of communication to be just as essential in scientific as religious writing. He constantly jibed at scientists, both ancient and modern, who wrote obscurely. One of the reasons he was hostile to chemical experimenters was that they expressed their findings in allegories and "affected Obscurities." *

Scientific knowledge would become more widely dispersed if it were conveyed in language that everyone could understand. Wilkins always wrote in English. He justified publication of *Mathematical Magick* in part by pointing out that although similar books on the subject existed, there were "not any of them (that I know of) in our Vulgar Tongue." He thought of himself, however, as something more than a translator and compiler, emphasizing that his work contained "divers things very considerable, and not insisted upon by others." These "divers things" belonged largely to the realm of astronomy and mechanics, the former concentrated in the *Discovery* and the *Discourse,* the latter in *Mathematical Magick*.

The first of Wilkins's books, the *Discovery,* was not itself a direct defense of Copernicanism, though it assumed the validity of the new astronomy. Its primary purpose was to break down the traditional, medieval view of the universe, with its solid orbs and qualitatively differentiated celestial and sublunary spheres, and to show the essential similarity of the earth and the moon. As a corollary to the thesis that the moon and earth were both planets, Wilkins attempted to show that the moon was a "world" in much the same way as the earth, possibly having inhabitants of its own. In this way Wilkins became the chief English exponent of the doctrine of the plurality of worlds, which was so widely discussed in the sixteenth and seventeenth centuries.

Wilkins's work was important in undermining the concept of a closed, finite, hierarchically structured cosmos, and in suggesting that all the components of the universe were of equal value. Although he did not completely eliminate qualitative concepts from astronomy, he helped break down the tradition that assigned a particular value to each astronomical body and phenomenon. The major step was to show that the earth and the moon, and even other celestial realms, were composed of the same substances and were subject to the same scientific laws.

The idea of a plurality of worlds was an ancient one that had been revived by Nicholas of Cusa and Giordano Bruno. The concept gained new life from the telescopic observations of Galileo, which conclusively proved similarities between the earth and the moon. These similarities led later writers to extend the thesis, and to speculate about the possibility of life on other planets and the related question of the infinity of the universe. Scientists were not the only ones to be captivated by these ideas. Some of the earliest treatments of the plurality of worlds took a literary form. In 1620 Ben Jonson presented a masque at court called "News from the New World Discovered in the Moon." Nevertheless, in England the idea was still somewhat esoteric in the 1630's, and Wilkins hoped, by a popular but convincing treatment of the subject, to convert the general reading public.

Wilkins faced three major obstacles to broader acceptance of the new views. His initial concern was to show that the strangeness or novelty of the doctrine of the plurality of worlds should not itself lead to its rejection. It was also necessary to convince the reader that the new hypotheses did not contradict the principles of religion or challenge the validity of Scripture. And it required a new understanding of the physical structure of the universe. To convince his audience of the likelihood of a plurality of worlds, Wilkins tried to demonstrate that the earth and the moon were essentially similar. He explained that all parts of the universe, not just the earth, were subject to change and corruption. Contrary to traditional views, the heavens were not pure matter and thus exempt from alteration, but were composed of the same matter as sublunary bodies. In so arguing Wilkins was repudiating both Aristotle and the Schoolmen, who had been propounding the pure-matter view for centuries.

Wilkins based most of his description of the moon on recent telescopic observations, particularly those of Galileo. The moon he depicted was solid, compact, and opaque like the earth, and, contrary to popular opinion, was as incapable as the earth of shedding any light of its own. In addition both the earth and the moon had a surface of land and sea, were surrounded by a "gross vaporous air," and were probably alike in having seasons, meteors, and inhabitants. He denied that the spots observed on the moon represented any kind of deformity. In this connection Wilkins engaged in a lengthy digression on the nature of mountains, both earthly and lunar, which, as Marjorie Nicolson has shown, played a very important role in transforming the Englishman's conception of mountains and his attitude toward them. In the *Discovery* Wilkins denied the commonly held view that the earth's mountains were ugly excrescences, traceable to the aftereffects of the Deluge or to man's sin. Mountains had emerged at the time of Creation and were produced by "the Goodness and Providence of the Almighty." All natural things were good, having been created by God. If studied objectively, mountains "will be found as much to conduce to the Beauty and Convenience of the Universe as any of the other Parts." Wilkins is more tentative on the question of lunar inhabitants, which raised a number of theological and scientific problems. He concludes, cautiously, "I dare not myself affirm anything of these Selenites, because I know not any Ground whereupon to build any probable Opinion." Posterity, however, might "invent some means for our better Acquaintance with these Inhabitants." The idea of lunar exploration appealed tremendously to Wilkins, who waxed enthusiastic on the pleasures and economic benefits of interplanetary travel. But, returning to a realistic note, he consigned "such Imaginations" to the "Fancy of the Reader."

Wilkins's ideas, both the scientific and the speculative, enjoyed a wide currency in the years following publication of the *Discovery*. John Ray thought the moon was inhabited, and as late as 1698 Christian Huygens was willing to discuss the social, political, and intellectual life of lunar society. Langrenus's map of the moon dedicated to the King of Spain named one of the locations after Wilkins. Wilkins's work on lunar inhabitants and interplanetary travel had a greater influence on literature than on science. With the possible exception of Fontenelle's *Conversations on the Plurality of Worlds*, which was itself based on Wilkins's publications, the *Discovery* was the chief source of the wide literary currency given these ideas. The late seventeenth and early eighteenth century witnessed an outburst of plays and poems based on the idea of a plurality of worlds and lunar flights. Many of these treatments can be traced directly or indirectly to Wilkins.

Two years after publishing his views on the plurality of worlds, Wilkins turned to the task of explaining Copernicanism itself to the public. Although many of his arguments were scientific, he insisted that his *Discourse* was not an "Exact Treatise" on the new astronomy but rather an attempt to eliminate "those common Prejudices that men usually entertain against that opinion." Wilkins knew, of course, that he was not offering the first explanation of Copernicanism. Popular almanacs had discussed alternative theories of the universe and advocated either the Tychonic or the Copernican system. Nevertheless, there had been no extensive presentation of the problem outside the technical exposition of the experts.

Wilkins recognized that to convince the public he would have to break down ingrained mental habits and uncritical veneration for traditional and ancient authorities. He reminded his readers that even some of the astronomers who originally opposed Copernicus had come around to his point of view, and that nearly all the best contemporary astronomers were Copernicans. He admitted that there were a few well-known astronomers, such as Tycho Brahe and Nathaniel Carpenter, who rejected Copernican views, but only because of "an overfond and partial Conceit of their own Invention." Wilkins was writing just as the still strong Tychonic school was losing ground to the Copernicans. His own publications helped to turn the tide of literate opinion.

After disposing of traditional arguments contending that it was "natural" for the earth to be in the central position, Wilkins turned to counter the strongest astronomical arguments of the opposition, trying to refute not only Aristotle and Ptolemy, but his more modern opponents, Fromundus and Carpenter, as well. Although he relied to some extent on his own arguments and diagrams, he depended primarily on Copernicus, Galileo, and Kepler for his ammunition. His basic argument for the central position of the sun, like that of most Copernicans, was the "Convenience of this *Hypothesis* above any other," for it could "resolve the Motions and Appearances of the Heavens into more easie and natural Causes." Nevertheless, Wilkins did not confine himself to arguments of hypothetical convenience as had the earliest advocates of Copernicanism, but followed Galileo and other more recent writers in insisting that the system was not only hypothetically convenient but actually depicted the reality of the universe. He also mustered some metaphysical arguments on behalf of Copernicanism, particularly that of "Harmonic Proportion." The Copernican thesis revealed a harmonic relationship between the number and the distance of the planets, a harmony that would be disturbed if the sun were placed among the rest of the planets.

Wilkins then asked whether there were "sufficient reasons" to consider the earth incapable of the annual and diurnal motion Copernicus ascribed to it. His first hurdle is to dismiss the evidence of the senses. Traditionalists like Alexander Ross had argued that if the senses were deceived about the motions of the heavens, they ought to be equally deceived about the movements of the clouds. Wilkins replies that the senses are not "mistaken in everything, because it was so in one thing." He, like Galileo before him, indicates that naïve empiricism could lead to as many errors as naïve rationalism. He then proceeds to explain why motions really caused by the earth appear to occur in the heavens, and disposes of various other scientific and philosophic objections. Wilkins delivered his main attack against the position that if the earth moved, airborne bodies such as clouds would appear to rise and set like the stars, birds would be carried from the nest, and nothing could fall perpendicularly. He undertook several lines of refutation, almost all of them adopted from Galileo's *Dialogue Concerning the Two Chief World Systems*.

Wilkins finally moved to more positive arguments. The earth's motion would free the heavens from the incredibly fast rotation usually ascribed to them. The notion of the simplicity of Nature had made a considerable impression on Wilkins. To impute motion to the heavens would be to argue "Improvidence in Nature." Every common watchmaker knew enough to avoid superfluous movements in his machines. Wilkins concluded that the Copernican hypothesis provided a better explanation than any other. The mixture of arguments used by Wilkins have not all stood the test of time, but were calculated to appeal to the average man of the seventeenth century and they served their purpose well. His books were read avidly as soon as they appeared.

Two printings of the *Discovery* were issued in 1638. The book was reissued, with an additional chapter and some minor changes, in 1640, the year the *Discourse* first appeared. Both works were reprinted several times. Wilkins seems to have succeeded in making the findings of the new astronomy available to a wide range of readers, an important accomplishment when one considers the difficulty of presenting difficult and highly technical material in a clear, persuasive, and entertaining manner without unduly sacrificing accuracy. Wilkins's books were the most influential English defense of Copernican astronomy in the second half of the seventeenth century. After a thorough examination of the popular works on astronomy, Miss Nicolson has concluded that Wilkins was the most widely read of all such writers in the seventeenth century, and that he was probably responsible for the almanac-makers' final acceptance of Copernicus. Wilkins's works were probably more important than any until Newton's in convincing Englishmen of the superiority of the Copernican hypothesis over the Tychonic.

Wilkins's influence reached the Continent as well. The *Discovery* was translated into French in 1656 and circulated widely in France, where writings on the plurality of worlds and moon voyages had a great vogue. Francis Godwin and Wilkins were almost certainly the major sources of Cyrano de Bergerac's *Histoire Comique des Etats et Empires de la Lune* which appeared shortly after the translation of the *Discovery*. Fontenelle's *Conversations on the Plurality of Worlds* was almost certainly based on Wilkins's *Discovery*. A German translation of Wilkins's astronomical treatises appeared in 1713 with eulogistic foreword by Johan Doppelmayer, a professor of mathematics, who described them as the best explanation of Copernicus then available.

Galileo appears to have been the chief source for both the *Discovery* and the *Discourse,* though Wilkins also acknowledged great debts to Copernicus, Rheticus, and particularly Kepler. The *Discovery*'s treatment of the earth's similarity to the moon seems to be directly derived from Galileo's *Dialogue Concerning the Two Chief World Systems,* as does the explanation of the brighter and darker spots on the moon's surface. In the *Discourse,* Galileo's influence is even more evident. Many of Wilkins's proofs regarding the movement of the earth and his answers to critics of the heliocentric system are drawn directly from the *Two Chief*

World Systems, and several of his diagrams were lifted straight from Galileo's work. Wilkins's broad aims were much the same as Galileo's: to present to the public in an attractive, simple manner the best evidence in favor of Copernicus and the strongest arguments against common anti-Copernican prejudice. Like Galileo, Wilkins presented both the theoretical and the physical evidence for the Copernican world view. This dependence, however, should not suggest that Galileo was Wilkins's only source. His more imaginative statements on the plurality of worlds, for example, depended heavily on Kepler's *Somnium.*

Wilkins's most original contributions dealt with flight, a subject on which he was the most important figure in the seventeenth century. While he was not the first to consider the possibility of flight, he did more to make the subject popular than any previous writer. His *Discovery* was the first printed work on flight as a scientific problem, and his speculations on the subject set the tone of such discussions for over a century. Wilkins became involved with the mechanics of flight as an extension of his astronomical studies, taking up the problem seriously only after he had written on the plurality of worlds and speculated on the possibility of a moon voyage. Such a voyage obviously required a mode of transportation. In his earliest reference to interplanetary flight, in the first edition of the *Discovery,* Wilkins merely noted that the possibility had been mentioned by Kepler and suggested that posterity might discover what men of his day could not. When the *Discovery* was reissued again in 1640, he had added a chapter showing "That 'tis probable for some of our Posterity, to find out a Conveyance to this other World." The major difficulty was ascent from the earth, for which it was necessary to overcome the force of gravity. Wilkins believed that gravity, the attraction of condensed bodies or desire for union, affected all bodies. This attractive quality varied with distance, and ceased altogether once one got beyond the sphere of the earth's attraction, which he estimated to be about twenty miles beyond the surface; at that point travel would be rapid and easy.

Discussions of gravity during the early seventeenth century were still highly confused. The contributions of Robert Hooke and Christian Huygens and the rigorous formulation of Isaac Newton were several decades away. Wilkins drew on the most advanced work on the subject available to him, notably that of Kepler and William Gilbert. He vigorously assailed the traditional Aristotelian view of heaviness as a quality. The gravity problem was especially serious because if it took very long to escape the earth's attraction, the time required for the moon trip would create serious difficulties of food supply and rest. In his whimsical passages on space travel, Wilkins gave free play to his imagination. The tone suggests that readers who took him seriously certainly mistook his intent. For instance, Wilkins proposes that the music of the spheres might provide nourishment—after having denied that the music of the spheres existed. For Wilkins castles in the air and other "astronomical fictions" were simply entertaining but not serious matters.*

He gave more serious attention to the question of how the traveler would be conveyed beyond the "sphere of the Earth's Magnetical Vigour." Wings attached to the voyager's body were one possible solution; large birds taught to carry a man were another; and a flying chariot was a third. Wilkins continued to ponder the matter and in 1641 indicated that he was considering a lengthier treatment of the subject, which ultimately appeared in 1648 as part of his *Mathematical Magick*. Even in *Mercury* Wilkins had ceased to think solely in terms of fantasy and had been seriously considering methods of getting real contrivances off the ground. Yet basically Wilkins's treatment in *Mathematical Magick* is simply an elaboration of the types of conveyances suggested in the *Discovery*.

The first method considered in *Mathematical Magick*, transportation by spirits, is roundly rejected and his own enquiry limited to "Natural and Artificial Grounds." Nor was Wilkins greatly impressed with the idea of flying with the help of birds, however large, although he found Francis Godwin's account of a swan-driven chariot amusing. He was drawn to the use of artificial wings, the method most widely discussed during the seventeenth and eighteenth centuries. He felt that methods based on the imitation of nature, if not carried to extremes, would yield the best results. He cited reported cases of such flight in rebutting critics like Robert Burton, who ridiculed the efforts of the "newfangled Wits." Wilkins had no doubt that a device enabling men to fly would be "easily affected by a diligent and ingenious Artificer." He spoke favorably of a device consisting of a set of wings moved up and down in a bird-like fashion by two sets of springs.*

Wilkins's greatest enthusiasm was reserved for a flying chariot, which could "never be too big or too heavy, if the space which it possesses in the Air, and the Motive-Faculty in the Instrument be answerable to its Weight." * He realized that there was much to be learned about the properties of air and objects in air, but thought that experiments might lead to a "new Science, concerning the Extension of Bodies, in comparison to the Air, and motive Faculties by which they are to be carried." The motor faculty of the flying chariot would be springs similar to those he had recommended for man-attached wings. To determine the proper proportions of the wings would require considerable experimentation. Such difficulties as arose, however, might be overcome by "frequent Trials." Certainly "in these practical Studies, unless a Man be able to go to the Tryal of Things, he will perform but little. In such matters, . . . general speculation, without particular Experiment, may conjecture at many things, but can certainly effect nothing."

Wilkins's work on the problems of flight attracted considerable attention during the following decades in both scientific and literary circles. Among the scientists, Robert Hooke was probably the most interested in the problems of flight. While Wilkins was at Wadham College in the 1650's, he and Hooke both worked on models of flying chariots. One of Hooke's models, made with both springs and wings as Wilkins had recommended, was said to have sustained itself in the air for a short time. Wilkins communicated his enthusiasm to other scientists at Wadham. In 1650 William Petty reported the Oxford "Club" was busy with experiments, having performed Captain Bulmer's experiment "whereby wee undertooke to blow a Boy or a Boate over London Bridge, the Ground whereof wee conceive to bee by blowing of bladders or other instrument of the like kind of greater capacity." In later years the Royal Society took up these problems.

If many of the scientific group were enthusiastic, others were doubtful. Francis Potter, for example, was impressed by Wilkins's presentation but still worried that "many things may be performed in lesser models, which cannot be affected in greater." While not denying that flight was theoretically possible, he felt they had not yet begun to solve the theoretical or experimental problems. His reaction was probably fairly typical. Perhaps Wilkins himself became discouraged, for his interest in flight seems to have lagged in later years.

Again it was in literary rather than scientific circles that Wilkins's ideas had their more lasting vogue. Joseph Glanvill and Thomas Powell borrowed from him directly. Others used Wilkins's discussions as the basis of their own literary ventures or mentioned Wilkins's ideas. Defoe's novel *Consolidator* (1705) discusses Wilkins's work on flight. Robert Paltock's *The Life and Adventures of Peter Wilkins* (1751) is indebted to Wilkins for both its title and much of its content. Samuel Johnson's *Rasselas* (1759) also borrowed heavily from Wilkins and discussed flying and its difficulties much as Wilkins had.

Satirists had a field day with Wilkins's ideas. Alexander Pope referred to Wilkins's efforts in the following couplet:

> The head that runs at super-lunar things,
> Pois'd with a tail, may steer on Wilkins' wings.

Sir William Temple attacked the idea of flight as unmercifully as he attacked the other novel ideas of the virtuosi, and, as one might expect, Thomas Shadwell ridiculed it, in the *Virtuoso*. Addison was still laughing at Wilkins in 1719.*

Wilkins was also concerned to popularize the science of mechanics. *Mathematical Magick, or the Wonders that May be Proved by Mechanical Geometry* was, even more than the *Discovery* or the *Discourse,* a work of popular science. Its purpose was not to defend the validity of a relatively new scientific theory but to familiarize the average man with the basic and long-accepted principles of mechanics. Wilkins begins with a defense of mechanics as a liberal art that was, like astronomy and music, a "species" of "mixed mathematics." * The basic subject of mechanics was the relationship between weight and power. Weight was no longer to be considered a "natural quality, whereby condensed Bodies do of themselves tend *downwards*," but "an Affection," which might be measured. Wilkins hoped to spread the new, mathematical approach to mechanics to the general public. He then describes basic mechanical principles and discusses their application. He shows how, at least theoretically, the force of any mechanical faculty could move any weight, suggesting that a small child, using a machine composed of a hundred double pulleys, could easily move the earth itself. Another mechanical principle involving the relationship of time and speed to power, however, forced Wilkins to admit that his earlier fantastic examples could not be realized in practice.

His treatment of mechanics was considerably more primitive and traditional than his treatment of astronomy, a reflection of the relative states of development of the two fields. Although he did question some traditional concepts, he did not expound a coherent mechanical philosophy. He seems to have been familiar with the most advanced work in the field, including that of Galileo and Simon Stevinus. His outline of the fundamental problems of mechanics as the weight to be moved, the force or power to move it, and the distance and time involved, was probably derived from Galileo's *On Mechanics,* a small tract written in 1600 for the benefit of his private pupils. Its brief, elementary analysis of the basic machines is paralleled by Wilkins's, and it states the principles on which Wilkins relied so heavily. Both men express great admiration for Archimedes. Both use the human body to explain the basic principles of simple machines. More generally, both writers felt strongly that scientific knowledge should be disseminated to the public at large (Galileo not only wrote in the vernacular but appealed to as wide an audience as possible by casting his most important works in dialogue form). Finally, Wilkins, like Galileo before him, condemned mathematicians who hid their knowledge.

The second part of *Mathematical Magick,* "Daedalus," named after that mythological builder of machines, was concerned with machines rather than underlying mechanical principles. "It is a wonderful thing to consider, how Men's Labour's might be eased and contracted . . . , if such as were well skilled in the Principles and Practices of these Mechanical Experiments, would but thoroughly apply their Studies into the Enlargements of such inventions." A few years later Wilkins's friends in the Royal Society would devote themselves to just such experiments and greatly stimulate the development of the machinery that made possible the industrial revolution. In general Wilkins preferred to stimulate imaginations rather than provide blueprints. Many of his fanciful examples were derived from earlier writers, including Jerome Cardan and Giacomo della Porta, or from recent experimenters such as Cornelius Dreble. He describes a sailing chariot "by which a man may sail on the land, as well as by a Ship on the Water," "waywisers" that measured distances traveled by chariot, ships or men on foot, and "artificial images" that could move, produce sounds, or even speak. Such artificial images were particularly interesting to Wilkins, with his concern for the mechanisms of language and speech. He was also intrigued by the submarine. Dreble's experiments had convinced him that such a device was feasible.* One of Dreble's machines was an underwater ship that operated some ten to fifteen feet beneath the surface of the Thames. But with the submarine, as with the flying chariot, Wilkins's imaginings were accompanied by a realization that hard work and experimentation were necessary to make the dream a reality. At least some of Wilkins's contemporaries took his speculations on submarines seriously. Francis Potter wrote to John Aubrey in 1651 that if the water at the bottom of the sea always remained calm, then "I believe all other difficulties may be helped." Later Dr. Johnson also devoted serious attention to Wilkins's discussion.

Like his father, Wilkins was intrigued by the possibility of perpetual motion, a possibility that interested "many refined wits for divers Ages." Here again experiments were crucial, because "though many Inventions in this kind, may at first view bear a great shew of probability, yet they will, being brought to Trial, and will not answer in Practice what they promised in Speculation. Anyone who hath been versed in these Experiments must needs acknowledge that he hath been often deceived in his strongest confidence." Wilkins described a number of experimental methods and explained the defects of each.*

The influence of any book is difficult to assess, particularly one that does not pretend to originality. The book must have been initially popular, for two editions were published in 1648. The volume must be considered important, if for no other reason than that it captivated the imagination of the youthful Isaac Newton. Roger North, a Cambridge student, still found it useful in 1680 as part of his scientific education, and the instrument maker Joseph Maxon suggested that this textbook of mechanics be placed in every boy's hands to turn his thoughts to inventions. If ridicule indicates a wide public acquaintance, the book must have been very well known. But literary men borrowed from it as well as poking fun. Dr. Johnson borrowed ideas from it for *Rasselas* and for occasional pieces in the *Rambler,* and Laurence Sterne's *Tristram Shandy* also shows considerable indebtedness to Wilkins.

Wilkins's scientific interests during these early years seem to have been confined to astronomy and mechanics. He tended to associate the chemists with hocus-pocus and mystical religion. This, of course, was not surprising given his lifelong concern for clarity and precision in scientific exposition.

Wilkins's *Mercury, or the Secret and Swift Messenger* is not strictly speaking a work of popular science, but it does have considerable bearing on the development of scientific discourse. Unlike his scientific publications, it contained little missionary zeal. He said that he had written the sections on ciphers and cryptography—the major part of the book—for his own amusement, and then published them "to gratify my brother the stationer" rather than "for the publique good." Wilkins was overmodest in labeling *Mercury* a totally frivolous work. Its discussion of the nature of language and communication was a pioneering venture in an area that engaged the interest of Wilkins in particular and Englishmen in general throughout the seventeenth century. Words, after all, were only a means of conveying one's thoughts, and these words and thoughts could be made permanent by utilizing symbols, letters, or writing. With these it was possible to "discourse with them that are remote from us, not only by the Distance of many Miles, but also of many ages." Ciphers were an alternative means of expressing words and thoughts, a means much in demand when political intrigue, war, and revolution, made secrecy particularly desirable.

Wilkins discussed several modes of secret communication. His treatment of gestures led him to speculate on whether the deaf might be taught to speak by learning the motions of the mouth and tongue. Some years later John Wallis and William Holder, both members of the Royal Society, were to accomplish remarkable results in this field.

Although Wilkins did not present a complete theory of language and communication in *Mercury,* he had already begun to develop the concepts that he elaborated in later years. He defined communication between the ear, which is the instrument of learning, and the tongue, which is the instrument of teaching, as speech or language. Language was natural to man, though not innate; all languages were learned. Having set forth these propositions, Wilkins goes on to consider the barriers to communication caused by the diversity of languages and of the written symbols for them. He suggests a "Universal Character to express things and Notions as might be legible to all People and Centuries, so that Men of Several Nations might with the same ease both write and read it." His desire to create such a language obviously stems from his interest in the popular diffusion of knowledge. The use of Latin as the language of science restricted scientific learning to the well-educated, while writings in the vernacular could be read in only one country. A universal set of symbols, each representing an object of the physical world or a concept, that all men could easily read and write would mean that a "great part of our Times which is now required to the Learning of Words, might then be employed in the Study of Things." The time required to master the learned languages was constantly decried by educational reformers of the day, particularly those who had been influenced by Bacon and Comenius.

Wilkins was convinced that a simple, universal character was possible. The Chinese and Japanese, whose languages differed, had been using the same system of characters for a long time, and could read one another's books. Besides, some common characters already existed in the form of Roman and Arabic numbers, the astronomical symbols for the planets and heavenly signs, chemical notations of "minerals," and musical notes. He therefore saw no reason "why there may not be such a general Kind of Writing invented for the expression of every Thing else." At this stage, however, Wilkins could only advance a few tentative suggestions for the construction of such a universal symbolic language. He thought there should be as many characters as there were "primitive Words," Hebrew providing the best pattern because it contained the "fewest Radicals." Such a system of characters would be no more difficult to master than a conventional verbal language. He estimated some 7,000 to 8,000 symbols would be required to adequately express all things. "Although men of several countries should each of them differ in their Voices, and pronouncing Words, yet the sense would be still the same. As it is in the Picture of a Man, a Horse, a Tree; which all Nations doe express the same Conceit, though each of these Creatures be stiled by several Names, according to the Difference of Languages." The construction of the character would occupy Wilkins for the rest of his life.

The preceding brief outline of Wilkins's early scientific writings would be incomplete without some discussion of the methodological underpinnings of these works. For in the last analysis Wilkins's discussions of flying machines and cryptograms are far less important than the attitudes toward scientific endeavor that they convey.

Looking at the whole corpus of Wilkins's early scientific work we find him repeatedly preoccupied with the rejection of traditional authority. Although relying heavily on Galileo, Kepler, and Copernicus, he was quite willing to reject even their findings when experience proved them erroneous. There was a constant emphasis on free inquiry and experiment unconstrained by rules accepted a priori on the basis of authority. Insufficient attention has been paid to this declaration of independence and its concomitant rejection of dogmatism, distrust of metaphysics, and preference for tentative hypotheses.*

Wilkins's rejection of authority led him to a reevaluation of the relative merits of ancient and modern learning, a subject that engaged both scientists and literary men for many decades. Those who upheld the principle of authority, not surprisingly came down on the side of the ancients, whereas those who rejected it were naturally drawn to the view that there was no inherent superiority in ancient knowledge. The debate over ancients and moderns was, of course, an outgrowth of the humanists' revival of ancient literature. Its chief relevence for scientists of the sixteenth and seventeenth centuries derived from its use as a vehicle for attacking and defending the new scientific knowledge. It was usually the nonscientists who tended to pose the problem as ancients *versus* moderns. The scientists themselves saw the question not so much in terms of the exclusive truth of ancient or modern learning but of repudiating the principle of authority and advocating the progressive nature of truth.

Wilkins's attitude toward the ancients was, of course, determined by his attitudes toward finding truth. If all men were liable to err, then ancient men were too. Even if ancient error had been sustained for countless generations, it was error nonetheless. Novelty alone was not sufficient grounds for rejecting an idea. Though the newest style was not always the correct one, "neither should we be so superstitiously devoted to Antiquity, as to take up everything for canonical, which drops from the Pen of a Father, or was approv'd by the Consent of the Ancients." If novelty had always been rejected, there never would have been any improvement in knowledge and the world would have been condemned to the state of ignorance that prevailed just after the fall of man. Scientific knowledge, like all the arts, improved with time. Echoing Bacon, Wilkins insisted that truth was the daughter of time, and that there were still many truths left "to make some of our Age famous for their Discovery."

Wilkins's confidence in the superior knowledge of modern man did not mean that he underrated the accomplishments of the ancients. He had, after all, selected Archimedes and Daedalus as models in the fields of mechanical principles and inventions, and in arguing for the heliocentric theory was careful to note the supporting views held by some ancient philosophers "of the better note." Wilkins never disparaged ancient learning as such. Like most learned men who criticized the ancients on certain points, he urged continued study of them.

Because Aristotle was *the* authority, *the* philosopher, for his opponents, Wilkins had to come to terms with him. It has frequently been assumed that in opposing traditional views of astronomy and physics, scientists of the seventeenth century were also violently opposed to Aristotle. This was certainly not true of Wilkins or, for that matter, of many of his fellow scientists. It was not the philosopher himself, but the Aristotelian schoolmen, who were

the chief targets of Wilkins and other moderns. Aristotle the man
and the scientist was admired tremendously, not only for his great
knowledge but for his scientific method, which seemed to approx-
imate their own. Nevertheless, it was necessary to point out Aristotle's imperfections. Though a Master of "the art of Syllogisms,"
he occasionally made logical errors. He was certainly wrong in
some of his physical findings, such as the incorruptibility of the
heavens and the nature of gravity and weight, and on some religious questions as well. But the world was still "beholden" to him
"for the Greater part of our Learning." And if Aristotle "were
alive again, Questionless, he was so rational and ingenius a Man,
(not half so obstinate as many of his Followers) that upon such
Probibilities as these, he would have renounced his own Principles and come over to this side." On this point Wilkins and Galileo were in agreement. When it came to nonscientific matters,
Wilkins had even greater respect for "the Philosopher," as he, like
the scholastics, called him. He based much of his ethical argument, and even many of his principles of natural religion, on the
writings of Aristotle.

Wilkins accorded Ptolemy and Pliny a great deal of respect as
well. Nor was he alone in this attitude. When the scientists defended the study of Aristotle, Ptolemy, Euclid, and others in the
universities against radical reformers who wished to sweep away
all ancient learning, they were recognizing not only the specific
contributions of these thinkers but also the fact that modern scientific knowledge was an extension of their work, not a repudiation of it. Wilkins's criticism of the schoolmen, it must be
admitted, was hardly novel. Anti-scholasticism was a stock attitude among literary men by the sixteenth century. When the
scientists of the seventeenth century made their attack, they were
flogging a long-dead horse.

The second major barrier to acceptance of the new science, after
unquestioning acceptance of authority and ancient learning, was
the apparent conflict between religion and science. Wilkins devoted a large portion of the *Discovery* and most of the *Discourse*

to removing this stumbling block. Thus, in addition to explaining the new astronomy, Wilkins attempted to convince his reader that acceptance of Copernicus and the plurality of worlds did not contravene Scripture or injure religion in any way.

Wilkins was not the first to try to bring the new astronomy into harmony with religion. From the beginning Copernicus and his followers were forced to reject both a literal interpretation of Scripture and the use of Scripture as a standard by which to judge the findings of natural philosophy, for there were passages in Scripture that seemed to be directly challenged by their hypothesis. Copernicus was immediately attacked by both Catholic and Protestant theologians, including Luther and Calvin.* The controversy raged during the late sixteenth and early seventeenth centuries with astronomers like Tycho Brahe and Thomas Hill, as well as theologians, opposing Copernicus on Scriptural grounds. One of the attractions of the Tychonic system was that it did not seem to contradict the Bible as directly as the Copernican.

Attempts to reconcile Scripture and the Copernican hypothesis began to appear almost immediately throughout Western Europe. The Tycho Brahe-Christopher Rothmann controversy of 1590 was one of the first to deal with the problem. Edward Wright and William Gilbert were among the earliest to censure literalism in England. In 1609 Kepler, Galileo, and Paolo Foscarini became involved in the controversy. Galileo issued a "declaration of independence" for scientific knowledge against the claims of Scriptural authority in 1613. His arguments were adopted by Wilkins and by later controversialists. His first argument was that literalism could lead to abominable heresies, for Scripture mentions God as possessing hands and feet and attributes to him qualities like forgetfulness. The second, which was to be elaborated by Wilkins in the *Discovery* and the *Discourse,* was that God had "accommodated" his Scriptural revelation to the capacity of the vulgar, who, being rude and unlearned, would not accept things that seemed to contradict the evidence of their senses. Galileo further argued that the Bible was simply not concerned with the problems of natural science, which could only be probed through "Sensible Experiments and Necessary Demonstration." In 1622 Tommaso Campanella's *Apologia pro Galileo* elaborated these views. A few years later Nathaniel Carpenter of Oxford added his thoughts on the subject, and in 1630 Philip Landsberg joined the camp of those who maintained that Scripture was not to be used as a source of astronomical knowledge.

The more widely known the Copernican hypothesis became, the hotter the controversy over literalism raged. The 1630's and early 1640's witnessed several more attacks on the new astronomy. In England these were led by Alexander Ross and Nicholas Fuller.* Wilkins evidently felt that a spirited defense was required if the forces of literalism were not to destroy the advances that had already been made. His was the first, and so far as I know the only, systematic English presentation of the Galilean outlook on the relationship of scientific truth to Scripture. His contribution was to place the controversy squarely before the English public and to assure his readers not only that Scripture did not bar the acceptance of Copernican astronomy, but that a Scriptural basis for scientific findings was unnecessary. The reassurance provided by Wilkins was undoubtedly one of the factors that led to the widespread acceptance of the new astronomy in the mid-seventeenth century. He did, however, have the advantage of drawing on earlier writers, especially Campanella, and of being on the winning side from the beginning. Although literalism was still widely accepted by the general public, only a handful of intellectuals supported it, and they were already very much on the defensive. By 1650, when Wilkins's works were enjoying a wide circulation, the tide had already turned.*

The practical result of Wilkins's synthesis of earlier arguments was to free scientific studies from the limitations that religious doctrines or Scriptural passages might have imposed, and thus to establish science as an independent body of knowledge verifiable solely by its own standards of investigation. But while Wilkins wished to exclude Scripture from philosophical controversies and eliminate religion as a standard for scientific truth, he was not content to have religion and science go their separate ways. Quite the contrary. Although religion as such could not aid the scientists, science could help the cause of religion. Wilkins was convinced that the study of nature and the findings of science could help prove religious truths and make men more religious. Although he developed this point of view at greater length in later years, even in these early works he asserted that the study of Nature, particularly astronomy, proved the existence of God and Providence, and led to a "nearer knowledge and greater Admiration of the Deity." It is difficult to confidently hang the label Puritan on the man who thought God gave to Man an Upright Face, that he Might view the Stars, and learn Astronomy." *

Wilkins's writings on science and religion constituted the major statement of one side of the debate. Alexander Ross was the major spokesman for the other. He was perceptive enough to realize that most scientists would not risk the outright divorce of science and religion, but would attempt to achieve a similar effect indirectly by allowing only a one-way flow of ideas: nature and natural law might inform religion, but religion, and particularly Scripture, could not do the same for the new philosophy. Ross was quite correct in saying of Wilkins that "you may turn Divinity into Natural Philosophy," for that was precisely what the natural theology of Wilkins and his associates did during the next few decades.

Ross set out to block this approach by attacking Wilkins's techniques as undermining the fundamental doctrine of the unity of truth. But Wilkins did not deny the unity of truth or suggest that the truths of philosophy and religion might be contradictory. He argued, rather, that different kinds of truth were discoverable by different means. He did not belong to that Baconian or fideist school of thought which maintained that certain things could be true in theology and false in philosophy; he said only that philosophical truths were not to be found in Scripture. The real point of dispute lay in conflicting views of just what Scripture was and what truths it was intended to convey. Several approaches were possible. If Scripture were designed exclusively to convey religious truth and all incidental matters were means of accommodating God's word to the understanding of the vulgar, there was no need to assert any separation of religion and scientific truth. This was Wilkins's position. If one wished to save both a literal interpretation of all or nearly all Biblical passages and the new science, it was almost mandatory to assert the separation of the two kinds of truth and claim that what was true for religion was not necessarily true for philosophy. This approach was used by some of the followers of Bacon. If one were unconcerned with the new science and wished to assert a literal interpretation of Scripture, one simply denied the findings of science that seemed to contradict it. This approach, represented by Ross, could still maintain both the unity of truth *and* the literal truth of Scripture, and was adopted by Roman Catholics and Protestants of various types.

Having to his own satisfaction at least, solved the problem of freeing science from religious hindrances, it still remained for Wilkins to determine just what science was. He did not undertake this as a conscious task, but scattered throughout his early works are statements about the nature of science and scientific method. In *Mathematical Magick,* he divides knowledge into three types. Divine knowledge was directed at man's search for true happiness. The second and third types, natural and artificial knowledge, together comprised scientific knowledge. Natural knowledge included everything men knew about the frame of the universe or the course of Providence in the world. Artificial knowledge consisted primarily of inventions and the utilization of natural knowledge. Wilkins, however, also distinguished between the liberal and the illiberal sciences, the latter involving some physical activity such as manufacturing or trade.*

The distinction between divine knowledge on the one hand and natural and artificial knowledge on the other was obviously intended to isolate the scientific method from theological incursions. The distinction between natural and artificial knowledge bears some superficial resemblance to the later distinction between pure and applied science, and was one frequently drawn in the seventeenth and eighteenth centuries. For Wilkins it probably had little functional value, since he uses roughly the same mixture of theoretical reasoning, direct observation and experimentation in both. It was, of course, artificial knowledge that resulted in tangible inventions. Like most mid-seventeenth-century writers, Wilkins does not try to differentiate theoretical and experimental techniques, although later in his life he attempted to give the problem of scientific method a more precise formulation. The distinction between liberal and illiberal science was less one of the scientific technique than of social prejudice, and reflected the traditional categorization of knowledge.

Wilkins recognized that the progress of science depended on a proper approach both to the subject matter under investigation and to fellow investigators. Perhaps following the dictates of Nathaniel Carpenter, who so eloquently pleaded for freedom of inquiry, Wilkins insisted that those in "search of Truth" must "preserve a Philosophical Liberty." This liberty must be used to make impartial inquiries. The scientist must approach his task with "an equal Mind, not swayed by Prejudice, but indifferently resolved to assent into that Truth which upon deliberation shall seem most probable unto thy Reason." Liberty and impartiality are joined by a third scientific virtue—tentativeness. If there is "any doubt or obscurity" on a point of natural philosophy, we should "suspend our Assents," and although continuing to "dispute pro or con" on the matter, not settle our "Opinion on either side."

Scientific discussion also required restraint and modesty. In matters "where Victory cannot be had, Men must be content with Peace: . . . and it should be in all . . . Philosophical Contentions." This advice governed religious as well as scientific discourse. " 'Tis an Excellent Rule to be observed in all Disputes, That men should give *Soft Words* and *Hard Arguments;* that they would not so much strive to *vex,* as to convince an Enemy. If this were but diligently practiced in all Cases, and on all sides, we might be in a good measure be freed from those Vexations in the search of Truth."

While Wilkins was convinced that men "must labour to find out what things are in themselves, by our own Experience, and through Examination of their Natures" he was less certain just how "diligent Enquiry" and "thorough Examinations" should be accomplished. His earliest works, those on astronomy, are somewhat confused on scientific method and on related questions of epistemology. He frequently commented on the inadequacy of the senses, and insisted that "sense is but an ill Judge of Natural Secrets." At the same time that Wilkins hoped to convince his readers of Copernicanism through Reason, however, he also made much of the telescopic observations of Galileo, sense data that "plainly discovered" certain things "beyond Exception or Doubt." Astronomical knowledge was therefore superior to knowledge that depended on "Conjecture" and "Uncertainty." Thus Wilkins admits that the senses may be mistaken in some things, but indisputably correct in others.

There are several reasons for this confusion. Wilkins had not yet come to any firm conclusions himself about scientific method, nor had most scientists at this date. The only really confident party was composed of the sensationalist Baconians, who were not themselves scientists and who refused to recognize the importance of mathematical and other forms of abstract reasoning. Galileo, of course, favored both empirical observation and rational inquiry, but in what combination is still not clear. Wilkins recognized that both reason and sense data were required for scientific knowledge, but he could not spell out the relationship between them. When sense data yielded results that appeared to contradict the new science, he rejected them, otherwise he accepted them. He treated reason in exactly the same way. Traditionalists were attacked for excessive ratiocination, while the role of reason in the new science is repeatedly emphasized.

Although Bacon and Descartes grappled with the problems of

scientific methodology, the former emphasizing the role of the senses and induction, and the latter focusing on mathematics and deduction, like Wilkins, they admitted some element of the opposite method and did not successfully reconcile the two. It was probably not until Newton and Huygens that something approaching the modern scientific method was enunciated and then only in a casual and unsystematic way. Wilkins, at this point and in later years, grappled with this significant and difficult problem. It is hardly surprising, given the state of scientific philosophy, that he got no further than he did. In any event his work demonstrates that seventeenth-century English science was not committed, as is frequently asserted, exclusively to empiricism and experimentation.

Yet Wilkins clearly favored experimentation, particularly in *Mathematical Magick,* though he never made precisely clear what experimentation entailed. On occasion telescopic observations, for example, are called experiments, an apparent identification of experience and experiment. Yet for the most part, he uses the word experiment to connote some kind of trial. He particularly stressed the need for experiment in the development of machinery and other practical devices. There are two plausible explanations of Wilkins's increased reliance on sensory data and experimentation in *Mathematical Magick.* Oxford in his student days provided broad opportunities for mathematical and astronomical study, but it may not have offered similar opportunities for experimentation. As he came into contact with men actively engaged in experiments, Wilkins probably began to more fully appreciate this aspect of science. The shift to a more experimental approach may have taken place collectively within the group that later became the Royal Society. It seems likely that the 1645 group was more interested in discussion than experiment, and that only later, at Oxford and after they had formed the Royal Society, did they take on a more practical experimental program with Baconian overtones. A second and simpler explanation lies in the subject matter of Wilkins's earliest works. The *Discovery* and the *Dis-*

course, because they focused on astronomy, necessarily involved a greater emphasis on mathematics and logic. *Mathematical Magick,* because it concerned practice as well as the principles of mechanics, necessarily gave a larger role to experiment and observation.

Wilkins has been claimed as a Baconian because he emphasized so strongly that science could be used to lessen men's labors, increase the number of inventions, and provide the basis for action. But it must be noted that he was referring specifically to artificial knowledge, and not all scientific knowledge. In discussing astronomy, he deemphasized the practical benefits and focused on the joys of contemplation. If Wilkins spoke of the conquest of nature, he was speaking in terms of artificial knowledge. Many portions of natural knowledge could lead only to a better understanding of the operations of nature. Thus to classify Wilkins as a pure Baconian would surely be misleading. He thought highly of Bacon, and even occasionally referred to him as our "new Aristotle." He was throughly familiar with his writings and recognized him as one (but only one) of the heralds of the new philosophy. Nevertheless the approaches of the two men were quite different, a difference that can perhaps be accounted for by Wilkins's early encounter with astronomy where theory and mathematical logic were obviously crucial. Bacon, by contrast, had no interest in astronomy or mathematics. Although Wilkins found Bacon's arguments on the progressive nature of truth and the relationship of ancient to modern knowledge useful, and his views in the *Advancement of Learning* about a real character stimulating, he did not follow Bacon on the crucial question of epistemology. Nor did he view science as an exclusively utilitarian branch of knowledge. Samuel Hartlib, William Petty, and Robert Boyle may perhaps be designated Baconians, but this label cannot be applied to Wilkins, Seth Ward, John Wallis, or Christopher Wren, all of whom had a great appreciation for the theoretical as well as the empirical aspects of the new science.

The influence of Bacon on Wilkins and English scientists has frequently been stressed and perhaps overstressed. Such an emphasis fails to take into account the fact that the scientific movement in the seventeenth century was an international one. In order to assess influences, one must look at the European community of scholars, not just those of a single country. In this context, and it is precisely in this context that the English scientists viewed their own work, Bacon is an important but not commanding figure. For those Englishmen actually engaged in scientific pursuits, he undoubtedly ranked with but not above Galileo, Descartes, Copernicus, and others. Wilkins's own work, with its wide-ranging borrowings from the entire international scientific community, both typified and helped to shape the scientific consciousness of his day, and it is obvious from that work that the English scientific world did not acknowledge a single master or use the Channel as an intellectual moat. For those Englishmen who followed science without being themselves scientists, Bacon undoubtedly had a special place; he was the most prominent scientific figure with whom they could become familiar in casual study. Their preoccupation with Bacon may have led later scholars to assign him a more central position than he had in the eyes of the seventeenth-century scientists themselves.

As for specific influences on Wilkins, he relies on different sources for different problems. On the relationship between ancients and moderns and the progressive nature of truth, Bacon is certainly important. But so is Campanella. Wilkins's views on Aristotle are almost identical to both Galileo's and Campanella's. His writings on astronomy lean heavily on those of Galileo, Copernicus, Kepler, and others, and he is indebted to Campanella for some of his ideas on the relationship between science and religion. If a choice were necessary, Wilkins would have to be labeled a follower of Galileo rather than Bacon, but such a choice would simply obscure the basic eclecticism of his writing and of the scientific world his writing reflected. In any event, Wilkins's mixture of reason and empiricism is so similar to Galileo's, and so similarly imprecise, that there is no profit in labeling him a Baconian.

The purer empiricism of Bacon was in fact largely confined to nonscientists. No working scientist of Wilkins's breed could have completely espoused Bacon's epistemology, no matter how much he appreciated the value of experimentation. For scientific work then revolved principally around mathematical and astronomical problems that were as much theoretical and logical as empirical. Galileo remains the dominant intellectual light of the period, and basically he followed a mathematical-deductive rather than inductive method of inquiry. He routinely accepted unverified or unverifiable hypotheses so long as they appeared to be theoretically sound. This was Wilkins's position as well.

In Wilkins's early writings, the difficulties of relating scientific hypotheses to the ultimate structure of the world and of obtaining scientifically verifiable knowledge were not central. It was only in later years that Wilkins found it necessary to delve deeper into epistemological complexities. The early writings thus contain only his first steps toward a philosophy of science. We shall have occasion to examine his more mature views later. So far what we have seen is a highly articulate and successful popularizer, who, casting a wide net, sought to bring to the literate Englishman the best science of his day, but largely the science of others, not his own, and materials whose significance he himself did not yet fully appreciate.

III. Religion

Wilkins's early scientific writings stand as a kind of counterpoint to his duties as clergyman and religious commentator. His first religious work, *Ecclesiastes or, a Discourse Concerning the Gift of Preaching* (1646), was a handbook for aspiring preachers. It was followed by *A Discourse Concerning the Beauty of Providence* (1649), and a prayer manual entitled *A Discourse Concerning the Gift of Prayer* (1651) a companion volume to *Ecclesiastes*. All three works enjoyed a wide circulation and were reprinted several times.

Because Wilkins provides a key link in the argument of those seeking to establish a close correlation between Puritanism and science, an examination of his writings and activities in this period in order to place him somewhere along the line between Laudianism and extreme Puritanism seems necessary here. Wilkins was not a Laudian, but then neither were most Anglicans. Too often the identification of Laudianism with Anglicanism has meant the lumping of all anti-Laudians into a category labeled Puritan. In the 1630's and 1640's, many men opposed Laud without aspiring to the fundamental change in the Church of England generally associated with Puritanism. At the same time, some Englishmen who in their own day were considered Anglicans accepted the successive Interregnum establishments and signed the Covenant and Engagement. Between the extreme forms of Anglicanism and Puritanism there lies a broad middle ground in which it is difficult to clearly differentiate between moderate Puritan and moderate Anglican. Wilkins was either a moderate Anglican of the Fuller or Ussher variety or a Puritan in the Erastian mold. He was willing to accept any religious establishment that did not violate the fundamentals of Christianity, and he was particularly reticent about the form of church government he ultimately preferred.

Wilkins has been called a Calvinist. He certainly never considered himself one, though certain Calvinist doctrines in the modified form of Covenant theology appear in his early religious thought. In Covenant theology Calvin's strict predestinarianism was softened. Although found primarily among Puritans, these modified Calvinist views were also espoused by some moderate Anglicans. The Covenant elements in Wilkins's thought therefore do not prove that he was a Puritan.

The same must be said for his more general stance on predestination. The concept of predestination is absent from Wilkins's later thought, which suggests that his statements of 1651 do not reflect as strong a position as they might seem to. Nevertheless in 1651 noting the role of Christ in election, he said, "There was nothing to move him in us, when we lay altogether in the general heap of mankind. It was his own free grace and bounty that made him to take delight in us, to chuse us out from the rest, to sever us from those many thousands in the world, who shall perish everlastingly." Predestination was not, of course, a monopoly of the Puritans, but a doctrine adhered to by many Anglicans as well.

The Divinity to whom Wilkins advises his reader to pray in the *Gift of Prayer* is more a God of mercy, and less a God of justice, than that of the typical Calvinist. Reconciliation with God requires only true repentance. Although he expressed the typical Protestant view that man could not regenerate himself unaided, Wilkins believed that by prayer "we may regenerate and become new creatures." And though he supported the traditional doctrine that a "lively faith" would produce good works, most of his writing implies that all men could perform good works if they wished. In his later years he wrote as if all men held their salvation in their own hands by acting morally. This increasing emphasis on morality and natural theology at the expense of revealed religion, which pushed doctrinal problems such as predestination, grace, and election into the background, was typical of Restoration latitudinarians. But here again, some latitudinarians had initially been in the Puritan and some in the Anglican camp.

Though generally reluctant to express an opinion on specific questions dividing the religious parties, Wilkins did take an explicit stand on the controversy over extemporaneous versus set forms of public prayer. Anglicans favored set forms of public prayer, and the Presbyterians did not oppose this position; Independents and the sectaries generally favored extemporaneous public prayer. Wilkins urged a middle course: set public prayers, and a mixture of formal and extemporaneous elements in private prayer.

On Sabbatarianism, another of the hallmarks of Puritanism, Wilkins seems to have held a strict and essentially Puritan attitude. Puritans tended to dwell on sin and human failings more than their Anglican counterparts. For the most part Wilkins, who had a high opinion of man's capacities, does not concentrate on these topics. Yet his *Gift of Prayer,* does emphasize original and actual sin. Both Anglicans and Puritans, however, conceived the confession of sin to be a central element of prayer, so it is understandable that Wilkins should be more preoccupied with sin in a book on prayer than in his other writing. Particularly in his later works, man emerges as a basically good rather than sinful creature, although original sin remains, at least in theory.

Wilkins's attitudes toward Scripture during this period were far more liberal than his views on the Sabbath and prayer. We have already noted that Scripture was not to be considered a source of scientific truth and that its function was limited to religion. In "Divinity," however, it provided "an Infallible Rule" that "plainly inform[s] . . . of all necessary Truth." Nevertheless he argued that the "Negative Authority of Scripture is not relevent in those things which are not fundamentals of Religion." Some things in Scripture were "manifest"; others "crypticall and obscure." Only the essentials for salvation were manifest, although other truths—historical, doctrinal, or practical—might sometimes be found in Scripture. Doctrinal truth, however, was not among those necessary for salvation. While it was acceptable to "deal *pro* or *con* in Philosophy," it was improper to be "too bold with Divine Truths." When clarity was lacking, caution was required. In interpreting any particularly difficult passage, Wilkins thought the "most rational solution" was "to look upon it as a Hyperbolical expression . . . which are not to be interpreted according to the literal sense of the words, but according to the drift of the speaker." His approach to the Bible differed markedly from the fundamentalist, literalist tendencies of many Puritans.*

During his early years in London, and later as head of Wadham, Wilkins had many opportunities to discuss the religious issues of the day and make known his opinions on them. His position and his authorship of several important religious books notwithstanding, however, there is remarkably little that identifies him as an adherent of one or another party. Although Wilkins was accused of being both an Independent and a Presbyterian, there is no real evidence that he identified himself with either. He almost certainly accepted both the Covenant, which was associated with Presbyterianism, and the Engagement, which was associated with Independency. This led Anthony Wood and John Aubrey, both Oxford residents during Wilkins's tenure there, to considerable discussion over his party identification. On one occasion Wood considered Wilkins an Independent, and on another a "notorious complyer" with the Presbyterians. Aubrey, however, insisted that Wilkins had never been a Presbyterian. Wood's final assessment was that when the rebellion broke out, "he closed with the Presbyterians, having always before been puritanically affected, and took the convenant." Wilkins's behavior thus confused his contemporaries as well as later historians. His only modern biographer recognized that he was a moderate, but thought his temperament closer to "mellowed Independency" than the "stiffness" of the Presbyterians. Rather than becoming a member of either group, he accepted each in turn when it controlled the religious establishment. His willingness to comply suggests that he did not consider such compliance a very important issue. A number of known Anglicans took the Covenant and quietly kept their posts. There is nothing in his writings or actions before the Restoration to indicate that he accepted the Independent and Presbyterian view that the form of church organization was designated by God. After the Restoration, Wilkins made it quite clear that he regarded the form of church government as an indifferent question that should be settled on the basis of appropriateness and expediency. This position was, of course, typically Anglican. On one of the few occasions when he mentioned the Church prior to 1660, he would only say that the Church required public and private prayer, the ministry of the Word, and the administration of the sacraments.

Toleration was another divisive issue. Wilkins never openly favored either the toleration desired by Independents or the rigid establishment and repression advocated by Presbyterians. At Oxford and later as Bishop of Chester he always strove to bring together those of disparate views, and it is clear that he eventually favored a publicly established, comprehensive, and nonrepressive church. Furthermore, Wilkins never discussed discipline, one of the hallmarks of Presbyterianism. Nor does he suggest, at least prior to the Restoration, that morality should be enforced by an ecclesiastical jurisdiction. His attitudes on these questions seem closest to those of lay Erastians of either broadly Puritan or broadly Anglican persuasion. Wilkins's associations first with Dod and the Pym group and later with Lord Berkeley and the Elector, together with his reticence over questions of church government and his willingess to accept a variety of successive governments, strongly suggest that Wilkins simply did not consider these questions essential. In view of the fact that he openly adopts this "indifferent" view after the Restoration, there is every reason to believe that he had held it all along.

Wilkins's early associations indicate that he was anti-Laudian. His post-Restoration relations with High Church bishops and his later views confirm this supposition. The unsolved problem, then,

is whether in the early 1640's he favored a modified, purged episcopacy, perhaps along lines acceptable to Pym, Archbishop Williams, or Thomas Fuller, or the specifically Presbyterian arrangements so popular with the London clergy. It seems probable that,
like the lay leaders of Parliament with whom he was associated,
Wilkins favored the elimination of Laudianism and a return to
the comprehensiveness of Elizabeth, combined with a reduction
in the jurisdiction of the ecclesiastical courts. There is nothing to
suggest that he favored Presbyterianism as such. He was not involved in the Assembly of Divines, for example, like his friend
John Wallis. There is no doubt at all, however, that Wilkins was
antagonistic to the sects. He disliked their separatism, their lower-
class membership, and above all their mysticism and excessive
zeal. Still, a few of Wilkins's contemporaries alleged that even after the Restoration he was really a Presbyterian in disguise, and
that he accepted a deanery, and later a bishopric, under false pre-
tenses. But as we have already noted, nothing that Wilkins said or
did put him in the Presbyterian camp, except perhaps his willingness to take the Covenant. A better case for Presbyterianism could
be made against John Wallis, or even Edward Reynolds, who
became Bishop of Norwich. Both these men represented the Presbyterians at the several conferences between Presbyterians and
churchmen in the early months of the Restoration. Wilkins was
not even invited to these meetings. Nor, unlike leading Presbyterians, was he made chaplain to the King in 1660. If Wilkins was
called a Presbyterian by his enemies, he was also called a
Socinian. In both cases the labels were epithets rather than accurate designations.

Wilkins lacked one of the prime qualities of the staunch
Puritan—confidence that his views were correct. He frequently
noted that men were naturally prone to error, and that impartiality was a rare quality among men. Although these misgivings did
not lead Wilkins to skepticism, they do suggest why the fervor
and zeal of the Puritan were alien to his nature. Wilkins and
other latitudinarians suspected any allegiance based on claims of

infallibility or authority. While Puritans avoided the formal claim of infallibility because of its Roman Catholic associations, they were absolutely certain of their monopoly on religious truth. Tentativeness of judgment and unwillingness to find solutions based on authority, together with insistence that quiet discussion rather than violent argument or the clash of authorities was most likely to yield truth, were attitudes that Wilkins appears to have carried over from scientific investigation to religious thought. Wilkins was also distinguished from most Puritans by his greater emphasis on the moral aspects of religion and his increasing use of non-Christian moralists. These tendencies eventually became the dominant note of his religious writings. As early as the 1650's, Wilkins was recognized as a leader of the "Moral, Sober Party" and as an antagonist of the "fiery" and zealous group at Oxford. Indeed, Wilkins and others who emphasized morality and moderation over doctrine and zeal had to face the accusations and "persecutions" of those who called them "mere moral men, without the Power of Godliness."

Thus the answer to the question was Wilkins a Puritan is both yes and no. He was trained in that tradition and adopted Covenant theology. The direction of his preaching is similar to that taken by the group Haller has called the "spiritual brotherhood," that is, by such men as John Dod, Richard Sibbes, and John Preston. But of course the Anglicans, Archbishop Ussher, and Tom Fuller can also be seen as following in their path. Even if Wilkins can be fitted into this segment of Puritan thought, he selected among the strains of that thought, further developing some of them while dropping others almost entirely. He never possessed the zeal and intensity characteristic of the Puritan clergy. He largely abandoned doctrinal questions to focus on the moral elements of Christianity and the fundamentals of religion. In his hands "practical divinity" became personal morality. He increasingly emphasized natural religion and deemphasized Scripture, although he continued to assert its importance. In doing so he used reason more frequently than Scripture to support his position. All this, along with his lack of interest in questions of discipline and church organization, drew him closer to Anglicanism, which possessed the rational, liberal, tolerant traditions of William Chillingworth and Hales. Given these factors, together with his political conservatism and his associations with the aristocracy, it is not surprising that Wilkins accepted the Restoration and Restoration Anglicanism.

Wilkins's relationship to Anglicanism is just as unclear as his Puritan ties. There is no doubt that he was personally sympathetic to many Anglicans, chaplain to Lord Berkeley, and a close friend of Tom Fuller. While at Oxford, one contemporary remarked, Wilkins was far from approving "the ways of those in power." In fact when an Anglican friend there "bewailed to him [Wilkins] the Calamities of the Church, and declared his Obedience even then to the Laws of it: He incouraged him in it, . . . protecting both him and many others, by an interest he had gained, and made use of chiefly for such purposes." It was well known that at Wadham Wilkins protected many Anglicans and Royalists. Yet protection and sympathy do not necessarily imply agreement. There is some evidence that Wilkins was willing to accept episcopacy, one of the few issues dividing moderate Puritans from moderate Anglicans. In 1657 he is reported to have told both Oliver Cromwell and the Scots Presbyterian Dr. Sharp that he thought episcopacy should be reestablished. There are other points of similarity between Wilkins's position and Anglican thought. Both Wilkins and the Anglicans emphasized reason more than most Puritans and were more receptive to natural theology. Both discussed church government and ceremonies in terms of utility and expediency rather than divine institution. It could perhaps be argued that although his education and many of his views were Puritan, Wilkins's temperament was Anglican, and that, over a period of time, his personal inclinations, together with the results of political upheaval, led him to accept Anglicanism without violating any of his earlier beliefs.

Perhaps rather than trying to decide whether Wilkins was a

moderate Anglican or a moderate Puritan during the Interregnum years, it might be more useful simply to call him a moderate. This was certainly the pivotal aspect of his thought and action both before and after the Restoration. Latitudinarianism, rather than Anglicanism or Puritanism, seems to be the key feature of his religious outlook. Although most of the evidence on this trend in his thought comes from his post-Restoration writings and activities, there is a great deal to suggest it was well-developed long before 1660. The origins of his latitudinarianism are somewhat obscure. At Wadham he was tolerant of opinions he did not share, and willing to encourage and cooperate with members of all parties. It is probable, however, that Wilkins's latitudinarianism and tolerance of differing religious views goes back at least as far as his association with Dod. There are indications that Dod's views on the unity of the Church and toleration of internal differences made a great impression on Wilkins, an impression that was fortified by subsequent political and religious conflicts. It seems fair to say that Wilkins was a latitudinarian long before 1660.

Indeed one factor pushing him toward latitudinarianism may have been the failure of his views to fit snugly into either the Puritan or the Anglican mold. He and others in this intermediate position may have been peculiarly sympathetic to reconciliation efforts, and especially sensitive to the fact that there was little to separate the moderates of the two sides. It is perhaps no accident that the religious backgrounds and commitments of so many latitudinarians are not easily defined, and that many of them combined Puritan or semi-Puritan backgrounds with attitudes associated with Anglicanism.

In 1649 Wilkins published *A Discourse Concerning the Beauty of Providence,* one of his most popular sermons, and the one that, of all his writings, sheds most light on his reaction to the events of the 1640's. The sermon was intended to comfort those who had been adversely affected by the events of the past few years. It was essentially a plea to accept the recent upheavals in Church and

State because they had been ordered by God. Although Wilkins says nothing of King and Parliament, or Anglican, Presbyterian, and Independent, it is not difficult to see that he was displeased with the direction events had taken, and that the discourse was written to help others accept a world gone awry. The doctrine of Providence made men cheerful and thankful in times of mercy; in times of suffering it should make them patient and submissive. The doctrine of Providence, as propagated by Wilkins, had many affinities with Stoicism, and was a favorite of those influenced by Roman thought. Wilkins particularly admired the Stoics and was constantly citing "the divine" Seneca. Of all Wilkins's early writings on religious matters, the sermon on Providence most resembles the later works in its emphasis on the role of reason and natural theology, and its reliance on classical rather than Biblical tradition.

In the political sphere the doctrine led to an affirmation and acceptance of the status quo, and provided a rationalization for the political inaction and passive adaptation to political change that Wilkins himself practiced. Wilkins was a politically astute man who recognized that political facility or "prudence" was necessary in the rapidly changing times he lived in. Political expertise was as essential as scientific and perhaps even more difficult to acquire, "considering that great variety and inconstancy which there is in the judgments and affects of men, the clashing and intanglements of cross interest, the several changes and vicissitudes that befall humane affairs: I say all things considered it is not mere *integrity* without great *prudence,* that can preserve a man in a constant and clear reputation." As a practitioner of such prudence, Wilkins was attacked by his enemies for unprincipled cultivation of whoever held power at the moment, and lauded by his friends for the astuteness with which he pursued his own essentially moral goals through the political maze.

Curiously, Wilkins's *Ecclesiastes* and *Gift of Prayer* have been of most interest to literary historians, for they are pivotal works in the change in prose and sermon style that took place at mid-century.* Both were intended primarily to aid uninitiated ministers and laymen organize their thoughts and thus communicate them more effectively. We have already seen that one of Wilkins's principal intellectual preoccupations was the improvement of communication. His works on prayer and preaching, on communication between man and God, should be seen as one facet of a broader quest for more efficient and systematic modes of expression. *Ecclesiastes* was essentially a handbook of references to other divines, designed to aid clergymen in the construction of sermons, although Wilkins in addition hoped to combat conceptions of the ministry and the preaching that had developed as the result of the proliferation of sects. His habitual caution did not leave him. While he was willing to note the writers he considered most useful, he refused to include the work of any living author in that category. Nor would he say which authorities were best, for few would "agree in the same judgement." He expressed distaste only for "mysticall Divines, who pretend to some higher illumination." * In this category were Roman Catholic mystics such as Teresa of Avila and Francis of Sales, as well as Jakob Boehme, the favorite of the more mystical English sects. His selection, however, was not anti-Catholic as such, as he recommended some Roman Catholic writers, especially Lombard and Aquinas. Nor did he condemn scholastic theologians out of hand. His bibliographies contained a wide variety of subject matter ranging from materials on Scripture and church government to specific controversies and doctrinal problems. Scriptural materials were most important, and all a minister's studies were to be subordinated to them. Heathen writers, however, especially Plato and Aristotle, were particularly useful in connection with natural divinity. Wilkins also emphasized the Stoics, who appear to have been his favorites, and included some more modern writers, such as Raymond of Sabunde, whose views on natural theology were similar to his own.

Like other kinds of intellectual activity, preaching required rules and method. It was, of course, particularly important that the minister have mastered the art of preaching if he wished to instruct others, although academic preparation in languages, sciences, and divinity was also necessary. Two qualities were required: "A right understanding of sound doctrine, an ability to propound, confirm, and apply it to the edification of others." Unlike the humanists of the sixteenth century, who saw an intimate relationship between the possession and expression of knowledge, Wilkins here clearly reflects the later tendency to distinguish between knowledge and its communication. The art of preaching, Wilkins insisted, required knowledge, spiritual qualities "infused" from above, and the specific art of preaching, which could be acquired by human industry. If, as some of the more radical religious groups claimed, prayer and even the ability to pray came as a direct "infusion" from God alone, his *Gift of Prayer* and *Ecclesiastes* would have been not only vain and useless, but perhaps even blasphemous. The *Gift of Prayer* sought to provide those skills that could be learned.

The art of preaching fell into three categories: Method, Matter, and Expression. By method Wilkins meant the "art of contriving our discourses in such a regular frame wherein every part may have its due place and dependence." Proper organization helped not only the minister but his audience, who could thus "understand and retain a Sermon with greater ease and profit." The best method was that of "Doctrine and Use," associated with the "practical divines," most of whom were Puritan. Wilkins belongs to the school of sermon construction that divides and subdivides, although he warns against excessive subdivision.* His own sermons follow a simple, logical pattern, with only a few points and sub-points. It was this simplified organization that won so many followers during the Restoration. John Tillotson, for example, might easily have been guided by his father-in-law's manual in both method and style. Simplicity is the keynote of both construction and treatment.* Wilkins was opposed to the common Puritan practice of dissecting the text into minute parts and then enlarging on each. In explicating the text it was necessary to "follow from the words by a strong Logicall consequence" in the "most easie perspicuous phrase." If necessary, a doctrine might be mentioned, but particular care must be taken to show its "necessary dependence" on the specific text. Here again we see Wilkins's desire to avoid doctrinal issues. Proof, divine and human, was a fundamental element of every sermon. Wilkins makes no objection to the use of human authorities, including the Church Fathers, the decrees of councils, or the testimony of the heathens, to show truths "agreeable to naturall light." In many respects Wilkins visualized the sermon in terms of the ordinary rules of discourse, even though it had a special and peculiarly important purpose. For certain "notionall doctrinal points," for example, the nine topics of logic and rhetoric were helpful in the "invention of proper arguments." The application, rather than text or doctrine, was most important, an emphasis that reflected the priority Wilkins gave to moral questions.

In his treatment of prayer, we again find Wilkins's concern with organization and logic as central to all types of communication, even that with God. Like preaching, prayer must first be reduced to "Rules and Method," so it can be more easily and fully comprehended. To provide the "matter" for prayer Wilkins recommended keeping a spiritual diary of the sort common among the Puritans and not unknown among Anglicans.

It was Wilkins's comments on style, in both *Ecclesiastes* and the *Gift of Prayer,* that seem to have had the greatest impact. Although many of Wilkins's statements suggest that he was hostile to traditional rhetoric, he probably was not; he simply refused to discuss it because he expected the clergy he was addressing to have been exposed to such "preparatory studies" before their "entry in the ministry." For this reason Wilkins never makes clear his precise views on the relationship between logic and rhetoric. His chief aim remained clarity and directness. Sermons

must be plain and natural, not being darkened with the affection of Scholasticall harshnesse, or Rhetoricall flourishes. Obscurity in the discourse is an argument of ignorance in the minde. The greatest learning is to be seen in the greatest plainnesse. The more nearly we understand any thing our selves, the more easily we expound it to others. When the notion itself is good, the best way to set it off, is the most obvious plain expression.

Some rhetorical expressions might be used and were even "very proper and powerful" for expressing and exciting the affections, yet even in prayer it was best to lay aside . . . needless artifice, or affectation," and address God "with the same plainnesse, and simplicity as we do with men." Thus "flaunting affected eloquence" had to be eliminated, but not all art or care.*

Although Wilkins's sermons were not entirely novel in adopting a simple direct style, his scientific writings were among the first to be written in an unadorned yet careful prose. Wilkins opposed both negligence and affectation. The first led to expressing thoughts "in a rude, improper, unseemly manner." The other took two forms. One was overneatness and elegance inspired by the elaborate prose of the Ciceronians and the court preachers. The second was the use of mystical language so fashionable among the sects at the time he wrote. Because *Ecclesiastes* had such a great influence on the preaching, as well as the general prose style, of the Restoration, and because it has received so much attention from literary historians interested in the development of the style associated with Tillotson, I have discussed Wilkins's ideas on style at considerable length. Some literary historians, such as R. F. Jones, have emphasized the role of science in the development of the new prose style. Others have found anti-Ciceronianism or Puritanism to be key factors.* But all use Wilkins's *Ecclesiastes* and his later comments in the *Gift of Prayer* and the *Essay Towards a Real Character, and a Philosophical Language* (1668) as evidence.

There can be no doubt that the chief influence on *Ecclesiastes* was the traditional Puritan sermon style. From at least the third quarter of the sixteenth century, Puritans practiced a system of logical exposition that reduced the imaginative and decorative elements in sermons to a minimum, insisting that the style be simple, plain, and direct. They disapproved not only of literary allusion, but also of farfetched metaphors and classical citations. The method was based primarily on the Ramist logic and in form followed a structure based on the categories of doctrine, reason, and use. Each of these divisions were in turn divided and subdivided, often very extensively. Although the underpinnings of this well-developed genre were elaborate organization and scholastic logic, Puritans wished to appeal to the heart as well as the mind. The traditional scholastic method was taught in the universities, but the major development of the style, and its peculiar association with Puritanism, came from the "spiritual brotherhood." John Dod was one of its chief advocates and set the example for many younger men. Dod's sermons were very much along the lines Wilkins later advocated, perhaps the only difference being that Dod's method was more elaborate. An examination of Dod's sermons, together with the rules set out by William Perkins and other Puritan advocates of the plain style, makes it clear that Wilkins's *Ecclesiastes* was a part of the Puritan preaching tradition. In time, however, the Puritan's emphasis on plain language was obscured by the tremendous complexity of their "method," with its countless subdivisions and their minute dissections of the text. Wilkins and later Restoration writers retained the natural, direct language, but reduced the method to a simple outline form and eliminated textual division.

While the spare, plain style thus has many associations with Puritanism, it was also advocated by many Anglicans. It was basically the court preachers, particularly the Laudians, who used a complex, learned, and witty style. Thus it is difficult to distinguish Puritanism from Anglicanism on the question of style unless we confine ourselves to a simplistic confrontation of Laudians and Puritans. Until we know more about the kind of Anglicanism accepted by the large majority of communicants and clergy from the beginning of the century to the Restoration, we cannot really make meaningful comparisons between Puritan and Anglican preaching styles or indeed between any other aspects of Puritan and Anglican thought. Nor is it possible to make a simple correlation between scientific ideas and a spare style. Alexander Ross, who defended scholasticism, Aristotle and the Ptolemaic system, and who was in almost every respect the epitome of obscurantism, defended the plain style against the rhetorical in philosophical matters, in terms almost identical to those of the Royal Society. It is thus difficult to argue that the origins of the plain style lay solely in the new scientific movement and Bacon's insistence on plain style.

Wilkins was almost certainly influenced to some degree by the Ramist logic and rhetoric which had such a great influence on the chief Puritan theologians of the early seventeenth century. Not only is his method of division reminiscent of Ramism, but his tendency to distinguish between logic and rhetoric, or form and content, is consistent with that approach. Ramism itself encouraged the development of a plain style, for its rigorous separation of logic and rhetoric put a constraint on eloquence by reducing rhetoric to an unnecessary adornment to the logical argument. Unlike the Puritan practitioners of Ramism, however, Wilkins did not regard it as a method of obtaining knowledge, but simply as a method of presenting known data, useful only as a means of classification and schematic arrangement.*

Another probable influence on Wilkins was the anti-Ciceronian movement, which George Williamson considers the chief element in the development of the plain style. The anti-Ciceronians, too, advocated a simple, relatively unadorned prose. According to Williamson, anti-Ciceronianism simply involved replacing the oratorical Ciceronian style with the brief, plain style associated with Seneca. He argues that Wilkins's attack on rhetorical flourish indicates his anti-Ciceronianism, and points to his praise of Seneca, and particularly his echo of the Senecan view that philosophy concerns things, not words. Furthermore, although the method of "Doctrine and Use" is usually associated with Nonconformity, it was commonly used by Roman Catholic orators as well and seems to have stemmed from Seneca's *Epistles*. William-son's explanation of Wilkins's plain style as directly due to Senecanism may not be completely convincing in view of other competing influences,* but certainly it cannot be ruled out. Wil-kins's frequent references to Seneca, his great admiration for him, and his emphasis on the communication of ideas rather than the elegance of words, all indicate that the Senecan influence was there.

In Wilkins, then, the various intellectual forces behind the plain style seem to have met. On the edge of the division between Puritan and Anglican, he drew from a general non-Laudian preaching tradition that had much of the plain style. As a partici-pant in the scientific movement, he shared the scientists' concern for accurate, simple, and well-organized communication. And as a classical scholar, he drew on the Senecan tradition. Perhaps, as recently suggested, the change in style is traceable not to a specific group or movement but to a basic change in the intellectual climate of seventeenth-century England. Wilkins, involved in many intellectual developments, and particularly attuned to the latest scholarly fashions, became a central figure in the new synthesis of style that accompanied the new habits of thought. Wil-kins's own contribution was to simplify the organization of the Puritan plain style and to contribute to the dominance of the plain style after the Restoration. Through the Royal Society, he ensured its success in the field of scientific prose, and his own works on preaching and prayer helped introduce the style first among latitudinarians, and then among Anglicans in general. The style and "method" of the earlier Puritan and later lati-tudinarian sermons were much alike, although they differed sig-nificantly in content. Doctrine became less and morality more important for the latitudinarians, and their citations, although not frequent, were likely to be drawn from classical writers, particularly the Stoics.

Although Tillotson has frequently been given the credit for the change in sermon and prose style, it surely belongs to Wilkins.

Until recently, however, only Edmund Gosse viewed Wilkins as the pioneer and argued that "The praise given to Tillotson properly belonged to Wilkins. . . . [He] learned to write English from his study of the Bishop of Chester, who he enthusiastically admired." Wilkins's preeminence had now been confirmed by Louis G. Locke, the author of the most complete study of Tillotson.

Wilkins's own sermons follow the model, and are in practice even simpler than his "method" would suggest. His earliest known sermon, the *Discourse Concerning the Beauty of Providence,* is a simple but logically ordered discourse. Its cool tone, simple organization, and appeals to reason and non-Christian moralists make it an obvious forerunner of the Restoration style of Tillotson, William Lloyd and, of course, Wilkins himself. His delivery was described by one of his followers: "He spoke solid truth, with as little show of Art as was possible. He exprest all things in their true and Natural colours; with that aptness and plainness of Speech, that grave Natural way of Elocution, that showed he had not design upon his hearers. His plainness was best for the instruction of the simple. . . . He applied himself rather to their Understandings than Affections."

At first the sermon style advocated by Wilkins was adopted only by Wilkins, Tillotson, Joseph Glanvill, and other clerics of a latitudinarian bent. Samuel Parker indicated that the new style of preaching was at least initially considered peculiar to that group. William Lloyd and Gilbert Burnet, liberal churchmen and personal friends of Wilkins, also advocated the forms suggested by Wilkins.* The only conspicuous latitudinarian group that rejected the new approach were the Cambridge Platonists, who preferred a more mystical and often very learned and obscure style.

Within a few years, the Wilkins style had become general to Anglicanism. In 1662 the King himself, in a directive to the archbishops, asked for its semi-official adoption. Even Robert South, a conservative Anglican, became a strong proponent of the new style. And soon after, in 1670, John Eachard argued that simpler sermons might save the clergy from the contempt into which they seemed to be falling. Others who wrote specifically on the subject of sermon construction followed Wilkins's canons. Glanvill and Burnet have already been mentioned. James Arderne's popular manual on sermon writing was simply Wilkins's *Ecclesiastes* in Restoration dress. The style that Wilkins popularized became the standard one of the next decades, and his *Ecclesiastes* was remembered and used long after his death.*

Although some authorities have claimed that Wilkins's modification of the Puritan plain style was helpful in bringing Presbyterians into the Church, presumably because they were familiar with it, current studies of Restoration Puritanism indicate that Puritan sermons no longer followed the plain style. Nonconformist sermons consisted of exact logical analysis, exact division, and much subdivision, and they emphasized grace, sin and damnation. They thus differed substantially both in form and content from the sermons of the latitudinarian Anglicans. Although not many years earlier Puritans had ridiculed Anglicans for their rhetorical flourishes, in 1668 Robert South could taunt John Owen with the same charge.

The origins and influences of stylistic movements are nearly always complex. Some have found Puritanism, others Senecanism and still others scientific discourse to have been the major foundation of the Restoration style. All these seem to have been significant not only in the Restoration style generally but in that of Wilkins, who was such a key figure in its development. It does not seem probable, as R. F. Jones has suggested, that it was the scientific movement that first affected prose style and then imposed its style on sermons. There were too many advocates of other versions of the plain style that had developed at the same time or even earlier who were not scientists. Puritanism, however, does not provide the complete answer either, because similar views were fairly widely held by non-Laudian Anglicans and even Roman Catholics. Anti-Ciceronianism was clearly present among the advocates of the plain style, but Senecanism may have been more of a symptom that a cause. Moreover, we do not know just why the latitudinarians were the first Restoration advocates of the plain style, although it must be noted that as a group, they, like Wilkins, were peculiarly sympathetic to the new science. Wilkins was not only a latitudinarian leader and a reformer of prose and sermon style, but the key figure in the founding of the Royal Society. It seems probable that it was at least in part owing to his personal activity and influence that the new stylistic credo was adopted by both liberal churchmen and the Royal Society. Puritanism, Anglicanism, latitudinarianism, Senecanism and the new science are thus all related in one way or another to the plain style—and to Wilkins, its leading proponent.

IV. The University Years: Oxford Under Puritan Rule

In 1648 Wilkins became Warden of Wadham College, Oxford. Until the Restoration of Charles II in 1660, he lived the relatively quiet life of a university don. As head of one of the most flourishing colleges of Interregnum Oxford, Wilkins was often involved in university-wide politics. On some occasions, for example during the educational conflict that broke out in 1653, his influence extended beyond the academic community. But his towering achievement of these years was the fostering of a scientific movement at Oxford. The small beginnings of the 1645 group grew more substantial, and, under the cultivation of Wilkins, eventually blossomed into the Royal Society.

The circumstances surrounding Wilkins's appointment as Master of Wadham College are unclear.* The political situation was extremely fluid during the early months of 1648, with Parliament and the army at odds and Presbyterian-Independent animosity increasing. It cannot be assumed, therefore, that appointments during this period necessarily represented the views of any one of the rival political and religious groups. Wilkins was as eminent as most of those selected to fill the headships at Oxford, although he was less strictly a religious figure than the others. It is not clear whether he was considered a Presbyterian or Independent candidate. Wilkins stayed on at Oxford long after most Presbyterians had gone, and survived the expulsion of Independents after Richard Cromwell became Chancellor.

The government began to concern itself with the universities as soon as it could, given the pressure of events. For like other English governments of the time, it realized the necessity of controlling the chief intellectual centers in order to control the Church. Ecclesiastical reform necessarily implied a change in personnel at the universities, particularly in view of the fact that both universities, and especially Oxford, had been dominated by Laudians. The first tentative steps in this direction were taken in August 1641, when a bill to regulate the universities was introduced. Soon the universities were ordered to remove the Laudian embellishments of the last decade. Shortly afterward, however, Oxford became the scene of active military operations. Lord Saye and Sele appeared in the city with a troop of parliamentary horse. Only a month later Oxford was occupied by Royalist troops and refortified. The city became the headquarters for the Royalist army, and the university an armed camp. So many students left that university life all but collapsed between 1643 and 1648. Royalist control lasted until the summer of 1646, when Fairfax, who like Saye took special precautions to prevent destruction, seized the city. This time parliamentary control lasted until 1660. A committee to regulate the university was appointed. College elections, the granting of leases by colleges, and many other actions were forbidden without parliamentary approval.

It was not until May 1647 that an order for the visitation of the university was issued. Its purpose was to correct the "offenses, abuses and disorders . . . of late times." The visitation was conducted primarily by Presbyterian clerics, but final control of the university, like that of the Church, was to remain in lay and parliamentary hands. In August the Board of Visitors was given enlarged powers, and thus armed it began to summon the heads of houses and those in charge of college and university accounts.

The delays and lack of firmness occasioned by quarrels among the various Independent and Presbyterian factions in London allowed the Laudian elements who dominated the university time to perfect their plans for passive resistance. For the most part the Visitors were simply ignored. It was March 1648 before the visitation could begin in earnest, and the powers of the Visitors pressed so firmly that they could no longer be ignored. This time, with troops standing by to overawe the recalcitrant, most heads of colleges appeared. Although Parliament had not planned on wholesale ejection, the refusal of a large number of the university officials to recognize the authority of the Visitors led to many removals.*

In April the summoning, ejection, and replacement of heads gained momentum. On the seventh Dr. John Pitt, Wilkins's predecessor at Wadham, was removed for "high contempt and denial of the authority of Parliament." On April 11 the Chancellor, Lord Pembroke, arrived in Oxford and presided over a sparsely attended Convocation that afternoon. It was on this occasion that Wilkins received the Bachelor of Divinity degree. More ejections followed. Mrs. Fell, wife of the Dean of Christ Church, refused to leave only to be carried out on a chair by soldiers. At All Souls a composed Gilbert Sheldon refused to surrender his keys, and the future Archbishop of Canterbury was marched off under guard. From All Souls the Chancellor and Visitors "with a great rabble after them," proceeded to Wadham College, "where they act the same things, dash out Dr. Pitt's name . . . and enter into his place Mr. John Wilkins, and forthwith gave him possession." Although Pitt was probably not present, it was necessary to break open the doors. But "Mr. Wilkins was put in Possession, before any Violence was offered to any Man's Lodgings," and his name entered in the college's buttery book.

The next few days were busy ones. The Visitors issued numerous orders, such as that forbidding use of the Book of Common Prayer in the colleges and halls and requiring that the Directory be used in its stead. Wilkins and the other college heads were warned that "they will Answere the Contrary at their Perills." On April 17, the colleges were ordered to present their rents, seals, and account books to the Visitors under a similar threat. This demand was posted on the gates of Wadham and the other colleges but was generally disregarded. Most bursars refused to comply; Wadham's had disappeared.

The hostility of the Royalists toward the new appointees was very open, but curiously their violent diatribes against the new heads did not include Wilkins. The pamphleteer who wrote that the university was "now filled up with a company of Harpys and Stinking fellows," and who castigated each of the heads unmercifully, could only say of Wilkins, "At Wadham (the World in the Moon) Wilkins . . . is put in." Another scurrilous Royalist effort had as little to say. "One Wilkins the Writer of the Man in the Moon dropt thence into his [Pitt's] place." It would seem that except for his fame as a writer on astronomical subjects and the knowledge that he was chaplain to the Prince Elector, he was either relatively unknown or not considered particularly unpalatable.

Not long after Wilkins became Warden, he left the university to accompany the Elector on his return to his ancestral lands.* He was probably gone no more than a few months, for he was busy at a variety of business on the university's behalf during the fall, and soon became an important figure in university administrative circles.

Wilkins's continental tour should not be taken as an indication that matters had settled down at Oxford. Puritan rule, even after its consolidation, did not mean serenity. The conflicts between Presbyterians and Independents, and between Royalists, Commonwealthmen, and Protectorate supporters, all had their reflections in the university as well. First the Presbyterians seemed to be dominant. Soon after the establishment of the Commonwealth, however, their position was undermined, and the House of Commons demanded that the Visitors obtain the university's submission to the Engagement. For the most part, the university was not favorable to the Engagement, and there were several attempts to evade it. The Delegates, Wilkins probably among them, met in Vice-Chancellor Edward Reynolds's lodgings and drew up a petition "wherein the sense of the Engagement might be declared, so that no offense might be given to such consciences as should scruple at it." Their request was accepted by Convocation, their petition, or a very similar one, was sent to London in the care of Wilkins and Henry Langley, the head of Pembroke College. They delivered it in November. The petition, however, was unsuccessful, and the Engagement was tendered at Oxford. Early in November the Visitors insisted that Wilkins and the other heads obtain signatures from the colleges. We do not know in great detail what occurred at Wadham, or what role Wilkins played in the matter, though the fact that he was chosen to deliver the petition suggests that he supported it. His college was probably one of the slowest to press the Engagement on its members, for months later, on February 6, 1650, Wadham was ordered to take the oath. Although lists of the submitters were required, Seth Ward, a resident of the college, seems to have avoided taking it. Wilkins may have been lax with others as well. He himself almost certainly took the oath. It is not likely that he would have been permitted to remain Warden of Wadham otherwise, and his views on such matters allowed him in good conscience to accept whatever government was in power. Submission to the events of the political world was one of the guides to conduct that Wilkins retained throughout his life.

Wilkins's views and example may have convinced some of those dissatisfied with political events to stay on at the university, but there were some major losses, including Vice-Chancellor Reynolds and Edward Pococke, Professor of Hebrew and Arabic. The university was not generally sympathetic to the changes in Whitehall, and would have preferred to "live quietly and peaceably" without signing a pledge of fidelity to the non-monarchical government. Most of the university, nevertheless, did accept the Engagement, though in an "angry sullen spirit." Even with such oaths, however, the religious complexion of the university was far from uniform. Many Presbyterians and some Anglicans stayed on during the period of Independent rule. For those willing to accept the Covenant and later the Engagement, there were few problems. As far as religious observance itself was concerned, Puritan forms certainly dominated, but well-attended Anglican services were held covertly with the knowledge of a large portion of the university community at the nearby home of Dr. Thomas Willis. The coffee houses that sprang up in Oxford about this time were known to be patronized by Royalist and Anglican wits and virtuosi.

Political and religious affiliation did not always determine personal relationships or university policy. Seth Ward, a known Anglican, was given the Savilian Professorship of Astronomy. Pococke remained until he refused the Engagement in 1650. In 1654, when he was charged with reading the Common Prayer in his country Berkshire parsonage, he was defended by Vice-Chancellor John Owen, Wilkins, Seth Ward, and John Wallis, all of whom made a special trip to convince the Triers of their errors. On another occasion Wilkins went out of his way to protect the Anglican Fell's right to remain in Oxford although Owen wished him removed.

Quiet submission was often an acceptable substitute for theological orthodoxy. This was as true for Anglicans as it was for the various brands of Puritans, for men of high status as well as low. Party lines were often difficult to draw. There were few overt differences, for example, between Presbyterians and Independents, even though Wood thought the Independents affected a more flamboyant style of dress. The difficulty of precisely labeling a man's views is evident in the case of John Conant, Vice-Chancellor between 1657-60. He is usually considered a Presbyterian, but he originally resigned his fellowship rather than sign the Covenant, which required him to abjure the good order of the Church of England. He nevertheless accepted the Rectorship of Exeter and probably took both the Covenant and the Engagement, the latter with qualifications. Conant was willing to cooperate with the parliamentarians once they had won, but refused cooperation during the war. Wilkins, as we have seen, is even more difficult to categorize. There is nothing to indicate that he was then or ever had been a Presbyterian, or that he favored Independency. If he was a Puritan, his must have been Puritanism of a rather indistinct sort, and it is likely that he was gradually moving toward a moderate Anglicanism.

All this does not mean that the universities were immune to religious divisions and pressures. By and large the Presbyterians were the more powerful faction until about 1650. Thereafter the Independents, particularly Thomas Goodwin and John Owen, played commanding roles. After Richard Cromwell became Chancellor, the power of the Independents began to wane. Wilkins was relatively unaffected by these shifts and remained an influential figure in the university throughout the decade he spent there. Almost immediately after arriving at Oxford, Wilkins was made a delegate. The Convocation Register suggests that Wilkins served for the whole time he was at Oxford and thus was involved continuously with what was, to the extent the Visitors allowed, the university's major policy-making body. He also served on several of the subdelegacies frequently appointed to deal with specific matters.

Shortly after replacing the heads of the colleges, the Visitors turned their attention to professors and lecturers, and personnel matters became a part of Wilkins's administrative chores. John Wallis replaced Peter Turner, and Seth Ward replaced John Greaves, as Savilian Professors of Geometry and Astronomy. Wilkins was one of the four persons recommending Wallis for the post. Ward received his post not through the efforts of Wilkins but through those of Greaves, the man he replaced. Although Ward and Wallis were probably not appointed until October 1649, in September they were already being instructed to make use of the mathematical books in Sir Henry Savile's library. Wilkins was one of the three officials expected to show them where these were kept. The substitution of Ward for Greaves created many problems for the delegates, most of them over the question of whether Greaves should be compensated for his loss. Wilkins was one of the subdelegates assigned to deal with the problem. On February 19, 1650, Wilkins went to London to present the delegates' view on the matter and to handle other university business.

Wilkins was frequently sent to London by the delegates, particularly to deal with the London committee. He was dispatched together with the Proctor Phillip Ward to present the university's congratulations to Oliver Cromwell when he became Protector. Not long afterward he and Dr. John Palmer represented the university in a lawsuit. In 1656 he went on behalf of the delegates who then wished to promote the study of civil law.

Late in 1652 Wilkins accepted a new position that further increased his authority in the university. On October 16, the Chancellor, Oliver Cromwell, for all practical purposes put the chancellorship in commission. Wilkins, together with John Owen, newly appointed Vice-Chancellor, Thomas Goodwin, a confidant of Cromwell and Master of Magdalen College, Jonathan Goddard, Cromwell's physician and a member of Wilkins's scientific circle, and Peter French, canon of Christ Church and brother-in-law of Cromwell, were appointed to consider all dispensations and grants that required Cromwell's consent as Chancellor. Three of them normally acted on such matters, Owen, Wilkins, and Goodwin, and more particularly Wilkins and Owen, perhaps because they resided permanently in Oxford. The power granted them was evidently considerable, for occasionally even the delegates, deciding on some matter, added that they had "obtained the Consent of those who have the Chancellor's power delegated to them." The authority Wilkins exercised in this capacity lapsed when Richard Cromwell replaced his father as Chancellor. But even then Wilkins undertook numerous administrative tasks. Like most college officials past and present, Wilkins was required to provide letters of recommendation. In 1653 he was chosen one of the five delegates of the university press and served until 1659. He also served on a committee to revise the statutes of New College so that divines would replace canonists, and a committee assigned to deal with beggars so "that they may no more trouble the university." Perhaps because of his town background, he several times represented the university in negotiations with the city fathers of Oxford.

Walkins put his talents as a mediator to good use within the university as well. Throughout the period he was at Wadham, there was constant friction between the colleges, the Visitors, and the parliamentary committee, particularly over elections. The colleges frequently tried to follow traditional patterns and statutes in defiance of the Visitors or the parliamentary committee in London. As early as June 1648, the Visitors forbade the fellows at Wadham to hold an election fixed by statute for the following day. During the summer of 1648 expulsions continued at Wadham and elsewhere. In July the Visitors set up a committee to examine scholarship and fellowship candidates, with the power to "approve such as they shall judge fitt to be preferred." Wilkins served on this committee, so perhaps for a time Wadham had somewhat less difficulty in obtaining the candidates it wished.*

As the colleges began to function more normally, their desire to regulate their own affairs intensified. After the purges had been carried out, there seemed to be no reason why they should not resume their earlier independence. This feeling was shared by many of the heads of houses, the delegates, and other university officials, including Wilkins. On March 16, 1650, the university petitioned the London committee for a general return to free college elections. There followed a quite confused interlude in which the London committee and the Board of Visitors issued a series of orders alternatively affirming and denying the right of the colleges to independent elections. A new Board of Visitors, all residents of the university and including many heads of houses, probably reduced the level of tension somewhat, but by July 1653 the Board was again claiming the power to approve all appointments. In the course of intervening in a disputed Wadham election, the new Board apparently reversed its predecessors finding that Wadham was "in a statutable way" and insisted on its own power of appointment. Yet by November it had compromised on a system somewhere between direct appointment and free election. Late in

1654 still another Board of Visitors, one that included more Presbyterians but still had an Independent majority, challenged Wadham's right to fill fellowships.

The following year the whole question of independence for the colleges against the authority of the Visitors entered a new phase. The academics, Wilkins among them, decided to petition the Protector in defense of their privileges and rights. A subdelegacy, of which Wilkins was a member, met on February 5 to discuss their demands. They wanted the powers of the Visitors drastically reduced, especially in relation to the colleges, so that they exercised no more authority than each college's statutes gave its own local Visitors. A few days later, when Wilkins and the subdelegates met with the Visitors to discuss their proposals, the Board asked them to adjourn to an adjoining room and wait while the Visitors considered the matter. According to Wood, "they waited till past nine of the clock, continually expecting to be called in, but the Visitors . . . departed without taking any notice of the Subdelegates who had waited so long upon them." Finally, Thankful Owen, head of St. John's as well as a Visitor, returned, confessing that the rest had left after a rather heated discussion. The Visitors had decided they could not treat with the subdelegacy, and that their papers, which Wilkins had provided as requested, should be sealed up. Wilkins and his associates understandably feared that "their paper was detained in order to make some disadvantageious representation of it." They thought their next move should be to "procure another Delegacy to give an account to the University of all passages in the said address to the Visitors, and after that to proceed to petition, being very sensible how deeply their interests in this place were concerned in this business, and resolved also to bring it to some issue by all regular and peaceable ways." They were convinced that the whole university, with a few minor exceptions, would agree with them. Shortly afterward Goddard wrote to one of the subdelegates, perhaps Wilkins, from London, indicating that the Protector and his Council were sympathetic to their views and expected to make changes concerning the Visitors very shortly. The subdelegates then conferred with the Vice-Chancellor, John Owen, and decided to do nothing further at that time. They were never asked to make a report, and were willing to "let the business fall asleep," supposing now the "visitors would use their power with due moderation and discretion." As a matter of fact, the Board did very little that year.

Each year seemed to bring a new crisis. In 1656 a major conflict arose between John Owen and Convocation over university reforms. After Convocation had refused some of his proposals, Owen called together the Visitors who accepted them and, for a time, it seemed likely that the powers of Convocation itself would be reduced. Owen, however, was finally persuaded to abandon his efforts in that direction.

The attempt of the Visitors the following year to enunciate disciplinary orders affecting the colleges led to another revival of the independence movement. The university insisted that nine years was long enough to "purge and correct all humours and malignities," and they were now certainly capable of running themselves. Wood felt that the Presbyterians were leading the movement to annul the Visitors' commission. Though most of the Visitors were indeed Independent, such men as Wilkins, Goddard, and Peter French can hardly be characterized as Presbyterians. But if party lines in these conflicts did not fall neatly into Independent and Presbyterian categories, groups certainly did exist. Wilkins, Goddard, and Ward "us'd their constant endeavor to oppose the Fury, and moderate the Heats of the fiery giddy Party, and to advance the interest of Learning." Walter Pope suggested that Wilkins and Goddard, as heads of the "Moral, Sober Party," were anxious to obtain the mastership of a college for Seth Ward.* The resignation of Oliver Cromwell and the appointment of his son Richard as Chancellor seems to have had some effect on the situation, for we subsequently hear very little of trouble in the university, which seems to have been left largely to itself. Nevertheless, in 1658 John Wallis was still petitioning on behalf of the university for Visitors who would purge Oxford of its "peccant or malignant humours," but at the same time not lessen its power, freedom, and traditional rights.

Despite the Visitors' constant interference in the colleges, it does not appear that Puritan rule brought any significant changes in academic matters. Most of the Visitors' efforts were spent in enforcing the old statutory requirements regarding disputations and other academic exercises, rather than reform. No new chairs were established. The government did insist that the existing professors and lecturers perform their duties. Much effort was expended on preventing absenteeism, for the new authorities, like their predecessors, found it difficult to enforce residence requirements. On the one occasion that the Visitors found Wadham's academic program deficient, they simply ordered the college to observe its statutory exercises and discipline.

These statutes called for an estimated twenty-four hours a week of academic activities, either lectures or disputations. Wadham undergraduates were expected to spend some three hours a day at logic and three hours a week at lectures on Greek and Latin writers. All Bachelors and Regent Masters were to dispute twice a week. Twice a week, too, all members of the college were to report to the hall to dispute in logic, natural philosophy, or metaphysics. Wadham's theological disputes occupied two hours every other week in the college's ante-chapel. In addition to the statutory program, of course, Wadham's students received work in a variety of subjects from their tutors. Furthermore, under the influence of Wilkins, Ward, Christopher Wren, and Laurence Rooke the sciences became a predominant feature of collegiate life. Even the college manciple Christopher Brookes, was a mathematician and mathematical instrument maker. The statutes assisted this development to some extent, for during the long vacation students could substitute arithmetic, geometry, or geography for classical studies.

Neither the Visitors nor the parliamentary committee in London did anything to encourage scientific studies with the exception of the appointment of able people to fill the Savilian professorships. Talented persons held these posts both before the Puritans appeared on the scene and after they ceased to influence the university. When the Commonwealth government considered changing the statutes of the colleges and university, it made no moves or even gestures toward emphasizing science in the university. If, as has been so prominently argued, the Puritans were the great champions of the new science against traditional learning, it is strange that they failed to take advantage of this sterling opportunity to reform the university, and indeed expended most of their efforts on enforcing obedience to the old curriculum. The Visitors were, in fact, basically concerned with a religious reformation. They wanted to eliminate the "corruptions" of the past, not to alter traditional education. Disputations in theology and logic went on much as before, and perhaps even with increased intensity. In fact it appears that the new philosophy was interdicted in some colleges by Presbyterians who feared that it would lead to innovations in religion, and that intellectual liberty would inspire religious speculation as well.

The Puritans might also have been expected to make a widespread effort to substitute the use of English for Latin, but this movement, which has been associated with the Puritans, seems to have affected only such trivial matters as the language used in keeping the Registers of Convocation. The Visitors and the London committee insisted on the use of Latin by the scholars at all times. Wilkins was ordered to have Greek and Latin "striktly and constantly exercised, and spoken" at Wadham, not only in academic situations but also in "familiar discourse" within the college. That orders on this matter were repeated on several occasions suggests considerable opposition within the university. Sometime earlier in the century the practice had apparently become obsolete, and Puritan authorities no less than Anglican tried to force the university back to an earlier pattern.

At various times the Visitors contemplated a general revision of the statutes of the colleges and the university, but as a vehicle for eliminating any vestiges of popery rather than as a means of educational experiment. Wilkins was involved in the negotiations for changes in the Wadham and university statutes. By and large the proposed changes dealt with the intensity, sincerity, and quantity of worship. The tension between the colleges and the Visitors was based less on substantial policy differences than on the colleges' feeling that they could and should handle most matters themselves, and that their statutes adequately provided for the religious education and welfare of their members. Wadham's statutes, for example, required, twice-daily service and a catechist to instruct on alternate Thursdays. Wilkins and the fellows also had the power to make rules for sermons and were directed to assist in Sunday and fast day services. Divinity disputations were a required part of college life, and Wadham's chaplain, Gilbert Stokes, was himself a "continual disputant" accustomed to "ferret" the students "from one hole to another with subtilties."

Although some heads, such as Owen and Goodwin, preached frequently at Oxford, it is unlikely that Wilkins did so regularly, except perhaps within the walls of his own college. Notes of a sermon Wilkins delivered probably in 1656 appear in a notebook of sermons by such Oxford notables as Reynolds, Owen, Conant, and Wilkinson. Wilkins's theme was that the compassion of God extended to all, and that men should as much as possible imitate God in his mercifulness and in his pity. This note of kindness toward one's neighbors recurs repeatedly in Wilkins's later preaching.

Two posthumously published sermons were also delivered to university audiences. One, offered on some public occasion, concerned knowledge and its pitfalls; it will be discussed later in the context of the educational controversies that shook the universities during the decade. The second, perhaps directed at Wadham's fellows, stressed the proper choice of companions by both students and teachers. For the most part Wilkins emphasized the long-familiar theme that good companions help produce good men and that wickedness was contagious. He spoke of the importance of communicating with companions or students in order to influence them. "Studious and retired" men he found to be frequently defective in this most important means of promoting all types of knowledge. Scholars often lacked a "ready, voluable, popular Rhetoric," which was essential, particularly in promoting "practical Religion." Men should be "more free towards one another in communicating their doubts, temptations, comforts; warming their affection and building up on another by mutual conference." It was necessary to strive for those qualities that made scholars acceptable and useful: "a readiness to communicate," humility, "awareness in owning our own weaknesses . . . anothers gift or preheminences," and the suspension of "rash censures, bitter expressions or whatever may exasperate." "Dower" disciplinarians with their "sower and rigid severity" and "proness to censure"—perhaps a dig at Owen and Goodwin and the board of Visitors generally—were thus deprived of "many opportunities of doing good to others." Wilkins himself seems to have been remarkably adept at teaching and criticizing without alienating others.

In spite of this continued commitment to religious teaching and preaching, Wadham and the other colleges were repeatedly bombarded with detailed orders insisting on more rigorous observance. From these and other actions of the Visitors, it is clear that even though purged, the collegiate bodies were not responding properly. This resistence seems to have resulted from a combination of college resentment toward outside meddling and the traditional laxness of the undergraduates. The "Puritanism" of the Visitors was largely confined to the constant battle for more religious observance against a faculty and student body that did not substantially disagree with the government's theology but resented their continual interference. The Visitors' efforts may be labeled Puritan zeal, but they should also be seen as the usual efforts of educational administrators to keep students and faculty hard at work on the subjects that justified the university to society and the State.

In other areas a distinctly "Puritan" policy is difficult to detect.

Most of the Visitors' actions regarding manners and morals were directed at overcoming the effects of several years of slack academic discipline, when the university was something between a court and a barracks. Even the Royalist Wood felt the scholars remaining in 1648 were "much debauched, and became idle by their bearing arms and keeping company with rude soldiers." In many respects the Visitors' attempts to regulate the moral activities of students differed slightly if at all from those of their Laudian predecessors. Nevertheless some changes were made that can be considered Puritan. Shortly after Wilkins's arrival in Oxford, efforts were made to break up the traditional May Day celebrations and Terrae Filius speeches. Sermons were encouraged more than they had been in the past and Sunday observance was scrutinized more closely. Perhaps the most obvious attempt at change was made by Independents and sectaries who, led by Vice-Chancellor Owen, tried to eliminate traditional academic costume. By and large Presbyterian and Anglican academics favored the traditional garb, but even Laud had considerable difficulty in trying to enforce scholarly costume, for garish gowns, boots and spurs, and other fashionable clothing were always cropping up to plague the Archbishop. Owen, like many of the undergraduates, preferred "fashionable aparrel" and "long hair." When Owen became Vice-Chancellor, enforcement of academic dress lapsed, and he attempted to eliminate it entirely. With the Independents' rise to power, hoods were seldom worn even in the "Solomn meetings" of the University. Owen on such occasions usually kept his hat on, "and that, many time cockt," as if to show his contempt.

Wadham's statutes required dark clothes or black gowns and square caps both within and without the college gates. It seems likely that Wilkins's college tended to be traditional on this matter. There were few Independents associated with it, and Walter Pope, Wilkins's half-brother and a Wadham fellow, defended "those decent distinctions of Degrees, Caps and Hoods." Pope, however, indicated that most of the heads and M.A.'s disagreed with him, and that victory depended on the old Cavalier scholars who came out "in troops" to vote for retention of traditional dress. In this as in other areas, there was little for the Anglicans to alter in 1660.

When such Anglicans as Clarendon looked back at Oxford they recognized that, despite the change in personnel and religious observance, very little had altered. The universities

yielded a harvest of extraordinary good and sound knowledge in all parts of learning; and many who were wickedly introduced applied themselves to the study of good learning and the practice of virtue, . . . so that when it pleased God to bring King Charles back to his throne, he found the University abounding in excellent learning, and devoted to duty and obedience little inferior to what it was before its desolation.

His statement suggests that Puritan rule had not given rise to any fundamental change in education, and that another shift in personnel would largely restore things to their prewar condition. Given the opportunities of over a decade to establish major educational reforms, it must be concluded that the Puritans desired none. Such reform as did occur involved a change in personnel based on religious and political connections and the additional discipline required to bring a university that had almost ceased to function back to its original state.

It was not from the Puritan establishment but from the sects that the principal threat to the continuity of the universities came. Throughout the Interregnum political and religious radicals attacked the existing system. Their hostility did not, however, become a serious threat except for the two brief periods when they were closest to political power, in 1653 and again in 1659. On these occasions there was a real fear that the universities might be destroyed. In 1653 the Barebones Parliament seriously discussed "suppressing Universities and all Schools for Learning, as heathenish and unnecessary." The collapse of the Parliament and the establishment of the Protectorate ended the possibility of suppression by the government. The major figures of the Protectorate were well-educated members of the upper classes who attempted to conserve some semblance of traditional institutions against radical change. It was only after the Protectorate's collapse that the universities were again threatened. In 1659 the radicals intended "to rout up all and to ruine those things that smelt of an Academy, never rejoycing more than when they could trample on the gowne and bringing humane learning and arts into disgrace."

William Dell and John Webster, both former army chaplains, who were probably supported by members of the Barebones Parliament, were the radicals' major literary representatives. They were answered by many, but Wilkins and Seth Ward jointly supplied the most effective defense against their complaints. Dell had recently become Master of Gonville and Caius College in Cambridge through the influence of the sects. His attack was based on the premise that religious insight was obtained through spiritual illumination, not reason and learning. Since faith could not "be learned as human arts and sciences can, to wit, by the teaching of man," a learned ministry produced by the universities was not essential. Although Dell has been cast as an educational reformer, reform was at best a peripheral concern to him. His primary aim was to spiritualize the Church and declericalize the ministry, not to alter the university. Thus he argued that humane learning, if kept distinct from divinity, had some value, and universities should be permitted to exist if they confined themselves to the secular learning that made useful citizens. The lower schools, he thought, should be increased in number and made more practical. The number of colleges or universities should be expanded to end the intellectual monopoly of Oxford and Cambridge. Students in colleges spread throughout the country could study on a part-time basis, working at a useful calling the rest of the time, thus eliminating idleness and increasing working-class attendance. His suggestions on reforming the curriculum, however, were fragmentary. He recommended that the universities should esteem those branches of mathematics, geometry, and geography that "carry no wickedness in them" and are "besides very useful to human society."

Webster proved to be the more formidable opponent, at least for Wilkins and Ward, precisely because he did have a great deal to say about how the universities should be reformed. His religious outlook, however, was hardly distinguishable from Dell's. Webster did more than indicate a desire for practical secular education, and provided, in his *Academiarum examen,* a long attack on the universities and an alternative program focused on the sciences. Although his tract reflects a mind without any real comprehension of the scientific method and does not accurately depict the actual state of the sciences in the university, it cannot be dismissed with Dell's as the work of a semi-ignorant man advocating a particular view of religious truth. For Webster did have considerable interest in, if not knowledge of, the sciences and was one of the period's more effective propagandists of Baconianism. His interest, however, does not so much indicate that Puritanism fostered science, as that scientific interests were spreading among all types of people and religious sects.

In the face of the apparent threat, university-educated Puritans and Anglicans closed ranks against the sects.* This was one of the earliest instances in which those who had opposed one another on other political and religious questions came together to defend traditional institutions against republican, unlearned, and usually lower-class onslaughts. This reaction directly contradicts the views of R. F. Jones, who argued that Anglicans and Puritans had distinct educational philosophies, the former emphasizing Christian humanism, the latter utilitarianism. There is little to support Jones's picture of the Puritans as condemning philosophy, poetry, rhetoric, and the classical languages. The Puritans who controlled the universities between 1648 and 1660 did little to indicate hostility to the tradition of Christian humanism, the classics, the Church Fathers, or the study of Latin and the other classical languages. When examining the replies to Dell and Webster, it is difficult to distinguish Puritan from Anglican on this ground. To present the conflict as reforming, Baconian, Puritanism against traditionalist, scholastic, Anglicanism is to greatly oversimplify the matter.

The controversy centered around two major issues. The more important was religious—whether or not the clergy should continue to dominate and control the intellectual life of the nation, and whether the alliance between religion and learning should be maintained. Two groups sought a change. The first was composed of secularists who were often republicans, although they included monarchists like Thomas Hobbes. These men were more active in 1659. The other group consisted of religious radicals who denied the necessity of clerical learning and wanted the universities to cease functioning as seminaries. It was the second group, which included Dell and Webster, that produced the most important tracts.

The second major issue, the curriculum, was related to the first. Those who distrusted the intellectualization of religion did not necessarily oppose all education, but advocated a secular, practical education. They fastened on utilitarian, inductive science as a substitute for the older learning, which they opposed, without really understanding what they advocated. For they had little knowledge of or concern with what had actually been accomplished in science. Baconianism became a conveniently erudite slogan with which to disguise the distrust of the uneducated for theoretical and esoteric knowledge and the usual plea of the anti-intellectual for "practical" education. Bacon became their hero both because his utilitarianism appeared to them a return to common sense from the suspect realms of philosophy, and because his separation of religion and science seemed to remove a threat to religion. Their naïve infatuation with induction led them to slight key deductive and theoretical aspects of science, and to ignore the distinctions between magic, astrology, and the sciences. This concentration on induction was a means of reducing science to the mundane manipulation of directly observable material to which the average man was accustomed and of which he approved.

Given Wilkins's advocacy of a learned ministry, his desire to promote the study of science, and his position as an Oxford don, it is not surprising that he entered the lists, even though very few of those in his position had the courage to do so openly. Owen, then Vice-Chancellor, indicated that the university community itself and its outside defenders were willing to do very little. The cause of the universities, "which ought to have been held sacred, but was now exposed to the greatest danger very few ventured heartily to defend. Nay, such was the pitch of madness, that to have stood up for gownsmen, would have been reckoned a violation of religion and piety." Wilkins was ready to lend his pen to the cause, but, it must be admitted, not his name: he and Seth Ward signed their tract with just the last letters of their names. At least as early as 1646, Wilkins began to feel that the critics of the universities were making unreasonable proposals, although he was not totally out of sympathy with reform. The *Vindiciae academiarum* of Wilkins and Ward, unlike other replies to Dell and Webster, challenged them on both the religious and the scientific issues. Wilkins became interested in the question first and then enlisted Ward's help. Together they dealt with the relationship of religion to learning and the necessity for scientific reform in the universities. Wilkins examined the first issue, and they both treated the second, although Ward, having been asked by Wilkins to undertake this task, did so more extensively.

Wilkins had advocated a learned ministry at considerable length in *Ecclesiastes,* and the alliance of religion and learning more generally in the *Gift of Prayer*. His ideas had not changed. He denied the radicals' contention that the universities were incapable of "fit[ting] men for the Ministry," and that the system of theology taught there was either harmful or useless. The universities had never sought to teach spiritual knowledge or to provide the gifts that came directly from the spirit of God. Nevertheless, of the three gifts required for the ministry, the university could supply one. It could not provide the spirit of God, which enabled a man to understand the mysteries of the Gospel and affected his heart so he might instruct others. Nor could it provide natural ability. Yet it could teach "a distinct and methodical comprehension of the severall subjects to be treated of, together with the meanes or advantages that help to facilitate the worke of instructing others."

Wilkins also dealt with Webster's contention that Scripture contained warnings against philosophy. He replied "If that prohibition were to be understood absolutely . . . , why doth he here pretend so much to the knowledge of it himself, and to the Advancement of it in others? The same answer that he will make for his own vindication, will serve his Objections." Wilkins recognized that the radicals had not really thought out one of their basic problems. If humane learning were dangerous for religion, and they agreed science was a branch of humane learning, the same arguments might be used against the sciences they proposed to promote. Wilkins adds that on careful reading, the Biblical passages in question condemn not the use but the abuse of philosophy.

In the midst of the controversy Wilkins delivered a sermon before his Oxford colleagues expressing his desire for a balance between knowledge and religion in university life. He took as his text the favorite antinomian passage, "For in wisdom there is grief; and he that increaseth knowledge encreaseth sorrow," so frequently used to deprecate the value of learning and education. But he turned the text into a defense of knowledge and a statement of the proper relationship between religion and learning. He acknowledged the imperfection of all knowledge. Man's natural thirst for knowledge, he admitted, was hampered by "the blindness" of his understanding, "the intricacie of things themselves; the many dark recesses of nature, the obscurity of causes and effects." Once attained it "inflames the appetite to a more impetuous craving" and leads to "vast desires, jealousies, impatience,

[and] emulations." Besides these general imperfections, each kind of knowledge had its own peculiar weaknesses. The learning "which consists only the form and paedogogy of Arts or the Critical notion upon *words* and phrases, hath in it this intrinsical imperfection, that 'tis only so far to be esteemed, as it conduceth to the knowledge of things, being in itself but a kind of pedantry, apt to infect a man with . . . pride, and affection, and curiousity, as well render him unfit for any great employment."

Scientific or "real knowledge" also had its failings, not only among ancient but also modern practitioners, who despite "diligent and exact" observations were at times deceived by "casual and fortuitous events." Citing Bacon he noted the difficulties of scientific investigation and suggested that "sense itself . . . our chiefest guide" might lead to error as well as truth. History, too, had its defects. Like many modern historiographer, Wilkins noted that history was often written "according to the Author's interest and prejudices, and so seldom contain[ed] an impartial . . . representation of the Truth." Despite their imperfections, knowledge and wisdom were worth struggling for. Wisdom was not only a "most excellent thing in itself," but "of all other things in the world doth bear in it the fairest appearance and probability of affording satisfaction to the mind." Secular knowledge must nevertheless be coupled with a holy life, for it was "practical divinity" alone that would lead man to heaven. As usual Wilkins warned against disputing about religion and emphasized its practice. He also warned scholars that an excessive concern for knowledge at the expense of piety was dangerous, and that it would naturally lead to the kind of attacks they were now witnessing. At the same time, he castigated the "folly and madness" of those "unreasonable men" who thought it better to be "idle, ignorant and cheerful" than learned. In short, Wilkins provided a rationalization for the existing combination of traditional knowledge, scientific investigation, and religious observance in university life.

Unlike the radicals, few of the scientists at Oxford wished to separate religion and science, and some of them, including Wilkins and Ward, published works showing the close relationship between the two. Several members of Wilkins's scientific circle, both during the 1650's and during the Restoration, were among the major proponents of a natural theology that did not seek to separate philosophy from religion but used the former to prove and buttress the latter.

Although Wilkins defended the university's role in creating a learned ministry, he did not consider this its sole function. The university had the duty of providing a secular education as well. Unlike the reformers, Ward and Wilkins had no wish to change the existing class structure in the university. One of the reasons Ward cited for not giving excessive emphasis to scientific studies was that gentlemen needed an education broad enough to make them "Rationall and Graceful speakers, and be of an acceptable behavior in their Countries." Some knowledge of the sciences, however, was becoming part of a gentlemanly education. Just as he had absorbed the literary culture of the humanists earlier, the gentleman was now supposed to have at least a passing familiarity with new scientific developments, and might pursue science as a hobby. Restoration culture and the activities of the Royal Society showed that a leisure class with scientific interests was by no means impossible.

The most important portion of the defense of the universities by Wilkins and Ward was their reply to the radicals' plea for scientific reform. It is worth outlining this debate at some length because it seems to have had an unfortunate influence on many modern scholars, who have tended to assume that sectarian attacks on the universities couched as defenses of science do indeed indicate scientific deficiencies in the universities and devotion to science among the sectaries.

Ward and Wilkins concentrated on their most important opponents, Dell, Webster, and Hobbes. To Dell they replied that Oxford and Cambridge did not monopolize learning, and that proliferation of universities would not lead to a general increase in learning because the advancement of learning required a learned community. It was Webster who bore the brunt of their attack because "it was not so much an ingenuous affection to the advancement of learning, as a forward and malicious prejudice against the universities that put him on to this worke." Not only was Webster ignorant of the reforms of the last few decades, he was actually a threat to improved education because of his wild accusations and ignorant statements. Wilkins complained that even though the *Examen* would appear "slight and contemptible" to judicious men, it might influence "weaker persons" more "apt to take accusations for convictions." Once again Wilkins's instinctive reaction was to reach out to the broader public. He comments on the difficulty of enlisting academics to carry on these propaganda chores: "It is a part of that Scholastick imprudence, which men of our profession are subject unto, to sit downe and satisfie ourselves in our owne knowledge of the weakness of such Adversaries, without taking any pains to satisfie others, who are not so well able to judge." *

Wilkins pointed out the major defects in Webster's argument. The first was his belief that the universities were still slavishly Aristotelian. The attack on Aristotle and Aristotelian philosophy has always been considered a cornerstone of the scientific movement, and there is no denying that the authority of Aristotle, as well as considerable portions of his philosophy, had to be abandoned before progress could be made in many areas. Nevertheless, the most violent anti-Aristotelians were not the scientists, who were cautious in their opposition and quite willing to preserve large portions of his findings so long as his authority was not permitted to prevent freedom of discussion. Wilkins argued that such freedom already existed at Oxford in full harmony with Aristotelian studies. He noted that those who were really acquainted with the universities "know there is not to be wished a more generall liberty in point of judgment or debate, then what is here allowed. So that there is scarce any Hypothesis which hath formerly or lately entertained by Judicious men, and seems to have in it any clearnesse or constancy, but hath its strenuous

Assertours, as the Atomicall and Magneticall in Philosophy and Copernical in Astronomy &c." Wilkins also denied Webster's contention that the sciences were not being taught: "Witness the publick Lectures of our Professors, the Positions or Questions maintained in the public Exercises of the Universitie for Degree, & in private Exercises of Colledges, besides the Instructions and readings of many Tutors, where in all the principall things which this Author doth accuse us to be ignorant and enemies unto, are taught and owned." Although Mark Curtis is correct in insisting that to properly assess the teaching of science in the university, one must look beyond the universities' statutes to the private and semi-private instruction of tutors, it is clear that the new views were also recognized in public exercises. Wilkins went so far as to assure Webster that the students were "so well learnt" in the sciences that they "have here many young boyes . . . that are able to reform this Reformer, in those things, wherein he thinks us all so ignorant, and himself so great a Master."

The lack of university instruction in astronomy and mathematics had been one of Webster's chief complaints. He had insisted that in astronomy the Ptolemaic system was still being taught, and was maintained by the authorities "with much rigor, severity and earnestness." As far back as Wilkins's own youth this had not been true, and both Wilkins and Ward hotly denied the charge. Ward said "there is not one man here" with any astronomical interests "who hath not received the Copernican System (as it was left by him, or as improved by Kepler, Bulliandus, or our own Professors, and others of the Ellipticall Way)." Nor was mathematics being slighted; geometry and arithmetic were "sincerely and profoundly taught, Analyticall Algebra, The Solution and Applications of Aequations, containing the whole mystery of both those sciences," are "faithfully expounded . . . by the professor of Geometry, and in severall Colledges by particular Tutors." Webster had been particularly foolish in arguing that only "private spirits" practiced mathematics because two of the three figures he mentioned, William Oughtred and Henry

Briggs, had been intimately connected with the universities and had done considerable teaching there, the former at Cambridge and the latter as Savilian Professor of Geometry at Oxford. For some reason historians have tended to follow Webster in overlooking the importance of these professorships in the diffusion of scientific knowledge. Wilkins and Ward also denied that the atomical and magnetical philosophy, or chemistry, was neglected, and ridiculed Webster's proposals that the university devote itself to natural magic and astrology.

The pseudo-scientific was a recurrent note in Webster's writings. He recommended astrology as well as astronomy. Chemistry he thought should seek the Elixir, and anatomy the discovery of the true signature of "Invisible Archaeus." Wilkins had for a long time been suspicious of just such advocates of chemistry because of their association with mysticism. Webster also condemned the schools for neglecting the mysterious in favor of the peripatetic philosophy, and applauded Boehme and the Rosicrucians for their appreciation of the mystical symbolism in nature. Wilkins did not approve of these views either. Mystical language, particularly that of Boehme and the Rosicrucians, had never appealed to him, nor did mystery in the sciences. In his concern for the mystical language of nature, Webster also criticized the universities for their failure to develop a universal character. This struck close to home, for Wilkins had been interested in the character for a long time. He wrote "What a loose and wild kind of vapouring is that about *Cryptography,* and the *Universall Character* wherein he supposed the Universities to be wholly ignorant, not of them having so much as touched at these things." Wilkins and Ward were both working on a universal character at the very time Webster wrote, and Ward in his answer showed precisely the kind of work they were doing.

The last major dispute between Webster on the one hand and Wilkins and Ward on the other concerned logic and method. The study of logic was attacked by Webster as well as by many other anti-scholastics of the sixteenth and seventeenth centuries. Wilkins's response was to remark maliciously that Webster could hardly be expected to reform logic since he understood so little of it himself. Ward, however, gave sounder reasons for rejecting Webster's reforms, although he, too, was incensed at Webster's description of how logic was taught. Ward denied that logic, which was merely "A systeme of rules directing us to the knowledge of truth," led to either internecine war or obfuscation, and defended it as a means of abstracting notions by examining the agreements and disagreements of things. He denied that belief in the "entity" or existence of logical notions was a necessary part of logic, so that this complaint of Webster's "may concern others, but not our Universities." Furthermore, he scoffed at Webster's belief that induction would replace deductive logic. The idea of replacing the syllogism with induction was foolish. Each had its proper function and utility. "Logick is universally subservient to the enquiry of all truth. Induction is ridiculously applied to Mathematicall truths, and Syllogism to be applyed to Physicks." Very much aware that the cult of induction among the unlearned derived from Bacon, he noted "it is a misfortune to the world, that my Lord *Bacon* was not skilled in Mathematiks, which made him jealous of their Assistance in all natural Enquiries."

Webster's emphasis on the utilitarian applications of science to the exclusion of its abstract and speculative aspects sometimes strikes a sympathetic chord with modern readers. Wilkins and Ward recognized, as modern historians sometimes have not, that Baconianism was frequently adopted by men who had no understanding of the scientific movement and who were primarily motivated by religious and political convictions. Similarly, the mere mention of mathematics, chemistry, or astronomy has too often been taken as proof that a writer really understood the new scientific developments and welcomed the consequences of scientific discovery. The pitfalls in such an assumption become clear from a look at Webster, who exhibited a naïve combination of science, mysticism, utilitarianism, magic, and quackery. It has also been assumed that advocating the standard of practicality necessarily implies appreciation of the scientific method. The friction in our day between "practical" groups who demand a utilitarian and vocational education and the "academics" who urge study of the liberal arts and sciences indicates that one cannot equate utilitarianism and science. Many would-be reformers, including Webster, had no appreciation of the speculative and abstract aspects of scientific inquiry. The naïveté of sectarian views of science is suggested by Richard Overton's expectation that the immortality of the soul might be tested by experiment, and the Quaker Edward Burrows's wish for laboratory tests to determine whether the bread and wine of the Eucharist really changed into the body and blood of Christ.

It has rarely been noted that throughout the educational controversy of the 1650's neither side opposed the inclusion of the sciences in the university. Although the university authorities, whether Anglican or Puritan, did little specifically to promote science, none of them opposed it either. By mid-century only a handful of men like Alexander Ross even thought of attacking science. Webster's assertions that the universities were hostile to science were simply not true. The scientific movement was never seriously threatened either during the 1650's or during the Restoration, whatever amusement the wits might have had at the expense of the scientists. Thus any attempt to identify pro- and anti-scientific movements in this period, and then match them with Puritanism and Anglicanism, is thus rather futile.

Nevertheless, Webster was not alone in his criticism of the universities' scientific offerings. Robert Boyle, who had not attended the university, seems to have been initially impressed by the arguments of the radicals. He expressed some surprise that the "chief professors and heads of colleges" discoursed and argued "in a way so far from servile that if all the new paradoxes have not found patrons there, 'tis not their dissent from the ancient or the vulgar opinions but juster causes that hinders their admission." Many non-university men joined the criticism. Owen attributed the widespread attack to the university's having sunk for a time to a "mere rabble," so that it became a topic of conversation among people who knew nothing about it. "Our critical situation and our common interests were discussed in journals and newspapers, by the most ignorant and despicable. Nor was any creature so miserably stupid, as not to entertain fears or hopes on account of our situation." Ignorance on the part of outsiders certainly played a large part.

Thomas Hobbes had also attacked the universities, though hardly from the same point of view as Dell, Webster, and the sectaries. Hobbes argued in *The Leviathan* (1651) that the universities were far behind the times on scientific questions, and practiced only scholastic arguments and philosophy. Of course he also disliked their clerical bent, and he thought that constant discussions and "democratical Principles" had helped plant the seeds of rebellion. Hobbes, for all this "slighting of the Universities," was not as clever as he thought, Wilkins insisted. Long before Hobbes's works were published, there were many at Oxford, said Wilkins, who were well-versed in the principles Hobbes claimed to have invented. But Wilkins left the specific rebuttal of Hobbes, as well as the more malevolent remarks, to Ward, who wrote "his Discourse seemes like that of the seven sleepers, who after many yeares awaking, in vaine addressed themselves to act according to the state of things when they lay downe." Hobbes had left Oxford about 1608, nearly a half a century earlier. What the university needed was intellectual freedom rather than Hobbesian authority. Hobbes, Ward argued, really wished that "Aristotleity may be changed to Hobbeity, & instead of the Stagyrite, the world may adore the great Malmesburian Philosopher." *

Although the educational controversy of the 1650's did not cease with the publication of the *Vindiciae* in 1654, the book made a considerable impression. No other scientist felt it necessary to make any extended statement on the subject. Many of them found the universities sufficiently satisfactory to spend much of their lives there. Wilkins, Jonathan Goddard, William Harvey, Ralph Bathurst, Isaac Barrow, and Isaac Newton served as heads of colleges. Ward, Wallis, Briggs, Greaves, Wren, Petty, and Willis accepted appointments as professors or lecturers. These men, while aware of the defects of the university, were willing to work within its framework. Recognizing the debt the new sciences owed to the past, they were unwilling to cut themselves off from the intellectual traditions the universities represented.

From the time of his arrival in 1648, Wilkins, as we have seen, was an important if not preeminent figure in university circles. His defense of the universities added to his prestige. From the day Richard Cromwell replaced his father as Chancellor, Wilkins became an even more powerful personage; he was the most conspicuous university representative at the elaborate installation ceremony. Richard Cromwell's Chancellorship does not seem to have reduced the tensions between Visitors and colleges, but it does appear to have given Wilkins a more important role in the university. Although the commission to execute the office of Chancellor was eliminated when Richard became Chancellor, Wilkins was soon instructing him on how to address the university and sending him copies of letters of former Chancellors so he might imitate their style and form. Wilkins seemed to feel no embarrassment in issuing instructions to Richard, or at least his secretary, and to some extent continued to act as if he were still on the earlier commission. Wilkins's talents were evidently much appreciated by Richard Cromwell. Late in 1658 it was rumored that Wilkins would replace the recently deceased Lord Rous as Provost of Eton, but this appointment did not materialize, apparently because Oliver Cromwell had designated someone else for the post shortly before his death. There were also rumors for a time that Wilkins would supplant Owen as the chief powerholder in the university, and some thought he would even be made Vice-Chancellor. His marriage to Richard Cromwell's aunt doubtless contributed to his rise in status and these rumors of advancement.

In 1656 Wilkins married Robina French, the widow of an Oxford colleague, Peter French, and youngest sister of the Protector. Very little is known of her, not even the date of her birth. Her first husband was a Puritan (probably Independent) minister, who had for several years been a Visitor of the university (from 1651 until his death in 1655), a canon of Christ Church, and a Trier. He had also served with Wilkins on the commission to execute the Chancellor's duties. Just when Wilkins met Robina French is unknown, but it is likely they were acquainted several years before their marriage since French and Wilkins had many occasions to see each other on university business.

Wilkins's motives in marrying Robina were suspect. John Evelyn thought he had "married the *Protectors* sister, to preserve the *Universities* from the ignorant Sacreligius Commander and Souldiers, who would faine have ben at demolishing all, both places and persons that pretended to Learning." Others felt it was less a matter of protecting the universities from outsiders than a case of internal academic politics. Walter Pope suggested that Wilkins married to still the opposition to him that was emerging in the university, and that the marriage "gained him a strong interest and authority in the university, and set him at safety, and out of the reach of his adversaries." Pope echoes Evelyn in asserting that the marriage "also preserved the University from running into disorder and confusion." Another observer, expecting university politics to be affected, wrote, "From Oxford I am informed, yt Dr. Wilkins of Wadham is like to prove ye man of men there, having lately married ye Protector's Sister, . . . troubles Dr. Owen and others of ye Grandees there, who forsee yt hee will overtop them all." Timothy Holdon of Queen's College thought that Owen might be replaced by "Dr. Wilkins who is the rising sun since his marriage with the Protectors Sister."

Wilkins had his own story of how the marriage came about, and it made no mention of university politics. Some years later when the Archbishop of Canterbury suggested to Wilkins that he had married "too near unto you know who," Wilkins, who had just become Bishop of Chester, replied "I never sought the match. Being proposed to me, I excused myself, which was interpreted a flat denial. When the same matter had been oft solicited, twas oft repulsed: I was at last given to understand; that to persevere in that resolution would not well consist with the safety of my Person; as the posture of affairs stood at that time." What this threat to Wilkins might have been is not clear; it may have been related to the conflict with Owen and Goodwin. Pope, too, suggested that the marriage "set him at safety," and that Wilkins had put into the "Port of Matrimony." It is not impossible that pressure was applied from within the college. In talking to the Archbishop, Wilkins would naturally emphasize his reluctance rather than the advantages the match gave him at the time. The local wits made what they could of the situation. One penned the following verse:

> Wadham's Warden with great strife
> Hath lost Eaton and got a wife
> She's nasty: we may gather hence,
> Twas not love but Christian Prudence.

Wilkins was frequently criticized for his marriage, not because it brought him worldly advantages, but because it was supposed to have required exemption from the Wadham College statutes, which forbade a married Warden. It was widely believed that a dispensation to marry against college statutes had been granted only because Wilkins had married into the Cromwell family. But the dispensation that made Wilkins the only married Warden of Wadham for nearly two hundred years had been granted him by the parliamentary Visitors several years earlier, long before Robina could have been a prospective wife, as part of the campaign against popish practices.

We know little of this "useful" marriage with a perhaps "nasty" wife. The family, which included two young daughters by Robina's earlier marriage, no doubt lived comfortably in the Warden's spacious lodgings. There is no record of any further children.* Wilkins's marriage to the Protector's sister does not in itself necessarily imply anything about his religious outlook. Two of Cromwell's daughters were covert Anglicans, and one, Elizabeth Claypole, was almost certainly a Royalist. Another daughter, Mary, was married in 1657 in an Anglican service. Since Cromwell apparently did not enforce ideological conformity on his immediate family, there is no reason to believe he expected it of his brother-in-law.

Very little is known about Wilkins's relationship with Oliver Cromwell. He must have come into at least occasional contact with the Protector after his marriage. Perhaps it is significant that although Dr. French was invited to preach before Cromwell numerous times, there is no indication that Wilkins received a similar invitation. Nor was he invited to preach before Parliament. Wilkins evidently did not think very highly of Cromwell, for he once told Gilbert Burnet that the Protector combined the qualities of enthusiasm and dissimulation. Wilkins, however, apparently discussed the problem of church government with Cromwell about the time the latter considered transforming the Protectorate into a monarchy. Wilkins later told Burnet that he had often insisted to Cromwell that "no temporal government could have a sure support without a national church that adhered to it, and he thought England was capable of no constitution but episcopacy." He felt confident that Cromwell would turn to episcopacy "as soon as the design of his kingship was settled." * Considering Cromwell's approach to church government, this seems highly unlikely, but the subject may have been a topic of conversation between them. In any event Wilkins did not use his connections with the ruling family for private gain. He "made no other use of that alliance," said Burnet, "but to do good offices, and to cover the university from the sourness of Owen and Goodwin."

Although most of Wilkins's time during the Commonwealth and Protectorate was spent at Oxford, he made occasional visits to London, particularly after 1656. He preached now and again in important London pulpits. In February 1656 John Evelyn heard him at St. Paul's preaching before the Lord Mayor. His sermon had as its theme that obedience was preferable to sacrifice, a message that recurred frequently in his post-Restoration sermons. Preaching engagements could prove embarrassing. On the occasion of a public fast day for the persecuted Piedmontese a few months later, Thomas Manton, the well-known Presbyterian minister, invited Richard Baxter and Wilkins to share his Covent Garden pulpit. Manton, who succeeded Baxter in the pulpit, had unfortunately chosen the same text, and had to constantly refer back to Baxter's sermon "and to say every now and then, 'As it has been observed by my reverent brother.'" By this time Wilkins must have begun to feel terribly uncomfortable. It is reported that he "set cruelly uneasy, and reckoned that between them both, he should have nothing left to say," for Wilkins, too, had chosen the same text. He begged Manton to be excused, but Manton insisted that he deliver his sermon. Wilkins retrieved the situation

and by an ingenious artifice, . . . succeeded admirabley. Before he named his text, he prepared the audience by expressing the fears of their narrow-spiritedness, and little concern for the interest of God in the world. 'For' says he, 'without any knowledge or design of our own, we have all three been directed to the same words.' Which spoken with the majesty and spirit of that excellent person, so awakened and disposed the minds of the people, that he was heard with more regard, and was thought to do more good than both the former, though he had scarce a single thought throughout the sermon distinct from the other two.

The occasion for this theological sleight-of-hand is interesting largely because it indicates that during this period Wilkins was associated with two of the more moderate Presbyterian clerics.

Wilkins probably had many things on his mind besides his spiritual duties at this time. He was seen in and about London most frequently during the early months of 1656, around the time of his marriage. Science and art seem to have joined preaching and romance. Wilkins and John Evelyn called on John Barlow, the "famous Paynter of fowls, Beasts & Birds," and Evelyn visited Wilkins at Whitehall. That Wilkins should be at Whitehall is surely attributable to his marriage. On this occasion Evelyn first met Sir Paul Neile, whom he notes as "famous for his optic-glasses." Ralph Greatorex, the mathematical instrument-maker, was also present, and showed the two "his excellent Invention to quench fire." Evelyn and Wilkins were evidently close friends. On March 11, 1656, Evelyn invited Wilkins, Dr. Taylor, Robert Boyle, and Mr. Berkeley to dine with him at Sayes Court. That afternoon he presented Wilkins with a "rare Burning-glasse." After dinner the group called on Colonel Blount, "to see his new invented Plow." On April 14, Boyle, staying at St. James Court, went with Wilkins to see some rarities. Thus the scientific group at Oxford was maintaining close contact with Londoners of similar bent.

The alliance with the Cromwell family that probably accounts for his sojourns in London may have led Wilkins to cross literary swords with the leading republican theorist, James Harrington, soon after his marriage. Harrington's *Commonwealth of Oceana* had appeared in 1656 and immediately aroused much discussion. Its espousal of republicanism ran directly counter to the aims of certain key supporters of the Protectorate who were seeking to develop the anti-republican elements of the new constitution. Shortly after the publication of *Oceana,* for instance, a committee whose moving spirit was Nathaniel Fiennes, the son of Lord Saye who had been requested as Visitor of Wadham, adopted a petition urging that the Protectorate become even more monarchical and Cromwell become King. Harrington's supporters were associated with the anti-Protectorate movement and were active in its downfall. Wilkins apparently supported the Protectorate as the closest approximation of the traditional constitution then available.

Wilkins, perhaps lacking the time or the inclination to undertake a reply to Harrington himself, asked Matthew Wren, cousin of the future architect and son of the imprisoned Bishop, to respond. Wren belonged to the scientific coterie that Wilkins led, but his choice of a known Anglican and Royalist is puzzling, even though Wren proved to be Harrington's ablest critic. His reply to the *Oceana* led to a pamphlet war of several years' duration. Besides arguments about the theoretical validity and practical value of Harrington's schemes, numerous personal insults were exchanged, many of them directed at Wilkins and his scientific activities.* The dispute was not really about science, however, and the exchange of insults was a side issue. There is no reason to think Harrington was hostile to the scientific movement.

The Wardenship of Wadham, then, was hardly a retreat for Wilkins. His activities ranged far beyond his college into university administration, public controversy, and London society. As we shall see shortly, his most important efforts were concentrated within the scientific circle he built up at Oxford, but he was already becoming a figure of some national prominence with a reputation raging far beyond that circle. It was during the period of his Wardenship that Wilkins became a man of affairs, who, by virtue of his position, his interest in science, and his literary and political talents, seems to appear near the center of every conflict that affected the educational and scientific interests he was committed to protecting.

V. The University Years:
Science at Oxford

Although Wilkins became deeply involved in university administration and even political controversy, his real achievement rested on his Wardenship at Wadham and his role in promoting science at Oxford. Under his leadership Wadham attained its greatest influence and prestige, and became one of the most populous colleges in the university.

The reasons for Wadham's preeminence are not hard to find. Wilkins not only followed a policy of encouraging men of all persuasions to come there, but was able to attract important scientific scholars no matter what their religious and political beliefs. Seth Ward, the new Savilian Professor of Astronomy, a known Anglican and Royalist, came to live at Wadham "Invited thereto by the Fame of Dr. Wilkins." Christopher Wren, also a Royalist, came in 1649. Although "that miracle of youth," as Evelyn described the brilliant young Wren, became a fellow of All Souls in 1653, he kept his rooms at Wadham. The mathematician Laurence Rooke, who would become Gresham Professor of Astronomy, left Cambridge "for the sake of Dr. Wilkins . . . and of Dr. Ward," and brought several of his students with him. The mathematician William Neile, son of Sir Paul Neile and grandson of the Archbishop of York, also came "for the sake of Dr. Wilkins . . . by whose instructions and those of Dr. Seth Ward he greatly cultivated and improved his genius in mathematiques."

These names leave no doubt that Wilkins's scientific reputation was partly responsible for the flourishing state of Wadham. But there were other factors as well. He maintained the traditional west country ties of the college and added a large cluster of students from Northamptonshire. Politically the range at Wadham was certainly very great. Not only were Royalists like Wren and Ward in residence, but also Parliamentarians, including the sons of Sir Francis Russell and General John Disbrowe, both allied by marriage with the Cromwell family.

Perhaps the most important reason for Wilkins's reputation was his policy of moderation, which enabled students and fellows of diverse backgrounds and markedly different points of view to live together. From the start he sought a workable compromise under which students of all persuasions could live amicably. Later detractors, who claimed he advocated comprehension during the Restoration simply as a means of favoring dissenters, were clearly wrong. At Wadham he quietly created a "comprehensive" college. Wadham thus proved to be a haven for Royalists and moderates. The Royalist and Anglican Matthew Wren wrote to Wilkins in 1657

Those men Sir, who have the good fortune to have part in your friendship, are not more in love with any of your virtues, then with the generous freedom you maintain in an Age overrun with passion and sourness: It is not enough with you, for the ruining of a man, to be told that he is of such a party or persuasion, but Truth and Merit are never strangers to your good opinion, in what Country soever they have been brought up: This is the Prerogative of your judgment, which being able to pass sentence upon every particular, is not put to take things in grosse upon the credit of any faction or company of men.*

In a period when fear of proclaiming Anglican sentiments was common, Wilkins encouraged at least one Anglican to maintain his beliefs, and used his influence to protect many others. It is hardly surprising that William Lloyd, a Restoration bishop who had lived at Wadham, felt Wilkins had "governed with praise," and "left a very grateful Remembrance behind him." Wilkins's policy of moderation and support for those in danger because of their religious views extended beyond the college walls. He went out of his way to ask the local Major General not to banish the future Dean Fell from Oxford although Owen and the Presbyterian heads were anxious to get rid of him. Fell would not treat Wilkins so kindly later. On another occasion, Wilkins, together with Owen and Wallis, tried to prevent the ejection of the Anglican scholar Edward Pococke.

Wilkins did a great deal to improve the college's physical setting as well as its intellectual environment. It was under his rule that the elaborate formal gardens were created. Despite financial difficulties the college allotted substantial sums to create the fashionable walkways, with their "prim parterres, straight alleys, clipped borders and hedges," in whose center stood a dial in the form of a figure of Atlas holding up the world. Once the garden had been laid out, Wilkins provided it with elaborate water works. "Amongst the Water-works of Pleasure, we must not forget an Engine contrived by . . . John Wilkins, . . . whereby, but of a few gallens of water forced through a narrow *Fissure,* he could raise a *mist,* and might see an exquisite *Rainbow.* . . . But what kind of *Instrument* it was that forced the water, I dare not venture to relate." Robert Hooke thought this a marvelous device. His gardens gave Wilkins the opportunity to play practical jokes on unsuspecting passersby. For these he used a hollow statue he had constructed, "which gave a voice and uttered words by a long conceal'd pipe that went to its mouth, whilst one speaks through it at a good distance." Shortly after Cromwell had sent a notice to the university encouraging members to preach the gospel in Virginia, Mr. Ashwell was walking toward the "statue of fflora" in the Warden's garden when Wilkins whispered through the pipe, "Ashwell goe preach the Gospel in Virginia. The voice amazed him, and at the next return, it repeated the same words. At another return it said, Ashwell, for the 3rd and last time, goe preach the Gospel in Virginia." Wilkins then "wheeled about and mett him: asked him what ayled him to look so affrighted: He said if ever man heard a voice from heaven I did; the Dr. said you have always derided such fancyes; but he persisted in it, till [Wilkins] unridled all to him that he might have a quiet in his mind, and suffer no harme by a delusion."

If much of the university was dour during these years, Wadham certainly was not. Wilkins sought in many ways besides practical jokes to alleviate the "sourness" that so many complained of. Oxford, according to one music historian, "seems to have been the only place in the kingdom where musical sounds were allowed to be heard." Many of these sounds emanated from Wadham. In addition to frequent chamber concerts, Wadham played host to the world-famous violinist Thomas Baltzar in July 1658. "About that time it was, that Dr. John Wilkins, warden of Wadham coll. the greatest curioso of his time, invited . . . [Baltzar] and some of the musitians to his lodgings in that coll. purposely to have a consort, and to see and heare him play. The instruments and books were carried thither, but none could be perswaded there to play against him in consort on the violin." But the concert was not to be stopped, and Anthony Wood, the chronicler of the Oxford scene, himself saved the evening. "At length the company perceiving A.W. standing behinde in a corner neare the dore, they haled him in among them, and play, forsooth, he must against him. Whereupon he . . . took up a violin, and behaved himself as poor Troylus did against Achilles. He was abash'd at it, yet honour he got by playing with, and against, such a grand master as Baltzer was." For the scientific group at Oxford, music provided a subject for scientific analysis as well as pleasure. Christopher Wren, for example, was interested in the development of new musical instruments.

Literature, particularly of the satirical variety, also flourished at Wadham. In 1658 *Naps upon Panassus,* containing several satirical poems "from some of the Wits in the Universitie," appeared. Most of its contributors were Wadham men. One of these, Thomas Sprat, later the author of the *History of the Royal Society,* was particularly encouraged by Wilkins. The publication of Sprat's portion of "Three Poems upon the Death of His late

Highnesse Oliver" by Dryden, Sprat, and Edmund Waller was probably due to Wilkins's efforts. Also contributing to the literary life of the college were Walter Pope and such future "wits" as Sir Charles Sedley and John Wilmot. It was not only lighthearted satire that was cultivated, for Samuel Lee, a man of a more serious bent, indicated that Wadham was a "goodly Seminary of all polite Literature."

Living well obviously appealed to Wilkins, and good living evidently included good food. The Visitors insisted that students eat in the hall rather than in surrounding taverns or inns, or in their rooms. This was probably not much of a problem at Wadham, for Wilkins had somehow managed to get as Wadham's master chef Mr. William Austin, who had served as Prince Charles's cook when he was Prince of Wales. When Charles was restored, Austin was restored to the royal kitchen. In view of the impeccable credentials of the college's cook and the lively conversation of its Warden, it is not surprising that John Evelyn, on visiting Oxford, chose to dine at the college with his "excellent & deare Friend Dr. Wilkins."

Although Wilkins's rule at Wadham was extremely successful, it was clouded by an attempt to oust him as Warden. The causes and circumstances are unclear. Whatever the reason, in 1654 a number of the fellows petitioned the Protector and some of his Council for Wilkins's removal. Although the Visitors just a few months earlier had indicated that the Chancellor of the University, Oliver Cromwell, ought to serve as ordinary Visitor of the college in the vacancy of the Bishopric of Bath and Wells, Wilkins requested that the complaint be heard instead by the university Visitors "as the proper judges in cases of that nature." The request was granted, and the Visitors were given authority to decide the case. They called in both parties and asked the petitioners to bring in a written complaint. After initially refusing, the complaining fellows finally brought in "a paper contayning eight heads of grievances." The Visitors, on hearing the case, decided that Wilkins was "not guilty [of] the said grievances charged upon him." They noted that several of the complaints contained a "matter of scandall" to Wilkins and that he "hath beene much injured thereby."

It is difficult to even guess the basis of the complaints. Montagu Burrows has suggested that the appeal was made to the Council because the disaffected in the college wished to avoid the Visitors. This still sheds no light on the nature of the charges. It is perhaps significant that quite a number of fellows were absent during the period of the attempted ouster. Their absence may have provided the opportunity for the dissatisfied to act. It is possible that the stricter Puritans in the college found Wilkins too lenient with the Royalists and Anglicans who were flocking to Wadham. Or perhaps it was this tolerance coupled with a lack of religious enthusiasm. Both Wilkins and Ward had been much criticized and had become "liable to the Persecution of peevish People, who ceas'd not to Clamour, and even to Article against them as Cavaliers in their hearts, mere Moral Men without the power of Godliness." Pope noted the extremist "Party were rigidly and unmercifully Censorious against the Moral Men" and had attacked them from the university's pulpits. It is certainly possible that Wilkins's moderation, his unwillingness to discuss doctrine, and his emphasis on moral duties had alienated some. His position and role in the educational controversies of 1653 would also have displeased religious radicals.

Wilkins's enduring contribution to the history of Oxford and Wadham was not gardens, musicales, or banquets, but the development of a scientific group at Oxford which became the nucleus of the Royal Society. It was Wilkins more than any other one person who was responsible for making Oxford *the* center of scientific studies in the 1650's. His personality and activities drew men from London, Cambridge, and elsewhere, and his leadership led to the development of a permanent institution for the cultivation and propagation of science.

Just why Wilkins and Wadham became the center of the scientific group, we cannot be certain. But if the mysteries of leader-

ship cannot be completely untangled, one must agree with
H. A. L. Fisher that "in every wide intellectual movement there
are men who exercise an influence quite out of relation to the importance of their positive contribution to the advancement of
knowledge. Of such is John Wilkins, Warden of Wadham College from 1648 to 1659." Wilkins was less talented than Seth
Ward, Christopher Wren, or John Wallis, but his personality was
more winning. His ability to get along with men of an extremely
wide range of views and social backgrounds must have been in-
valuable, for the scientists ranged from staunch Anglicans like
Ward, Christopher, Matthew and Thomas Wren, and Thomas
Willis to Presbyterians and Independents like John Wallis and
Jonathan Goddard. He was at home in courtly as well as plebeian
circles, and was able to bring men who belonged to disparate
classes together. His geniality and good humor were characteristics that any organizer covets. Perhaps because his own scientific
talents were not great, he did not arouse jealousy among his
colleagues. In fact he particularly enjoyed encouraging young
men like Christopher Wren and Robert Hooke who were more
talented than himself.

Wilkins attracted some of the best scientific minds of his day to
Oxford. We have already noted that he played an important role
in bringing Wallis there as Savilian Professor, and that Ward,
Rooke, Christopher Wren, and William Neile came to Wadham
because he was there. These men, with the addition of William
Petty, Ralph Bathurst, Matthew Wren, Thomas Willis, and
Jonathan Goddard, an old Magdalen Hall schoolmate of Wil-
kins, made up the core of the Oxford scientific circle.

Wilkins was probably responsible for bringing Robert Boyle to
Oxford as well, though Boyle did not come until 1655 or 1656. As
early as September 6, 1653, Wilkins invited the young aristocrat
to join them. Boyle must have expressed some interest, for Wilkins wrote, "If I knew with what art to heighten those inclinations, which you intimate of coming to *Oxford,* into full resolu-
tions, I would improve my utmost will to that purpose." In

September 1655 Boyle visited Wilkins at Oxford "with whom he spent the day with noe small satisfaction." Boyle, like Evelyn, found Wilkins charming and his entertainments pleasant, and was impressed with his courtly speech and the "real productions of his knowledge." Wilkins was thus able to impress men not only with his civility and social graces but also with his intellectual abilities. Boyle's 1655 visit convinced him that Oxford was indeed the center of scientific activity, and he joined the Wilkins circle soon afterward. Wilkins did not confine himself to recruiting aristocrats. He gave the position of manciple or steward of Wadham to the talented but unknown mathematical instrument maker Christopher Brookes, the inventor of a new quadrant, "purposely to encourage his ingenuity."

He was also able to arouse enthusiasm in those as yet unconverted to science. Students at Wadham developed a remarkable interest in scientific subjects even if their own dominant interest lay elsewhere. Wilkins's own curiosity and enthusiasm were infectious. Wherever he was—in London in the early 1640's, in Oxford from 1648 to 1658, in Cambridge in 1659–60 and again in London in the formative years of the Royal Society—it was there that the nation's most creative and active scientific circle came into being.

Although it is clear from the comments of his contemporaries as well as the verdict of historians that Wilkins was at the center of the scientific movement at Oxford in the 1650's, to assess his personal contribution and that of his scientific group, we must indicate briefly just what the scientific conditions were when he arrived on the scene. The study of scientific subjects, as we have noted earlier, had been a feature of English intellectual life long before mid-century. Nor can it be claimed that Wilkins introduced serious scientific work to Oxford. It is simply not true, as both contemporary and later commentators have sometimes argued, that the universities provided little or no stimulus to the scientific movement in the earlier decades of the seventeenth century.* Most of the men involved in the mid-century scientific

movement had themselves received their earlier intellectual training at the universities. We have already noted that Wilkins's
scientific interests were highly developed during his student years,
and that by the time he left the university he had fully absorbed
the available writings of Copernicus, Kepler, Galileo, and others.

In mathematics and astronomy in particular, Oxford offered
the most advanced instruction in the country. The Savilian professorships had, since their foundation, drawn the very best minds
in these fields, particularly from the faculty of London's Gresham
College. Thus Christopher Hill's assertion that the most advanced
instruction was being carried on at Gresham in the end seems to
support the university's claim to competence in these fields. The
constant interchange between the Gresham and Oxford faculties
continued into the Interregnum and Restoration, with some
Greshamites always willing to leave for the supposedly backward
university. Scientific instruction of high quality was available at
Oxford to all who cared to take advantage of it. The tradition of
first-rate scientific scholarship was further strengthened when
John Wallis and Seth Ward came to fill the Savilian posts.

Nor had the biological sciences been entirely neglected before
Wilkins arrived. During the civil war, William Harvey came to
Oxford with Charles I. Harvey did not find university life antagonistic to his scientific inquiries, and in 1645 accepted the Wardenship of Merton College. There he found a congenial group of
men who understood his experiments and even collaborated with
him in his dissections.* Outside of biology, however, there does
not seem to have been a great deal of interest in experimental
work prior to 1648.

One of the chief reasons for the acceptance of the view that pre-
Puritan Oxford was anti-scientific, Puritan Oxford scientific, and
post-Puritan Oxford again anti-scientific has been that it seems to
fit the thesis advanced by Robert K. Merton, Dorothy Stimson,
Christopher Hill, and others that the progress of science and Puritanism were intimately and causally related. If we were not so
anxious to impose this hypothesis on the actual historical data, we

would realize that from at least the early seventeenth century, there was a steadily increasing appreciation of the sciences, especially mathematics and astronomy, at the universities, and particularly at Oxford. This was a continuous development whose peak occurred during the 1650's not because of Puritanism but because a group of men with widely differing political and religious beliefs found themselves together in a situation conducive to scientific work. They found themselves together partly because of political events and indeed partly because they were all seeking refuge from the religious conflicts connected with Puritanism. Early Restoration Oxford also exhibited a very high level of scientific achievement although the group led by Wilkins had by then largely dispersed.

Furthermore, the closer we look at the careers of those involved in the formation of the Oxford group, and then the Royal Society, the farther we are led away from Puritanism as a unifying feature. In fact very few of these men were Puritans. The most striking thing about their religious views and the progress of their careers is their ability to make peace with whatever government was in power, their toleration of disparate political views, their repudiation of all forms of dogmatic religion, and their tendency to move in the direction of latitudinarianism and natural religion.

We have already indicated that the Puritans had a unique opportunity to reform the university in a more scientific direction but showed no particular inclination to do so. Neither Presbyterians nor Independents made any conscious attempt to turn the universities into national centers of scientific learning. It is true that many of the scientists appointed to Oxford during this period were appointed by Puritans. But this is simply to say that all university appointments during this period were government appointments. Among those appointed, the correlation of scientific achievement with Puritan sympathies is at best random. Furthermore, there is some evidence that the Presbyterians attempted to prevent the cultivation of science. Simon Patrick reported "the new Philosophy was interdicted in some colleges" by Presbyterians who feared it would lead to religious as well as philosophical innovations.

Whatever the contributions of Wilkins's Oxford group of scientists, it must be remembered that it was not a totally new creation, but rather an offshoot and further development of the 1645 London group. That group's meetings broke up when several of its important members took posts requiring them to leave London. Wilkins, of course, left to take up his duties at Wadham. By the time he did so, he must have been one of the leading members of the London group, for soon after his departure several other members followed him to Oxford. During the next few years, it was the Oxford branch that was most active and most productive. If Wilkins was not the dominant person in the London group by 1648, there is no doubt that he assumed leadership of the new group at Oxford and was largely responsible for its success. John Aubrey, for example, described Wilkins as the "principall Reviver of Experimental Philosophy (secondem mentem Domini Bacon at Oxford)." Wilkins and his colleagues, whom Henry Oldenburg later referred to as the "Oxonian Sparkles," were undoubtedly the immediate predecessors of the Royal Society. Thomas Sprat, the historian of the Royal Society, goes so far as to say that the meetings in Wilkins's lodgings "laid the foundation" of the Royal Society, and Oldenburg, one of the Society's first secretaries, thought of the Oxford circle as the "embryo or First Conception of the Royal Society."

Initially Wilkins and his scientifically inclined friends at Oxford met in William Petty's rooms. When Petty left for Ireland in 1651, the meetings continued at Wilkins's lodgings at Wadham as long as he lived in Oxford. The most important members of the club were Wilkins, Wallis, Goddard, Ward, Rooke, Petty, Bathurst, Willis, Boyle, and Christopher and Matthew Wren. The total membership fluctuated; in 1652 there were thirty members. The group had its ups and downs. Although it was very active in 1655, a letter from Petty to Boyle in February 1658 suggests that for a time it did not meet. He wrote "I have not heard better news, than that the club is restored at Oxford." * Wilkins was frequently in London during this period, and perhaps his absences had led to a temporary collapse.*

Early in the group's history, the members adopted a set of rules to govern their meetings, rules that to some degree became the basis of the Royal Society's regulations. They called for weekly meetings at which members would perform or provide experiments. Since a six-week absence "without speciall occasion" led to exclusion, members were clearly expected to be active. Active participation was further ensured by the provision that any member who did not "upon the day appoynted performe such exercise, or bring in such experiment as shall be appoynted for that day, or in case of necessary absence provide that the course be provided for by another" had to pay a fine, and "shall performe his task notwithstanding." Either at Oxford or earlier in London, the group evidently had some difficulties with members who failed to perform the experiments they promised. Membership was formal, as in the Royal Society, and required a majority vote "of the company." Voting was secret so that it might "be free, and without prejudice." Each new member paid an admission fee to the club, two-thirds of which was used for instruments required for the group's experiments. Wallis indicated their meetings "were very numerous and very considerable. For beside the diligence of Persons, studiously Inquisitive, the Novelty of the design made many to resort thither." Perhaps the rules were drawn up when the novelty began to fade, for he indicated that when the project "ceased to be new," some "began to grow more remiss" or pursued their scientific inquiries at home.

It is not difficult to see why scientific activities attracted so many men during this period of religious and political upheaval. Science provided a respite, a non-controversial topic of conversation and joint endeavor, in which men of varying religious and political views might have "the satisfaction of breathing a freer air, and of conversing in quiet one with another, without being engaged in the passions and madness of that dismal Age." Natural philosophy was a neutral subject that Royalists and Anglicans like Willis and the Wrens could discuss with the Presbyterian Wallis. The 1645 group and the Royal Society specifically barred discussions of religion and politics. The Oxford group probably did the same. In all his dealings Wilkins tried to maintain a free and moderate atmosphere. His ability to do so undoubtedly helps explain his success in the Oxford group.

In other ways, too, political and religious upheavals proved to be a stimulus to the Oxford group as well as to science generally. Interest in science grew as clergymen and Royalist men of affairs were prevented from engaging in their regular professional duties. Science provided an outlet for creative energies diverted from normal channels. Matthew Wren, for instance, retired to Oxford and science only to return to politics after the Restoration. Others changed their professions. Walter Charleton noted that the "late Warrs and Schisms" particularly "discouraged men from the study of Theologie; and brought the Civil law into contempt"; and that many young scholars in the university turned to medicine and philosophy. Both Ralph Bathurst and John Wallis abandoned promising clerical careers for science. Anglican clerics frequently took up lay work such as medicine. Others, such as Joseph Glanvill, Thomas Sprat, and John Pell became interested in science while they were in effect biding their time until they could take orders in the Church of England. A good part of the scientific activity of the war and postwar periods, among both stay-at-homes and exiles, seems to have had its roots in the desire to escape from the turmoil of religious fanaticism and revolution.

Although no minutes seem to have been kept of the group's activities, the accomplishment of a great deal of productive work is evident from letters, fragmentary reports, and books published by its members either during the Interregnum or later. In areas that were well developed as academic subjects, particularly mathematics and astronomy, it is difficult to separate the work of the club from that of the university itself. Ward and Wallis, the Savilian professors, were busy teaching and lecturing as well as participating in Wilkins's group. Most of our information about mathematics in the university emphasizes the high level of interest and widespread teaching through public lectures, private instruction, and tutorials in the various colleges. It is possible that, because of their difficulty, mathematical subjects were not frequently discussed by Wilkins and his group, although Wallis's own publications indicate his concern with new problems, and he kept mathematicians in London and abroad informed of progress at Oxford. Ward, Wallis, Wilkins, and Charleton all commented on the high esteem mathematics enjoyed at Oxford.

Astronomical theories and observations were important to the group. They wasted little time in quarrels over the merits of the various systems; Christopher Hill's contention that the civil war "was fought between rival schools of astronomy, between Parliamentarian heliocentrics and royalist Ptolemaics," is as erroneous as Webster's belief that only the Ptolemaic system was taught at Oxford. As Ward indicated in the *Vindiciae,* the Oxford scientists were engaged in topics such as the refinement of elliptical theories. Ward himself had "excogitated a Method, whereby the Astronomy of the primary Planets may be Geometrically explain'd: & that as well according to the Elliptical, as the Circular Way. A thing of stupendious difficulty, requiring universal knowledge in the Mathematiques; & of inestimable benefit towards the Certification of Coelestiall Science." It was this type of work, rather than warmed-over disputes about the Ptolemaic system, that concerned the virtuosi. There is no evidence that Wilkins continued to have any particular interest in astronomy in these years, and he made no original contributions in this field.

The group as a whole probably spent more time on astronomical observation than theoretical speculation. They rapidly acquired new telescopes and other instruments, and important sightings, such as that of the comet of 1652, were made by Rooke and Ward, the latter delivering a series of lectures on the 1652 comet shortly after it appeared. The group was also particularly interested in improving the telescope, Wilkins and Christopher

Wren, for instance, trying to build a telescope eighty feet long so they could see the entire moon at once. Boyle, who had very little interest in astronomy before joining Wilkins's circle, provided telescopes to be used by other interested persons at Oxford as well as himself. Wren proposed a number of astronomical subjects for discussion, revealing an interest that later led to his appointment as Gresham and then Savilian Professor of Astronomy. Optics and microscopy were also highly cultivated. Wilkins, Charleton, and Matthew Wren have all left enthusiastic accounts of improved instruments and detailed observations from which Christopher Wren made drawings.

The 1650's began a "period of unsurpassed importance" in the teaching and investigation of anatomy at Oxford. As in other fields, there were roots extending into the past. A readership in anatomy had been established in 1624, but William Petty was its first important occupant. Petty was active in Wilkins's circle before his work in Ireland temporarily curtailed his scientific pursuits. During his short stay at Oxford, he, together with others in the club, became particularly interested in the anatomy of dogs and in chemistry. Before he left Oxford, Petty became involved in the famous case of Ann Green, whose body was to have been dissected after her execution. The revival of this supposedly dead woman by Petty and several of his physician friends was memorialized in a small tract, *Newes from the Dead*. The city authorities wanted to rehang Miss Green, but she was saved from that fate. She became a celebrity and Petty a local hero.

Thomas Willis was another important physician-experimenter in the Wadham club. It was during this period that Willis, an Anglican, and the future Sedleian Professor of Natural Philosophy and physician to Charles II, did much of his experimental work on brain anatomy. Wilkins's friends at Oxford also initiated the experiments on transfusions and injections which were to become famous during the Restoration. The versatile Christopher Wren "was the first Author of the Noble Anatomical Experiments of Injecting Liquors into the Veins of Animals." The idea of injections directly into the bloodstream came to Wren during a discussion with Wilkins and Boyle. After discussing the matter the three decided to try an experiment, which Wren performed before a group of observers. The experiment was repeated several times with a variety of liquids and became well-known throughout the university. In 1657 more injection experiments were performed. The following year the group was performing new anatomical experiments which involved opening a "vein and sprout[ing] medicines into it."

Chemistry also interested the group, although Wilkins was probably not a major participant in these activities. As we have noted, several years earlier he had ridiculed the chemists for their propensity to search for the fabulous. The arrival of Boyle in late 1655 or 1656 may have altered Wilkins's views, though we have no evidence that it did. But if Wilkins was suspicious, Ward in 1652 reported that eight out of the thirty members of the group had "joyned together for the furnishing of an elaboratory and for making chemical experiments" each week.

The Oxford group was interested in the practical aspects of science as well as the theoretical, and worked on inventing and improving a tremendous variety of mechanical devices, ranging from dials and flying machines to beehives. Wilkins and Hooke pursued flying experiments, and Hooke constructed a model which, with the help of weights and springs, "rised and sustain'd itself in the Air." The club tried several flying experiments, including the blowing of various objects over London Bridge. Some balloon-like constructions were also attempted. Other experiments involved perpetual motion, "new ways of Intelligence, New Cyphers," all of which had so interested Wilkins earlier, and "Ways of submarine Navigation," which he had discussed in his *Mathematical Magick*. The club also tried to improve coaches "for ease, strength and lightness," although it is not clear whether they ever concerned themselves with Wilkins's sail-driven coach. They also worked with "a speaking organ" for articulating sounds. Wilkins and his group considered, among other things, surveying and mining techniques, improvements in etching and engraving, new methods of wood turning, a device for weaving several ribbons simultaneously, "cheap and fair" techniques of embroidering for beds and hangings, and improved printing methods. This sort of effort suggests that the more practical and utilitarian attitudes of the Royal Society stemmed from the Oxford group rather than the 1645 group.

Wilkins's lodgings at Wadham contained a potpourri of mechanical devices and scientific instruments; Evelyn reported that "He had above his lodgings and gallery a variety of shadows, dyls, perspectives, and many other artificial, mathematical and magical curiousities, a waywiser, a thermometer, a monstrous magnet, a conic and other sections, a balance on a demi-cycle, most of them his owne and that prodigious young scholar, Christopher Wren." Although many of these sound very fanciful, most were practical instruments of one kind or another. During this period several members of the group were interested in sun dials, and many colleges had them installed. Wilkins himself was probably responsible for the design of Wadham's. The waywiser was a devise attached to a carriage to measure distances traveled. Wilkins's interest in such a measuring device went back at least as far as 1648 when he had suggested that by multiplication of a series of wheels, it was possible to develop an instrument "whereby a Man may know how many Miles or Paces he doth go in any space of Time, whether or no he do pass by Water in a Boat or Ship, or by Land in a Chariot, or Coach."

Sometime during the 1650's Wilkins became interested in developing an improved plow. Hartlib in a letter to Boyle reported he had "received a special commission from Sir Charles Culpepper, [who] . . . entreated me most passionately to put you in mind of the promise you were pleased to make unto him, about the new invented plough of Dr. *Wilkins*. He bids me to assure you, that if you can procure one for him, that you will lay a very great obligation upon him." Perhaps other agricultural implements were developed, for Wren indicated he had worked on "divers improvements in the art of husbandry."

Military matters had always interested Wilkins. Much of *Mathematical Magick* had been taken up with ancient and modern methods of fortification and assault. Now at Oxford he and the others, particularly Christopher Wren, concerned themselves with "new offensive and defensive Engines," "secret and speedier Ways of attacking Forts than by Approaches and Galleries," "inventions in Fortification," "inventions to better making and fortifying Havens, for clearing Sands, and to sound at Sea," and "Fabric for a Vessel at War." Wilkins himself worked on a double-barreled windgun. The university, after the Leveller uprising, designated Wilkins to investigate the engineering documents concerned with the local fortifications. Naval and maritime matters seem to have interested the Oxford group as much as they later did the Royal Society. They discussed new methods of sailing, improving war vessels and whaling techniques, developing submarine navigation, ways of making fresh water while at sea, as well as the best means "for reckoning Time, Way, Longitude, and observing at Sea."

The group was also interested in architecture. Wallis devoted considerable effort to such construction problems as the best means of supporting certain kinds of floors. He made a model of one such arrangement in 1650, which he "shewed soon after to divers in *Oxford,* and particularly to Dr. *Wilkins* then *Warden* of *Wadham* College." Their transformation into architects must have seemed quite natural to such scientists as Christopher Wren and Robert Hooke, for the connection between science and architecture had already been established at Oxford in the 1650's.

Among the many practical endeavors of the Wadham scientists, one that seems to have particularly appealed to Wilkins was the development of new types of beehives. As early as 1653 he was experimenting with glass hives, which he set up in the college garden. In 1654 Evelyn remarked that after dining with "the most

obliging and universally curious Dr. Wilkins," he was shown the
hives, and that Wilkins "was the first who shew'd me the transparent apiaries, which he had built like castles and palaces and so
order'd one upon the other to take the honey without destroying
the bees." Wilkins evidently gave free reign to his fancy in building them, for Evelyn notes they were "adorn'd with a variety of
dials, little statues, vanes, etc." Finding Evelyn so pleased with the
hives, Wilkins presented him with an empty one, which he kept
for many years in his garden at Sayes Court. Even the King
"came on purpose to see and contemplate" Wilkins's hive there
"with much satisfaction." On this project, too, Wilkins worked
closely with Christopher Wren, who sent reports of his colleague's
"pleasant and profitable Invention of a Transparent Beehive" to
Samuel Hartlib. The interest in bee-keeping, like so many other
practical concerns, was continued after the break-up of the Oxford group by the Royal Society.

At Oxford as in earlier years, Wilkins wished to spread scientific knowledge to a wider audience. In November 1653 he gave
"£200 towards the erecting of a College for Experiments et Mechanicks at Oxford," to be located "over the Schooles or in the long
gallery." It was to include "all the models of Inv[entive] Arts
. . . with a Tr[eatise] added to each showing the structure and
use of it." Nothing seems to have come of this proposal, however,
and perhaps Wilkins's £200 were absorbed by other experiments
or never actually materialized. Wilkins and his associates also
wished to make knowledge more readily available to all members
of the university community and to the public, in part by making
more efficient use of the Bodleian Library. They hoped to be able
to build a compendium of all knowledge, a project dear to the
hearts of Baconians and Comenians. But because of the uncertainty of "not knoweing what others have done before us" and to
avoid repetition of the work of others, they "conceived it requisite
to examine all the bookes of our public library (every one taking
his part) and to make a catalogue or index of the matters and
that very particularly in philosophy physic mathematic & indeed

all other facultyes, that so that greate numbers of bookes may be serviceable and many may at once see where he may find whatever is there concerning the argument he is upon." This cataloging was supposed to be completed in a few months, but several years later, in 1655, Hartlib reported that it was still unfinished. Another venture that occupied the Oxford virtuosi was the development of a universal character and philosophical language.

Although it is well known that both its predecessor, the 1645 London group and its successor, the Royal Society, maintained contacts with foreign scientists, the similar activities of the Oxford group are less widely recognized. Although it did not have a regular foreign corresponding secretary as the Royal Society did, it did carry on extensive correspondence with scientists elsewhere, particularly in Paris and Holland. Not only did scientific communication cross national borders with the greatest of ease, it transcended political divisions as well. In 1656 and 1657 Wallis, for example, was writing to the Royalist and Catholic Sir Kenelm Digby as well as Lord Brouncker in London. Digby, writing from Paris in 1658, was excited by the accomplishments of the Oxford group, and particularly wanted to be introduced "to your worthy and noble Colleagues and friends Dr. *Wilkins* and Dr. *Ward;* whom I exceedingly honour." Digby indicated that the accomplishments of the Wilkins circle were well-known abroad. "It is a worthy triumverate that you two and Dr. *Wilkins* do exercise in literature and all that is worthy. Your names are famous abroad and I hear of you from sundry hands."

Surprisingly enough, the scientific movement during this period was never seriously attacked. Far from being the peculiar reserve of one intellectual or religious group and the target of others, the new science was generally assumed to be making a useful contribution to human knowledge. Wood, however, indicated that some tensions existed, and that the Oxford scientists were not as modest as they might have been. Perhaps these tensions might most usefully be seen as the normal friction that arises whenever a younger group of academics, enthusiastic over new techniques and methodologies, seems to jeopardize the position of the older generation, or at least to undermine the prestige of their work. In any event no steps were taken to inhibit the activities of the Wilkins group. Even the more old-fashioned must have recognized that the virtuosi were their allies in defending the universities against the attacks of the radical sects.

The general recognition of the desirability of scientific activity was eventually symbolized by the creation of the Royal Society. The idea of such a society was hardly new even in the 1650's. Bacon had envisioned a similar venture many years earlier, and Hartlib had been advocating a government-aided scientific organization for many years. By 1657 the Protectorate government was interested; Oldenburg wrote to Boyle at Oxford that the Council had granted "your desires for the promotion of knowledge, which I suppose to be those that were couched in a certain petition you were pleased to import unto me at Oxford." The contents of this petition have not come to light, but Wilkins and his Oxford group were probably responsible for it.*

In May 1657 Evelyn mentioned a "mathematico-chemico-mechanical school," designed by "our noble friend Dr. Wilkinson [sic]," which would be a teaching institution and also serve to communicate scientific findings to the public. By 1657 several schemes for a variety of scientific institutions were being discussed. In January 1658 John Worthington informed Hartlib that the Council seemed willing to set up an institution for learning. Hartlib indicated that his son had discussed the matter with "Mr. Secretary," who proved suspicious, but fortunately had referred the matter to someone more sympathetic. It would appear that Hartlib was now also involved.

Richard Cromwell was even more willing to promote the cause of science than his father had been, perhaps partially because of his friendship with Wilkins. In December 1658 Hartlib had heard that Richard had plans "for contenancing and advancing of universal useful learning in due time." Hartlib hoped to see Wilkins made Provost of Eton, and "likewise president of the forementioned standing council of learning." This statement suggests that Wilkins was probably slated for a position of leadership in the projected "council of learning." His leadership of the Oxford group, together with his friendship with Richard Cromwell, lends plausibility to the suggestion. However, nothing much could be accomplished during Richard's brief rule. In the turbulent republican phase that followed, the matter seems to have been dropped. Evelyn wrote Boyle on September 3, 1659, that they could no longer hope for a mathematical college "much less, a Solomon's house," and proposed instead a private society where gentlemen could cultivate science. These preliminary efforts facilitated the rapid organization of the Royal Society after the Restoration. Wilkins's preeminent role prior to the Restoration helps explain his position afterward.

As early as 1658, however, Wilkins's group at Oxford began to break up, with many of its members returning either permanently or temporarily to London. The withdrawal of Wilkins to Trinity College, Cambridge, even in the absence of other factors, would have caused a decline in the group's momentum. In any event, the center of English scientific activity returned to Gresham College, where meetings drew into the scientific circle many men of affairs who could not have attended those at Oxford.

The drift of Wilkins and his friends to London and the subsequent organization of scientific activity there under the aegis of the Royal Society did not, however, result in a collapse of scientific activity at Oxford. Two mistaken assumptions have led to this view: first, that the science that existed there during the 1650's did not extend very deeply into the life of the university, and second, that its particularly flourishing state was due to specifically Puritan influences that later disappeared. A high level of scientific activity continued some time after the Restoration. Although many scientists did leave Oxford for positions in the newly reestablished Church or other situations previously closed to them, the Restoration itself did not suddenly denude Oxford of scientists. Christopher Wren went to Gresham College, but he returned to take Ward's Savilian chair after the Restoration. Wallis, Boyle, Willis, and Bathurst remained at Oxford. Nor did the creation of the Royal Society mean the end of a scientific group at Oxford. Though the number of members decreased, Boyle and Wallis still served as a focus for such meetings. In 1665, when the Plague forced so many members of the Society to leave London, most of them naturally flocked to Oxford to continue with their experiments. There was for a time even a plan for creating a permanent scientific society there, perhaps modeled on the Royal Society. Although the Restoration did see a marked increase in scientific activity in London, and the Royal Society did come to overshadow the universities, London did not necessarily flourish at their expense. One of the characteristics of Restoration England was a more general commitment of intellectual and financial resources to scientific pursuits, which permitted science to thrive in more than one place at a time.

Wilkins's departure from Oxford foreshadowed the later multiplication of scientific circles. In 1659 he became Master of Trinity College, Cambridge. The circumstances of his appointment to the best preferment at Cambridge are confusing, and were complicated by the political upheavals which occurred that year. The post had traditionally been an appointment of the Crown, and the Protector, Richard Cromwell, probably succeeded to this as well as other royal patronage. The Protector knew of Wilkins's accomplishments at Oxford, and according to one writer promoted him to Trinity "thinking he would be as serviceable in that as he had been in the other university." Shortly before receiving the appointment, Wilkins visited London frequently and was often seen in Richard's company. Edmund Ludlow even claimed that he was one of the three members of the Protector's "cabinet council," along with Lord Broghill and Colonel Phillip Jones. Whatever Wilkins's political role actually was, and there is little evidence elsewhere to substantiate Ludlow's portrait of him as a leading adviser to Richard Cromwell, there is no reason to doubt that

Richard "not only loved, but trusted him." Yet the appointment was formally made on petition of the fellows of Trinity College, and granted by Parliament. Just a few weeks after the death of the preceding Master, John Arrowsmith, Wilkins was incorporated doctor of divinity, which may indicate that he was already slated to become the new Master, and that the subsequent petition was a mere formality. That the fellows welcomed the appointment there can be no doubt, for they sent one of them on two journeys to London "on ye behalfe of ye Society petitioning yt Dr. Wilkins might be made our Master when the place was voyde." When Wilkins finally arrived in Cambridge, the college greeted him with a reception and suitable entertainment. A few months later a petition to Charles II stated the fellows had been particularly anxious to obtain Wilkins as their Master in 1658 because they "feared least some person either of mean sort or of factious principles should be thrust upon them." * It is clear that Wilkins's reputation for moderation had spread beyond the confines of Oxford, and that Trinity, which then enjoyed the highest prestige of any Cambridge college, considered him the ideal master.

Wilkins was confirmed as Master on August 17, 1659, and resigned as Warden of Wadham the following month. His legacy to Wadham was a tradition of benevolent and tolerant rule, the pleasures of scholarship as well as its rigors, and a new emphasis on science. He also left his "great telescope to the library," a fitting remembrance of the initiator of organized scientific enquiry at Wadham. Even his enemies acknowledged "allmost all that was preserved and kept up of Ingenuity and Learning, of good Order and Government in the *University of Oxford* was chiefly owing to his prudent conduct and encouragement." The move from Oxford to Cambridge brought few changes in Wilkins's style of life. Academic affairs were carried on in much the same way at both universities. Cambridge, like Oxford, had been affected by the political changes of the last decade. But although Cambridge experienced purges, they were not accompanied by

the bitterness of the Oxford ejections, perhaps because the Laudians had never captured Cambridge so completely.

Wilkins's rule at Trinity was short but successful. He used his
very considerable powers to reform the college, and "used great
diligence and care to put all things in order and settle the troubled affairs . . . with great prudence and reputation." Strict examinations and disputations were revived. Four months after his
arrival, new regulations were instituted. The B.A. examination
was improved, and evasion of the statutory requirements for the
degree was made punishable.

Wilkins was installed at Trinity just in time for the annual fellowship elections in late September and played an important role
in selecting the new fellows. Robert Creighton, one of the candidates, reported the circumstances of his own appointment. Shortly
before the election, he was watching a tennis game at the college
court when "the Ball was stroke by chance into the Eye of one of
[the scholars]; whereupon the Doctor [Creighton] cried out, 'O
God, O God, the scholar's Eye is stroke out.'" This event was
used by one of Creighton's competitors who "took an occasion
from it to accuse him to the Master (Dr. Wilkins) and Seniors as
a prophane person, and one that daily took God's name in vain,"
buttressing his argument by adding that Creighton never came to
their private prayer meetings. When all the Seniors met for the
election, Wilkins sent for Creighton and "charged him with it."
He examined Creighton's tutor, Dr. Duport, as well as others of
the Seniority, "who all vouched for his Sobriety, and that they
had never observed any thing to come out of his mouth, that
tended to prophaness or Blasphemy . . . tho' they believed he
might say some such words in relation to the Scholar's Eye."
Wilkins responded in a characteristically generous way. He said
"it look't like malice: and that it did not signify much if he neglected to come to their private meetings since he never failed the
public, nor his Tutor's Lectures." He therefore proposed that the
Seniors "lay aside the Informer and his Adherents, & elect the
accused and his; which they at his request consented to, & chose
him." The incident not only illustrates the great power of the

Master in College affairs, but suggests that Wilkins was not greatly concerned with observing all the religious niceties. The election of Creighton did not quite end the matter. The following day a note appeared on the screens: "He that informed against Dr. Crichton, . . . deserves to have his breech kickt on."

Although Wilkins did not remain at Cambridge long, he stayed long enough to spread his enthusiasm for science. Soon after his arrival he set about organizing a scientific group similar to the one at Wadham but it apparently did not survive his Mastership. Even so, during this period Trinity could claim the scientific leadership of the university. Cambridge as a whole seems to have been less committed to science than Oxford—in part because Cambridge's most scientifically inclined members, such as Seth Ward and John Wallis, had migrated to Oxford. Another related cause was the lack of endowed professorships at Cambridge to rival the Savilian chairs at Oxford.

If formal education in scientific subjects left something to be desired, private study was flourishing, particularly in the fields of botany and anatomy. The famous botanist John Ray, a fellow of Trinity College, devoted much of his time to scientific studies, and his student Francis Willoughby, the future ornithologist, obtained most of his scientific education at Trinity. Ray directed several younger men to the study of natural history. Later on Ray and Willoughby collaborated with Wilkins in trying to work out a scientific classification of plants and animals.

Isaac Barrow's scientific studies, like Ray's, predated Wilkins's Mastership. Like many Royalists and Anglicans who had planned a clerical career, he turned to science and medicine when advancement in the Church seemed barred to him. He returned to the college about the time Wilkins became Master, and the two soon became close friends. In 1662 Barrow obtained the Gresham professorship of geometry largely thanks to Wilkins's vigorous backing. Although Barrow was an Arminian and a staunch episcopalian, his religious beliefs never troubled his friendship with Wilkins; indeed the two men shared a latitudinarian bent.

Wilkins applied his Wadham policy of moderation and toleration of divergent views to the problems of Trinity, and while at Cambridge "joined with those who studied to propagate better thoughts, to take men from being in parties, or from narrow notions, from superstitous conceits and fierceness about opinions." Wilkins joined the Cambridge Platonists, referred to in the above passage, in their search for moderation and a simple faith based on reason. Several of the Platonists were his personal friends. Wilkins was instrumental in obtaining the Vicarage of St. Lawrence Jewry for Benjamin Whichcote, and he proposed Henry More and Ralph Cudsworth as members of the Royal Society. Cudsworth considered Wilkins a personal friend.

Contact and even friendship does not necessarily imply intellectual alliance, although there were many points on which the Platonists and Wilkins agreed. Like Wilkins, the Platonists taught that religion and science were complementary, and that reason was an important element in religion. Nevertheless, differences also existed. Wilkins had none of the Platonists' religious fervor. His religion was matter-of-fact. The Platonists' mysticism was totally absent in Wilkins, and he did not admire this quality in others. While the Cambridge Platonists to some extent took Plato and the Neoplatonists as models, Wilkins rarely mentioned them except to castigate the Neoplatonic cabbalists. If Wilkins drew on any ancient writers for his approach to religion and ethics, especially in his later years, it was Aristotle and the Stoics, not Plato. Nor could he, one of the most outspoken advocates of plain writing, have admired the Platonists' abstruse style. Science played a much more important part in Wilkins's life than it did among the Platonists. For the Platonists, especially Henry More, science was important largely to the extent it confirmed the existence of supernatural powers. Although Wilkins and indeed most scientists of the period shared this interest, it was not their primary motive for performing experiments. It is significant that More turned away from Cartesianism not because he was dissatisfied with Descartes's scientific findings but because of their implications for metaphysics and religion. More's interest in witchcraft can be seen as part of the same phenomenon—the attempt to find in nature proof of the supernatural. Wilkins had little part in this movement and was unsympathetic to occult studies. The one important idea that the Platonists contributed to the scientific movement, that of "plastic nature," does not appear in Wilkins's writings. His approach is more mechanical. Nor did he ever devote much time to botany, the area where the idea of "plastic nature" had its greatest vogue.

Still, the relationship between Wilkins and the Platonists was not simply social. John Ray was in many ways a Platonist, and yet to a considerable extent he modeled his natural theology on that of Wilkins. Wilkins and the Platonists proceeded from differing philosophical models and presuppositions, but as their thought related to the practical world the results were not dissimilar. They are properly associated as founders of the Restoration latitudinarian movement. They advocated religious charity and were tolerant of other religious views. It is curious that these qualities, together with the ability to survive a variety of regimes, have led both contemporaries and historians to admire the Platonists and to condemn Wilkins for time serving and insincerity.

Wilkins's tenure at Trinity coincided with the last hectic months of the Protectorate and its downfall. Unfortunately we know little of his role in these affairs. As we have seen he was a close associate of Richard Cromwell, and may even have been one of his important political advisers. It is very likely that he was among the very few to support Richard against the army leaders when the Protectorate's days were numbered. Wilkins may even have become a member of the small committee or cabal that Cromwell used when the Council of State came to include a large number of the regime's opponents, among them representatives of the army and out-and-out republicans.* When the Protectorate fell, like so many of its supporters Wilkins apparently became an advocate of restoration of the monarchy. Fauconbridge, Broghill, and Howard, all supporters of the Protectorate against the army, became Royalists when the Protectorate collapsed, and there are some hints that Wilkins did too. There are also suggestions that Wilkins was not altogether in favor of the Protectorate even while it lasted. Robert Creighton of Trinity felt that Wilkins really disliked "the Party he was supposed to be of," and in spite of his marriage "was at heart a true Loyalist, and had privately sent money often times to the King." Creighton claimed that Wilkins "always used his Interest with Cromwell in favour of the royall Party; who whenever he saw him come to him, would first accost him thus, 'What, Brother Wilkins, I suppose you are come to ask something or other in favor of the Malignants?'" Creighton may have been correct in his assessment of Wilkins's political sympathies, but it is more likely that he had a change of heart when the Protectorate collapsed and restoration of the monarchy appeared to be the only alternative to a series of military coups and a totally unrepresentative parliament.

The last months of the Interregnum were as confused at Cambridge as elsewhere. In February 1660, Samuel Pepys spent most of his visit to Cambridge drinking "many healths to the King" in a local tavern. Yet shortly afterward Parliament was still trying to form classical presbyteries in the colleges. Pepys reported that all the "old preciseness" was gone from Cambridge, and "that there is no such thing now-a-days among them." Shortly afterward the Convention Parliament was elected, and the political changes began to affect Cambridge more directly. Celebrations in favor of the monarch were no longer limited to toasts. On May 10, Wilkins and the other Masters were summoned to the schools accompanied by their "fellows and scholars in their formalities." With musical accompaniment they proceeded from the schools to the cross on Market Hill, where a proclamation acclaiming the royal return was read. On July 5, the university representative waited on the King at Whitehall with a congratulatory address. A series of congratulatory verses, *Academia Cantabrigiensis* (1660) was published by members of the university. Wilkins may have been a contributor.*

With the Restoration, Wilkins was forced to leave Trinity. His ejection was due not to his political or religious views, or to any personal antagonism, but to a prior legal claim that Charles II was obliged to recognize. But for this legal technicality, Wilkins could have expected to remain at Trinity. The heads of colleges normally retained their posts unless the head ejected by the parliamentary Visitors was still alive and pressed his claim. In such circumstances the intruded head usually obtained a good position in the Church, where many vacancies now existed. Wilkins himself became Dean of Ripon just two months after his ejection. The ejected Master of Trinity, Thomas Comber, was no longer alive in 1660, but before Comber died, Charles I had already appointed Henry Ferne to replace him, when the post became vacant, as a reward for his pamphleteering in the Royalist cause. With the Restoration, Ferne sought fulfillment of the promise made by the martyred king. Given the circumstances, it would have been exceedingly difficult for Charles II to refuse him.

The fellows and scholars of Trinity, however, begged for the retention of "Dr. John Wilkins, . . . appointed at their earnest petition," insisting that by "his prudent government and sweet conversation [he] both endeared himself to this Society, and hath made good that general fame, which had reported him eminent for learning, integrity, ingenuity, and other vertues fitt for the promoting of order, peace, and unity, and for ye discharge of such a trust." Their plea was unsuccessful. Wilkins was replaced by Ferne on August 3, 1660. Thus Wilkins, like many others, suffered in the aftermath of the Restoration from the confusion of myriad claims and counterclaims to offices and benefices. And if in his case both parties appear to have had justice and law on their side, this was true of countless others. At least Wilkins had the testimonial of the fellows to his successful Mastership. In less than a year he had been able to win the loyalty and respect of his colleagues. In the words of John Aubrey, he was "honoured there and heartily loved by all." *

VI. The Restoration

Both at the time of the Restoration and subsequently, there was a natural tendency to view the return of the monarch as a sharp disruption in the lives of those who had remained in positions of trust during the Interregnum. Walter Pope, for example, made much of his half-brother Wilkins's difficulties during this period. The seriousness of such disruptions can easily be overestimated. Wilkins did lose the Mastership of Trinity, but within a few months after the King's return became Dean of Ripon. Most clerics who lost one position soon found another, and many of the political leaders of the Protectorate were to be found in court and government circles under Charles II.

In political matters the King and many of his immediate advisers recognized that civil government could not be firmly re-established without the cooperation of the major powerholders, including those who had made their peace with the Protectorate. As lay politicians who had managed to survive successive regimes by moderate compliance were recruited into the new government, they tended to be sympathetic toward other politicians and clergymen who had done the same. Among the High Church clergy led by Sheldon, however, there was considerably more hostility toward conforming clerics, whom they considered at worst Puritans and at best time-servers. Generally speaking, Laudians were more anxious to exclude Puritans from the Church than Royalists were to exclude parliamentarians from politics. Only outspoken republicans and the regicides themselves were driven completely from public life. Even in the Church only the sectaries were expelled in 1660. And in 1662, when the decision was made to exclude a large portion of the Puritan clergy, those willing to accept the Act of Uniformity were left untroubled.

The returned churchmen, and the political faction of Clarendon, which represented the returned Royalists, were most hostile to clerical and other officials who had served under the Commonwealth and Protectorate. The anti-Clarendon factions, themselves compromised by Interregnum ties, were more sympathetic to moderate conformists. The relative balance among the pro- and anti-Clarendon groups, therefore, tended to ameliorate the sharp disruptions in clerical and political careers that might otherwise have occurred. Wilkins's career is a good example of this phenomenon. He was far more at home in secular and governmental circles than among clerics, and gravitated into the anti-Clarendon group, which became the principal source of his preferment. He received his most important early appointment before Sheldon and Clarendon were firmly entrenched and his later ones after their eclipse. While the Restoration did shift him from an academic to an ecclesiastical career, he, like most other moderates, managed to weather this storm as he had earlier ones.

As Wilkins's political beliefs became more widely known, it became clear that he was not dangerous to the regime. He was a firm upholder of the government, and his views on the proper structure of society were conventionally hierarchical and conservative. Society without government was simply a state of nature, which he depicted in terms very similar to those of Hobbes. To avoid constant warfare, men had formed governments and established laws that could only be maintained by the acceptance of religion by both rulers and ruled. Unlike many clergymen, Wilkins did not disdain politics. He respected "Wisdome," which, following Aristotle, he defined as the ability to choose "fit and convenient" means to achieve success in the "practical affairs of life." This required not only sensitivity to the temper and interests of other persons and a capacity for recognizing the proper moment for action, but also the ability to predict the consequences of action. Political wisdom thus involved both adaptability in the face of rapid change and the accumulation of experience. Following the humanists, Wilkins found that history could provide at least a partial substitute for first-hand experience. The political arts were, he thought, to be cultivated by public men and clergymen alike and Wilkins was thought by both his friends and his enemies to possess such political wisdom and dexterity. William Lloyd noted that "in great matters he judged so well, that he was not usually surprised by Events." And Anthony Wood remarked on his "rare prudence and dexterity in the management of worldly affairs." His ability to get along, on a fairly intimate basis, with several successive political regimes, and to obtain important positions from each of them indicates that he did not lack political talent.

He recovered quickly from his loss of the Trinity College Mastership, receiving the royal appointment as Dean of Ripon in August 1660.* Although his appointment must have been unpalatable to the returned exiles and impeccable Royalists who garnered most of the lucrative and prestigious places in the summer of 1660, it was made before they had an opportunity to seize control and before factionalism had hardened along party lines. The government was forced to act quickly on clerical appointments in the summer of 1660, for cathedral chapters had to be filled before new bishops could be chosen. Wilkins was thus installed as Dean before the bishops' ranks were filled with men hostile to him. His appointment could not have been a great surprise to the knowledgeable. His ouster from Cambridge, as we have noted, resulted from the accident of an earlier commitment by Charles I. He enjoyed a good reputation as a mediator between men of different parties and a protector of known Royalists and Anglicans. Moderate Anglicans, at least, recognized his "zeal" for the "unity of the church," and were familiar with "How he stood up in defence of the Order and Government: How he asserted the Liturgy, and the Rites of it" while still at Oxford.

The chapter at Ripon had been dispossessed over a decade before Wilkins's appointment and consequently had to be entirely reconstituted. The choice of the new canons was to some extent under Wilkins's control, for customarily the Dean and chapter recommended several candidates, one of whom would be chosen by the Archbishop of York. The first stall was filled by Henry Gresswold, who just a few months earlier had been at Trinity College with Wilkins. Another was given to William Lloyd, a former Wadham man, and a promising young divine of the Wilkins school.*

About the same time Wilkins became Dean, he was also presented with a prebendary at York Cathedral, a preferment of the Crown. Soon after receiving these appointments he took up residence in London; by November 1660, when he began regularly to attend the scientific meetings at Gresham College, any other permanent residence would have been almost inconceivable. Although for a time he had no regular clerical employment in London, Pepys heard him preach at the Temple three days before the Royal Society was organized. Soon afterward he accepted his second position with Gray's Inn. This time he became "Preacher" of the Inn with "an honorable maintenance." Although Wilkins did not remain at Gray's Inn very long as minister, his relationship with the Inn continued, and in August 1664 he was admitted as a member without charge. Such membership was granted to eminent persons as a sign of respect. The Inn and its environs provided for Wilkins not steady employment or exposure to the learning of the law, but rather some degree of social and intellectual prestige and a convenient place to meet and talk with many of the important people of his day.*

In spite of these various clerical appointments, for the first few years after the Restoration Wilkins was not actively engaged in ecclesiastical politics. He certainly could not sit with the Presbyterian delegations at the Worcester and Savoy conferences after accepting the Deanery of Ripon. Acceptance of the Deanery was itself an act of abjuration of the Covenant, which had been an oath favoring extirpation of deans and chapters along with the bishops. On the other side, the bishops, most of them returned exiles and uncompromising Laudians, would not select someone they considered a turncoat to represent them. Sheldon could

hardly have been sympathetic to a man who had been intruded at
Wadham on the very day he had been violently ousted from the
headship of All Souls. The failure of the early comprehension
schemes, which, given the fluid state of affairs in 1660 and 1661,
probably had more chance of success than later ones, was in large
part due to the exclusion of Anglican moderates. Although the
government already included liberals and ex-Protectorate supporters as well as Royalists, the Church for many years lacked this
balance. The Cavalier Parliament, which succeeded the Convention, also wished to avoid concessions. The result was the Act of
Uniformity of 1662, which permanently excluded a considerable
portion of the ministry from the establishment.

Wilkins seems to have conformed without hesitation even
though he did not approve of the new legislation. His own acceptance of the Act of Uniformity satisfied few. The High Churchmen viewed it with suspicion, the dissenters with distaste. Wilkins
nevertheless tried to persuade others to accept the Act, for he considered a single national Church essential and believed that minor
differences on church polity, ceremonies, and forms of prayer
should not prevent a peaceful settlement. He seemed surprised
and alarmed that many of those he considered moderates were
unwilling to follow his lead. In fact, he was divided from such
liberal dissenters as Richard Baxter, John Howe, Edmund
Calamy, and Thomas Manton, who like himself preached moderation and accommodation, by one crucial point. Although they
conceded that the practices on which they insisted were not required by Scripture, they argued that since these matters were
spiritually indifferent, those in authority might just as well yield
to them as they to those in authority. Wilkins argued that his
allies were being unreasonable, and that their needless scruples on
nonessentials would only succeed in destroying the unity of the
Church.* Among the important ecclesiastics of the Interregnum
only Wilkins and Reynolds, who had become Bishop of Norwich,
accepted preferments that enabled them to defend their beliefs
within the hierarchy.

Wilkins's decision to conform and accept the Church he did not consider perfect led him toward the leadership of an initially small but increasingly influential party of "moderate episcopal men who were then called Latitudinarians," and who supported the establishment but wished to broaden it. Wilkins was perhaps the most important and surely one of the most outspoken latitudinarians in the early years of the Restoration, and he soon gathered around him a group of rising clerics. Their latitudinarianism was partly a reaction to the unhappy fruits of narrow sectarianism in the civil wars, and partly a result of the increasing laicization of society that preceded and accompanied the wars. It embodied such intellectual traditions as the humanism of Erasmus, Castellio, and Acontius, the ideas of toleration developed among the sects, the liberal views of the Dutch Arminians, and the anti-dogmatic and questioning stance of the scientific movement. Anglicans like John Hales and William Chillingworth contributed much to the intellectual foundations of Restoration latitudinarianism, as did the Cambridge Platonists. The Cambridge group, indeed, must be considered a constituent part of the latitudinarian movement. But as Norman Sykes has noted, the line of connection between them and their latitudinarian successors is "devious and difficult to draw." That some connection did exist is obvious in terms of both ideas and persons. In the 1660's a shift occurred in latitudinarianism toward a more genial and worldly pragmatism. This change in direction, I think, reflects Wilkins's influence. Though a rationalist, he championed the analytical reason of science rather than the mystical reason of the Cambridge group. Reason in the hands of Wilkins and his successors was closer to common sense than the Platonists' "Candle of the Lord." He was more willing than the Platonists to become involved in day-to-day affairs and work for more liberal ecclesiastical arrangements. Wilkins's own tolerant views and his emphasis on rationality and moral theology were clearly not borrowed from the Platonists, for by the time he reached Cambridge his basic attitudes were already well established.

From about the time of the Restoration, Wilkins became the effective leader of the latitudinarian circle in London. John Tillotson, later Archbishop of Canterbury, was the most prominent member of the coterie of liberal young clerics that gathered around him. Just when the two met is uncertain, but it could not have been long after the King's return, for by the fall of 1660 Wilkins had nominated Tillotson for one of the vacant Ripon canonries. John Hacket, Bishop of Coventry and Lichfield, did not approve of his curate's new companions, and complained that Tillotson "is now fallen in with Dr. *Wilkins,* and is become a Presbyterian, and enemy of the church of England." Tillotson admitted his relationship with Wilkins but denied the charge of Presbyterianism. Of all the latitudinarians, Tillotson was the closest to Wilkins. The two men became colleagues at St. Lawrence Jewry in 1663, and shortly afterward Tillotson married Wilkins's stepdaughter.

Another member of the group was William Lloyd, whose religious outlook and preaching style Wilkins "formed," and who, like Tillotson, became one of the most famous liberal churchmen of the Restoration. Another Wadham protégé who entered the London group was Thomas Sprat, later Bishop of Rochester; Edward Stillingfleet, the youthful author of *Irenicum* (1660), a plea for a moderate ecclesiastical settlement, also moved in Wilkins's orbit. Although in later years he lost some of his latitudinarian sympathies, he was among the important members of this group for over twenty years. Other young clergymen attracted to Wilkins's entourage were William Outram and Simon Patrick, the latter probably the author of *A Brief Account of the New Sect of Latitude-Men* (1662), the earliest description of the latitudinarians and their beliefs. Gilbert Burnet, who met the group about 1663, soon became a convert and reported he "easily went into the notions of the latitudinarians."

The philanthropic layman Thomas Firmin, a Socinian who remained a communicant of the established Church, was also connected with the circle, as was John Locke, an intimate friend of

Firmin, Tillotson, and Stillingfleet. Another layman associated with Wilkins's group was Matthew Hale, the eminent jurist. Like Locke, however, his association may not have begun until the mid-1660's. The Wilkins circle also included those Cambridge Platonists who were living in London. Benjamin Whichcote and John Worthington, whom Wilkins had known from his Cambridge days, were among his closest companions, and Ralph Cudsworth, though not a regular associate, consulted Wilkins occasionally. By the mid-1660's Joseph Glanvill too could be found in liberal clerical circles and became one of the chief propagandists of the modern churchmen. For the most part, however, the Platonists preferred academic retirement to political activism, and the quiet pulpits of Cambridge to those of London where latitudinarian influences were most in evidence.

Most of Wilkins's associates were notable for their youth and their noninvolvement in the conflicts that had engendered the disputes of the civil wars. Wilkins, now in his mid-forties, and Whichcote were the exceptions. The group's opponents on both sides, the dissenters led by Owen, Baxter, Manton, and William Bates, and the High Churchmen, many of them returned exiles, were still to a large extent fighting old battles and revenging old wounds that meant little to the younger group, either intellectually or personally. The cluster of moderate young clergymen was a recognizable, though not closed group. Several of them were interested in science and were members of the Royal Society. Two of them, Sprat and Glanvill, became the most vocal defenders of the Society that Wilkins had done so much to create.

Wilkins, with his usual bent for gathering talented persons around him, was creating still another group of men who wished to engage in intellectual pursuits free of sterile wranglings. As at Wadham, he served as a rallying point not only for those who wished to avoid religious conflict, but for those who sought to establish a climate of opinion that would end the conflict itself, and lead to calmer, more pragmatic modes of discourse and action. Wilkins's most striking talent may well have been his ability to encourage critical interplay while avoiding the bitter feuding that so often marked the intellectual life of the seventeenth century. Lloyd went out of his way to emphasize that Wilkins "would not spare to give reasonable reproof and wholesome advice," and said "I never knew any that would do it as freely, and that knew how to manage the freedom of speech so inoffensively."

Wilkins added to his scholarly talent for facilitating fruitful and moderate discourse an eminently practical concern for supporting the discoursers. He helped Robert Hooke and Isaac Barrow obtain scientific posts and tried to obtain clerical positions for Lloyd, Stillingfleet, Tillotson, and his other companions. Much of his influence with his contemporaries seems to derive from his zeal "to promote worthy men and generous designs." And, once promoted, most of these men remained his close associates. Wilkins's circle thus became more than a group of young clergymen with a common philosophical or religious outlook. It soon became the outstanding spokesman for both a moderate ecclesiastical establishment and a new theology.

The latitudinarians' approach to church government was pragmatic rather than Scriptural. The civil government, they argued, had both the power and the authority to establish the forms of church government and public prayer. The individual's duty was to submit to the established forms even if inconvenient, provided, of course, they were not patently un-Christian. Wilkins certainly preferred the wisdom of the public authority on such questions to private judgment. The latitudinarians considered themselves sincere Anglicans; they not only favored the established episcopal system of church government, but also admired its constitution and liturgy, and expressed distaste for both Presbyterianism and Independency. They did not argue, however, that other forms were unacceptable. They favored "a settled Liturgy," without which there could be no "solemnity of public worship," and like Wilkins disapproved of combining private and public prayers. Wilkins preferred "a reverend Decency" in divine worship to "pompous Superstition or Popular Confusion," but was probably not entirely wedded to the existing liturgy. He and his group were willing to make alterations to attain the unity they desired. Wilkins insisted on the importance of public worship, and its protection and promotion by the secular government. He also indicated that ceremonies and the like received all their obligation from being instituted by the proper authorities, and were acceptable if based on "Reason and Prudence." His past activities and compliances would suggest that most liturgical forms that might have been established would have been quite acceptable to him.

Although the latitudianarians did not find it difficult to accept the establishment, they wanted "Mercy and Indulgence" for those who could not bring their consciences to comply, and broad "terms of Communion" designed to take in all "of any Reason, Sobriety, and Moderation." They hoped, therefore, that the "things indifferent" preventing the reunion of the dissenters would be altered. These included a few expressions in the forms of prayer and certain ceremonies and disputed doctrinal points. Wilkins's "club for comprehension," as Wood called it, became the bane of the High Churchmen, who viewed any changes as destructive to the Church of England. It was only when the attempt at comprehension failed that some moderates turned to toleration as the closest available alternative, but until at least 1689 comprehension rather than toleration was particularly associated with Wilkins and his followers.

The theology of the Wilkins group differed from that of their contemporaries in emphasizing rationalism, natural theology, and morality. The group stressed the compatibility of faith and reason and the unity of truth. Moderation, however, was the keynote of Wilkins's thought and also of that of the other latitudinarians. Their sermons, which in style followed the precepts of Wilkins's *Ecclesiastes,* concentrated on two themes, the practice of moral virtues and the necessity of moderation. This combination of rationalism and moderation led their opponents to castigate them as Socinians. Their concentration on practical morality rather than doctrinal questions inspired the same kind of attacks that had led Wilkins and Ward to be labeled "meer moral men" several years earlier. The emphasis on morality perhaps implied a rejection of Calvinism, for the latitudinarians preached that salvation was at least in part attainable by man's conscious effort and free choice. They were neither Calvinists nor Arminians, but something in between. The elect were irresistibly saved. The rest of mankind, however, was not necessarily damned and possessed sufficient grace to gain salvation if it tried. This combination of free grace and free will partially explains the apparent contradictions in Wilkins's earlier statements on predestination and good works.

Wilkins sought to refute the charge that mildness would lead to skepticism or indifference. Skepticism was the result of an unduly quarrelsome disposition. At the same time the equally dangerous fault of dogmatism stemmed from overconfidence and pride, from the mistaken insistence on all things as equally certain. Dogmatism most frequently arose when a system was accepted "by the bulk," instead of being subjected to a systematic analysis of its component parts. "As every truth is not of the same degree of evidence, so neither is it of the same necessity." Some things are essential to religion, others "are only superstructions," and zeal must be proportioned to importance. Those who were zealous on lesser matters and entertained "strong prejudices" on "weak grounds" gradually became "more censorious" and "soured in their spirits," as well as "cooled" in their zeal for the fundamentals of religion.

This brings us to one of the basic approaches of Wilkins and the latitudinarians, the distinction between the essentials and the nonessentials of religion. They spent a great deal of time emphasizing the essentials, although they refused to enumerate them for fear of causing still further quarrels. They focused on the tenets of natural theology, that is the existence of God, the immortality of the soul, the necessity of being religious, the concept of future rewards and punishments, and the necessity of living a virtuous life. Conversely they deemphasized such nonessentials as ceremonies, obscure doctrines, vestments, and the forms of prayer. Wilkins insisted that salvation depended not on fine theological points, but on the "weighty and substantial duties of righteousness and peace." If a point was much debated, it was not likely to be a crucial factor in the life of religion, for God made the fundamentals perfectly clear.

There were two reasons, Wilkins argued, why men should refuse "to insist upon the utmost rigour of things" and "comply with all gentle and prudent expedients" that would "heal and accommodate differences." The first, and perhaps the most important, was the fallibility of human judgment. If men would only recognize the impotence of human faculties, the prejudices arising from interest that "strangely bias a man's judgment against clear evidence," the obscurity and difficulty in all things, the fact that learned men have always differed and that it was "next to impossible" to "agree in the same apprehension of things," they would realize that dogmatic statements were rarely as certain as those who made them thought. A man "must believe what he can, and not what he will." If he were ready to change his mind when "better information" became available, that was all that one reasonably could ask. The second reason to avoid dogmatism was pragmatic rather than philosophical. Moderation provided security and refuge in an unpredictable world. While Wilkins insisted that he opposed a Machiavellian compliance that permitted one to become engaged only as far as one could safely retreat, and asserted that it was necessary to maintain one's beliefs openly, there was every reason to do this "without fierceness and bitterness." Others might label this attitude "lukewarmness" and "detestable neutrality," but society would cease to exist unless vehemence on small differences were abandoned. To avoid "recourse to Arms," it was necessary to adopt mutual forbearance. As for those now in authority, it would be singularly inappropriate for men who had just won release from suffering to inflict it on others. "Let a man but look indifferently, round about him, amongst the kinds of parties in our times, . . . and then, say whether both our common peace and the power of Religion hath suffered exceedingly."

Even if Wilkins and his colleagues did not regard themselves as partisan, they were quite distinct from both the nonconformists and the Sheldonians and were viewed by others as a religious faction. The latitudinarians were the object of considerable distrust, especially from the leading figures in the church hierarchy. They were characterized as an insincere

company of men that are prepared for the embracing of any Religion, and to subscribe to any Doctrine, rather than incur the hazard of Persecution; and that they esteem him the onely heretick that refuseth to be of that Religion that King or State professeth. . . . They are characterized as people, whose onely Religion is to temporize, and transform themselves into any Shape . . . and that judge no Doctrine so Saving, as that which obligeth to be so complying and condescending a humour, as to become all things to all men.

A shorter but no less hostile definition of a latitudinarian was, "a Gentleman of a wide swallow."

This general suspicion tended to focus on Wilkins. As one of the oldest latitudinarians, he was most likely to have had compromising contacts with the Interregnum governments. He was censured by "the great men of the Church," who "did malign him for his wavering and unconstant mind in religion." Anthony Wood, who sympathized with Wilkins's critics, thought the major defect in his character to be the lack of "a constant mind, and settled principles." Wilkins's conformity, like that of his latitudinarian associates, was suspect, and it was said "that they had no greater zeal for what they conform to; . . . and could be as well content with the contrary." * Despite their protestations of loyalty, the latitudinarians were considered by many to be dangerous to King and Church.

These "moderate episcopal men" were, as we have seen, quite distinct from the dissenters, though the Sheldonians liked to suggest that they were really fellow travelers of the Presbyterians and had only conformed to gain preferments. Although this surely was a false assessment of their beliefs and motives, the latitudinarians did try to win over Presbyterian dissenters to the Church. They recognized that the Presbyterians comprised too large a segment of the population to be simply ignored. On a personal basis, they had nonconformist friends, particularly among the Presbyterian leadership. The moderates were less sympathetic to Roman Catholicism, however, than their intellectual position about nonessentials implied; they were reported to be "all very zealous against popery." * Their fear of Roman Catholicism more than once occasioned serious soul-searching, for several efforts at obtaining concessions for Protestant dissenters would have extended the same concessions to Roman Catholics.

Wilkins's played a role in the moderate movement in part because of the appeal of his ideas and personality, but also in part because of his patronage connections. He rejoined his former patron Lord Berkeley, who presented him with the vicarage of Cranford in Middlesex. Cranford was about thirteen miles from London, not far enough to keep Wilkins from attending the meetings at Gresham College. Parish duties could not have kept Wilkins very busy, for he had few parishioners. He served the religious needs of the Berkeley family, when they were present, and their tenants and dependents. Wilkins succeeded Thomas Fuller at Cranford. They had become rather intimate friends by 1655. The two clergymen had much in common, not least their moderation and desire for reconciliation in the Church. Although Fuller had been a Royalist, his approach to religion and church affairs was strikingly close to Wilkins's. The sermons of the two men also had certain similarities: both used the plain style and emphasized morality and its application to everyday life.*

Berkeley had made it clear that this was precisely the sort of preaching he wanted. He was undoubtedly attracted to both Wilkins and Fuller by their moderation and desire for religious conciliation, for he took the same position in his *Historical Applications,* a volume that demonstrates the importance of lay thought in the latitudinarian movement. Historians of the Restoration have rarely noted that there were men in Parliament, particularly in the House of Lords, who opposed persecution and were latitudinarian in sympathy and belief. In a period when laymen were preeminent in policy-formation and administration at both central and local levels, one must not overlook their impact on clerical affairs. It would be difficult to distinguish the substance of Berkeley's *Applications* from the works of Wilkins or Tillotson. Like so many of this school, particularly those with a scientific bent, he hoped to combat "Speculative and Practical Atheists" through the study of Nature. He greatly admired the Greshamites, particularly Boyle, Sir Robert Moray, and "the famous and eminent learned Dean Wilkins." And like other latitudinarians, he insisted it was the practice of Christian virtues, not the profession of particular doctrines, that expressed true Christianity, and that the fundamentals not the paraphernalia of religion were what counted. Berkeley recognized that the role of conciliator, which Wilkins so often played, was not an easy one. Those "pious, learned and well disposed persons," who were zealous "to reconcile the Difference in Christian Religion," usually met "a severer fate (instead of their deserved Reward) to be abominated or at least disliked by all parties."

Walter Pope was obviously wrong, then, to write that Wilkins was "destitute of all Employment and Preferrment" when he became Vicar of St. Lawrence Jewry, one of the most prominent London parishes. Wilkins was then not only Dean of Ripon and a prebend of York, but Vicar of Cranford under a patron whose views were remarkably similar to his own and who apparently fully understood his difficult position. His stepbrother was probably correct, however, when he suggested that Seth Ward, the previous incumbent, now newly promoted to the bishopric of Exeter, had a hand in obtaining St. Lawrence for Wilkins. Ward was becoming an influential figure in High Church circles and may have had some influence with the Crown, which possessed the right of presentation.*

The location of St. Lawrence alone would have assured the importance of its pulpit even if such able and well-known clerics as Edward Reynolds, Seth Ward, and John Wilkins had not served as its ministers. The Guildhall, the center of city government, was within the boundaries of the parish, and there had been an intimate association between St. Lawrence and the Guildhall for centuries. The parish itself, though not particularly large, was composed largely of well-to-do, well-established people, many of whom were connected with the city government. The church-wardens, for example, were usually members of one or another of the London guilds. More significant than the congregation's wealth, however, may have been its sympathy for nonconformity. Richard Baxter, the most prominent nonconforming cleric of the Restoration, was frequently present and apparently quite influential in parish affairs. Thus the appointment of Wilkins provided the parishioners of St. Lawrence not only with a prominent authority on sermon-writing appropriate to their prestige and position, but also with a minister whose views on theology and church polity were compatible with their own.

The weekly lectures of John Tillotson contributed substantially to making St. Lawrence such an influential pulpit. His extremely popular sermons were attended by high society and young clerics. Tillotson was a man very much in the Wilkins school of divines, and it is almost certain that Wilkins was the most important formative influence on both the style and the content of his sermons. Many of the ideas and approaches that have been considered novel to Tillotson are simply an elaboration, and not much of an elaboration at that, of Wilkins's early writings. Burnet described the relationship between the two men:

But that which gave a last finish to his course of instruction was his close and long friendship with Bishop Wilkins. He possessed himself of all the richest stores of knowledge acquired by that great man, so as to perfect every one of them; for though Bishop Wilkins was the more universal scholar, yet he was the greater divine; if the one had more flame, the other was more correct. Both acted with great plainness, and were raised above regarding vulgar censures. But if Bishop Wilkins had a character so peculiar to himself, that perhaps, never man could admonish and reprove with such weight and authority, and in a way so obliging as he did; so no man know better than his great friend, the art of gaining men's hearts.

Their religious outlook was in fact so similar that Robert Hooke, an intimate of both, suggested that Tillotson write a "plain way to heaven" based on Wilkins's theological works. Both Wilkins and his son-in-law were noted stylists, but it is Tillotson rather than Wilkins who is usually remembered, probably because the student was the more skillful practitioner. Tillotson, of course, was not alone in following Wilkins's stylistic canons. Most latitudinarian divines did.*

If Wilkins did not draw the crowds at St. Lawrence that Tillotson drew, his sermons were still well-attended. Pepys, a connoisseur of sermons, noted in his diary, "Up and to church at St. Laurence to hear Dr. Wilkins, the great scholar, for curiousity, I haveing never heard him: . . . but was not satisfied with him at all." Most other listeners took away a far better impression. Tillotson counted him an eloquent preacher, as did Anthony Wood, albeit grudgingly. William Lloyd, also a disciple, admired the style and the content of his sermons.

On Easter Wednesday, 1663, Wilkins delivered a sermon on charity at the Spittle before an audience of wealthy City men, in which he particularly recommended that they support the clergy's recent scheme of redeeming "Captives from Slavery," and suggested the City companies increase their charitable contributions. Men, he said, using the traditional terminology, were only "stewards" for "the great Sovereign and Proprieter of the World." Some men were created poor simply so that others could exercise the virtue of charity. There is nothing to suggest Wilkins thought the poor vicious or despicable as many Puritans did. The Calvinists traditionally had held that charity and other good works were an indication of salvation rather than a contribution to it, but Wilkins insisted that God would "pass upon . . . our final Sentence according to these works."

In addition to his duties at St. Lawrence, Wilkins served as an examiner at St. Paul's School. On one occasion he examined the head forms in Latin, Greek, and Hebrew. Pepys, also present, thought "they did not answer in any so well" as his contemporaries had many years before, adding that "only in geography they did pretty well." Despite his very considerable commitments in London, Wilkins was often absent. He probably made occasional journeys to York and Ripon to perform his required duties there. The accounts of St. Lawrence suggest that his absences may have been fairly lengthy, for the parish occasionally hired someone else to officiate in his place for substantial periods. But he was in London at the time of one of its greatest disasters.

The plague that struck London in 1665 came as a great shock even to a city that had witnessed many earlier plagues. The death toll reached at least 68,000. The plague did not claim as many victims in Wilkins's parish as it did in many others, for by and large his parishioners were wealthy enough to find quarters elsewhere. So many fellows of the Royal Society left London, including Wilkins, that the meetings had to be discontinued. Almost immediately after the plague had subsided, the city was struck by the Great Fire. Once-crowded Cheapside, Wilkins's home, was so desolate that a contemporary wrote, "You may now stand where Cheapside was and see the Thames." Wilkins himself was not in the city when the fire broke out. Nevertheless, it was a tremendous blow to him personally. Not only did his church and his home burn, but the manuscript of his universal character and philosophical language, which was at the printers, perished in the flames, as did most of his personal goods and his library. Wilkins was not alone, of course, in losing his books, the tools of a minister's trade, for Baxter reported, "Most of the libraries of Ministers Conformable and Nonconformable in the City" burnt. From his home six miles from London he could see "the half burnt leaves of Books" fluttering in the wind.*

The churches of London were rebuilt slowly. Of the eighty-odd destroyed, only some fifty were restored. St. Lawrence did not, like many London parishes, build a temporary church or tabernacle. The congregation did, however, begin to make use of Guildhall Chapel, which was rebuilt more rapidly than most churches. Financial difficulties slowed the rebuilding program. Parishioners also had to rebuild their homes and other structures. The destruction of the London churches led to the unemployment of Wilkins and many other London ministers. There were "but few churches left in the City . . . and as for lectures none scarce are considerable for a competent maintenacy, but such as belong to Churches without the walls and they are full." Good livings were scarce and there would be heavy competition for them for several years. Wilkins did not sever his relations with St. Lawrence immediately after the fire, but he received no income from the congregation after June 1666.

The shock of the successive disasters of plague and fire engendered many sermons and much soul-searching. Wilkins delivered a sermon before the city magistrates, perhaps at the Guildhall Chapel, the main purpose of which was to urge their aid in rebuilding the destroyed churches of London. Whereas provisions had already been made by the City to "preserve mens Properties . . . to enlarge the passages and avenues, whereby the City may be rendered more safe, beautiful and convenient for Trading," they had been negligent, Wilkins charged, in rebuilding places of worship. Public aid from both the city government and Parliament was essential because those parishes which suffered most could least afford to rebuild. He expressed the hope, no doubt a little wryly, that ministers in these parishes would be provided "a sufficient maintenance" so that they would not have to live so precariously "upon the benevolence of their hearers."

The lack of interest on the part of the city authorities seems to have had another source than simple parsimony, for much of his sermon is a veiled plea to dissenters and others who did not fully approve the existing constitution of the Church to cooperate in the rebuilding program. Wilkins had two aims in this sermon; one was to convince dissenters that they had an obligation to help rebuild London's churches even though they were not in complete sympathy with the establishment; the other was to convince them that they could rejoin the Church even though they did not agree with it in all particulars. He tried to show that any man who subscribed to the principles of natural religion must find public worship a necessity, and deduced from this that the Church of England would satisfy that necessity. The rebuilding program would promote public welfare, for places of public worship were necessary not only for the government but for the maintenance of all religion.

Wilkins was evidently in financial straits at this time. He not only sold some land in his possession to Wadham College for £400, but repeatedly pressured the purchasers to pay him in one lump sum. Although Wilkins still had an income derived from the deanery of Ripon, his situation was very difficult, not only because there were many clergymen who shared his plight but because he was not looked upon with much favor or sympathy by the church authorities. His stepbrother said that the fire was a peculiar hardship for Wilkins not only because his marriage into the Cromwell family was still viewed with suspicion, but because "Archbishop Sheldon, who had the Keyes of the Church for a great time in his power, and could admit into it and keep out of it whom he pleas'd, I mean dispos'd of all Ecclesiastical Preferments, entertain'd a strong prejudice against him, so that he was now not only without any Place, but also without probability of obtaining one: so that his Fortune was as low as it could be." *

In his hour of distress Wilkins turned to Seth Ward, now Bishop of Exeter, who told Walter Pope of his great concern for Wilkins and said he wrote "to him oftener than I otherwise should, to keep up his Spirits and assure him of my utmost assistance." Ward was as good as his word, and helped Wilkins obtain two of the positions that relieved his penury. By November 6, 1666, Wilkins was collated to the Rectory of Polebrooke in

Northamptonshire. Polebrooke offered only a small income, but even that was welcome. Wilkins went to Northamptonshire at least for a time, although he was evidently not greatly taken with the benefice.* It is hardly surprising that Wilkins should have been unhappy with the twists of fortune that forced him to exchange an influential City pulpit so conveniently close to Gresham College for a small country parish.

Wilkins tried to find quarters in London, but the housing shortage was acute, and he, like many others, failed. Late in November, just a few weeks after taking on the Polebrooke charge, he was still searching. When the Council of the Royal Society discussed renting a house in Westminster for their meetings, Wilkins "offered to contribute something towards it, if he might have some rooms in it." Nothing came of this suggestion and Wilkins had to search elsewhere.

Ward evidently was a man to be relied on, for soon after he obtained the Polebrooke living for Wilkins, he found him another benefice as well, the Precentership in his own diocese of Exeter. Wilkins was installed at Exeter on July 11, 1667. About the same time he also obtained the stall in the cathedral that ordinarily went with the Precentership. If the Polebrooke living did not increase Wilkins's income substantially, the Exeter posts certainly did. The precentership alone was worth nearly £100 annually. Wilkins probably spent little time in Exeter, for cathedral clergy were rarely regular residents. He did come on some occasions, however, for he often visited Mr. Samuel Tapper, a local nonconformist, and he is known to have made a trip to Exeter in July 1667. About the same time that Wilkins became Precenter of Exeter, he also became the prebend of Chamberlain's Wood in Saint Paul's Cathedral. Thus by late 1667, just a little over a year after the fire, Wilkins was back on his feet again, largely thanks to Ward. Changes in the political scene, however, would soon relieve him of his dependence on Ward. The ouster of Clarendon and the subsequent decline in power and influence of Archbishop

Sheldon allowed Wilkins more direct access to the sources of influence and patronage.

The replacement of the Clarendon group by the Cabal administration had extensive religious as well as political repercussions. Not only did it symbolize a change in the policy of the government, it also signaled an effort to replace the existing ecclesiastical hierarchy with more liberal men. The early appointments of the reign had gone primarily to High Churchmen, who, led by Sheldon, had done much to obtain the repressive Clarendon Code. Once these appointments had been made, there was little even a tolerant monarch could do. As early as 1665 Charles began selecting non-Clarendonians, but of course there was no opportunity for mass appointments as there had been in 1660. The major disagreement between Charles II and the churchmen arose over the question of nonconformity. The bishops as a group favored repression, and voting as a bloc under Sheldon's direction, they were able to pass or frustrate nearly any legislation before the House of Lords. By 1667 Charles was thoroughly sick of the bishops and their repressive policies. The fall of the Lord Chancellor that year provided the King with an opening for religious reform. Charles dismissed the most prominent Clarendonians from the Privy Council; Sheldon was clearly out of favor, and his supporters George Morley, and John Dolben were driven from court.

Nevertheless, policy changes in a liberal direction were still extremely difficult to initiate and were perhaps doomed to failure from the beginning. While the Cavalier leaders were dismissed from the government and court, the composition of Parliament, which had approved the repressive measures, was unchanged. The bishops might be out in favor, but they could continue to exercise their voting strength in Lords and their influence in Commons. Furthermore the government itself was weak and was held together only by its opposition to the Clarendon faction. Although its leading members favored a more liberal religious policy, this, too, proved a disruptive factor, for some favored comprehension, others toleration. Of the latter, some were in reality interested in obtaining toleration for Roman Catholics and, if that were not possible, would not necessarily support toleration for others.

Even so, the situation looked more promising than it had for some years. The Duke of Buckingham, who was now chief minister and probably already Wilkins's patron, was widely known to favor toleration for all parties. He and Lord Ashley set out to subvert the policy of Parliament and pushed plans for comprehension and toleration.* In many ways 1667 seemed a propitious time to broaden the religious Establishment. Not only were the chief opponents of this policy discredited, but the heroic action of nonconformist ministers, many of whom remained in London during the plague, worked in their favor. For some time open meetings of dissenters in London, contrary to the law, had been "connived at," probably on command of Buckingham and the King.

The first attempt at comprehension was a feeble and ill-planned effort. Sir Robert Atkins drew up a bill embodying the advice of Thomas Barlow, who like Wilkins was a liberal churchman in the Buckingham circle. The bill was to be introduced by Colonel John Birch. Birch, however, became so hesitant that the session ended in December before he made his move, and the plan collapsed. The opposition was led by Sheldon, who seemed to possess more political sophistication and skill. The Archbishop immediately began to canvass episcopal votes, which he claimed were needed more than "at any time, these many years before." A rash of pamphlets both for and against comprehension soon appeared, and the last months of 1667 saw much discussion and debate. Buckingham was watched closely, for he was known to favor some kind of accommodation and was expected to play a significant role. The King himself was more enigmatic. In the past he had favored relief for Protestant dissenters, but he was widely and correctly believed to really be concerned with promoting toleration for Roman Catholics.

Although Wilkins was the author and chief proponent of the

1668 comprehension proposals, he probably worked very closely with Buckingham. One of the first preliminary moves came from Lord Keeper Sir Orlando Bridgman, who dispatched Sir John Baber, the King's physician, to inform the Presbyterian leadership that the government wished to discuss terms for comprehension and toleration. On January 4, Wilkins informed a group of liberal ecclesiastics of "his design and his ideas as to what might be yielded without damage to the dignitie and spirit of our Worship to effect an understanding among all moderate Protestants to the peace of the Kingdom." Significantly two of the five clergymen he consulted, Bishops Ralph Ironsides and Walter Blandford, were former Wardens of Wadham College who had continued Wilkins's moderate policies there. Bishop Reynolds wished to add an Indulgence for those who could not be comprehended, and they "all promised to consider it for a future time." A few days later Wilkins had a two-hour conference with the King, which probably resulted in an agreement on the terms Wilkins had drawn up and a pledge of royal support. This was followed by a series of conferences in which the government and Church were represented by Wilkins and Hezekiah Burton, Bridgman's chaplain. By the time they met and Wilkins presented his proposals on January 12, the nonconformist leaders, represented by Richard Baxter, Thomas Manton, and William Bates had already been informed that the court was favorably disposed to comprehension for Presbyterians and toleration for Independents, and that they must be willing to cooperate with those who favored toleration for Catholics. It was also understood that while they could offer suggestions, they were not to alter Wilkins's basic plan, which was based on the King's 1660 Declaration of Breda.

Basically what Wilkins offered was a formula by which dissenters, particularly the non-episcopally-ordained clergy, could become ministers in the establishment without submitting to reordination. There was to be a subscription expressing approval of the established doctrine, worship, and government of the Church in all things necessary to salvation. In return, certain requirements that had been objectionable to Puritans from at least the time of the Hampton Court Conference, such as bowing at the name of Jesus and the use of the cross in baptism, were to be eliminated. Wilkins also proposed a review of the Book of Common Prayer after the comprehension bill had passed. Although he had no personal objections to a more ambitious scheme, he refused to give in to many of Baxter's requests on the ground that there was a limit to what Parliament would accept. Even Manton and Bates recognized this, and after discussing the problem with Wilkins agreed not to tell Baxter everything because "Mr. Baxter might well ruine our plans with temper and love of disputation."

Baxter and Wilkins had most difficulty in agreeing on a formula for the dissenting ministers. The Presbyterians insisted that no formula that in any way implied reordination was acceptable. Although Wilkins insisted "those Consciences must be accommodated who took them for no ministers who were ordained without Bishops," his originally mild wording was made even milder. At the same time the declaration approving the doctrine, worship, and government of the Church avoided any specific mention of the Thirty-Nine Articles in order to spare the sensitivities of the Churchmen. Wilkins's conversation with the Presbyterians probably involved only comprehension, at least initially. He probably did not personally handle the negotiations with John Owen concerning toleration for Independents. In any event, Owen evidently ignored Wilkins's proposals for indulgence and prepared his own, which emphasized doctrinal orthodoxy. Wilkins's plan would have allowed Independents to hold services and build places of worship. They were to pay for this privilege, the money collected to be used to build badly needed churches in London.

Soon after the meetings with dissenters had led to agreement, Wilkins called in Barlow, and the two took the compromise measure to the liberal Anglicans convened at Oxford. Walter Simon has suggested that Wilkins used his position as mediator to deceive both Anglicans and Presbyterians about the others' demands regarding toleration, and that Barlow and Reynolds cooperated in these deceptions. The Presbyterians only acquiesced after "being assured by Mr. Wilkins that the Bishops would take no less." The bishops were then persuaded to accept indulgence as a concession to the Presbyterians. In any event, after the final discussion with the churchmen at Oxford, Matthew Hale, who now dispensed with "his maxim of avoiding to engage in matters of State," shaped Wilkins's amended proposals for comprehension and toleration into a bill.

Thus far Wilkins and his party had moved quietly. It was hoped that surprise would permit the government to push the bill through before opposition could be organized. Wilkins himself, however, was responsible for its disclosure. He had hoped for Seth Ward's assistance and had even given him a copy of the proposals. Ward, who was much indebted to Sheldon for his recent translation to Salisbury and did not in any case approve such moderate measures, turned a copy over to the Archbishop, who quickly organized his forces. Not only did he canvass the bishops' votes, but he immediately "stir'd up a Party in the House of Commons." Its core was the High Churchmen, but another group, conceiving the bill as designed to foster papism, opposed it as well. The whole situation regarding Roman Catholic toleration was a confused one. The King's speech would mention Protestants only, and Wilkins's proposals were not quite clear on the point. Although Roman Catholics were excluded from taking advantage of comprehension, it is not certain whether or not his toleration proposals would have excluded them. Wilkins was not immune to anti-papal fears, and had argued that "if dissenters were not taken in, popery would invade us." * The ambiguity on the question of Roman Catholic toleration created additional opposition. Furthermore, there was a good deal of confusion over what precisely was being offered. This was particularly true because Owen's toleration proposals were bruited about along with Wilkins's.

Thus when Parliament opened on February 6, the opposition was well organized. The House of Commons was so enraged that they did not wait as usual to give precedence to the King's speech, which they knew would propose a method of uniting his Protestant subjects. Instead they asked that the existing ecclesiastical laws be enforced, and moved that if any new laws on religion were submitted, their proposers "might come, as a proposer of new laws did in Athens, with ropes around their necks." Sheldon's hand was clear: the petition for Royal enforcement of the acts of uniformity was introduced by Sir Edward Nicholas, a close friend of both Clarendon and the Archbishop, who just a few days earlier had been informed by Sheldon of his plans to wreck the bill. Hale introduced his bill on February 13, but it was by then already doomed to failure. On March 4 the still irate Commons requested the King to enforce the laws against conventicles and unlawful nonconformist assemblies. Although the King's speech on March 11 again mentioned Protestant reunion, the House moved, after a discussion of toleration and comprehension, that no indulgence be granted, and went out of its way to insist that the King's Declaration of Breda could not repeal Parliament's ecclesiastical legislation without parliamentary consent.

It has been argued that the parliamentary discussions of March and April, which focused on comprehension rather than indulgence, were less violent, and that as late as April, Wilkins's proposals still had some chance of success. Wilkins, however, was probably convinced that the bill was foredoomed to failure, and seems to have absented himself from London for several weeks. He probably realized that the mounting pressure for a renewal of the Conventicle Bill would stymie even a revised version of his own legislation. Wilkins's proposals relied on parliamentary action and eschewed the use of the dispensing power as a means of relieving dissenters of their disabilities, a method much discussed in the 1660's and finally used briefly in 1672. The goal was thus to obtain liberalization without using the prerogative powers to overturn parliamentary legislation. And this was quite impossible without a sympathetic Parliament.

Wilkins's efforts were not appreciated by the ecclesiastical hierarchy. Burnet noted "that those who had set it on foot, came to be looked on with an ill eye, as secret favourers of the Dissenters, underminers of the Church, and everything else that jealousy and distaste could cast upon them." There was no doubt in the public mind that Wilkins was responsible for the comprehension scheme. Anthony Wood noted that Wilkins had a "club for comprehension and limited indulgence for dissenters," which he described in typical High Church fashion, "schismatically managed against the canons of the church." He indicated that the "club" was widely known among the London clergy, and that Wilkins and Tillotson had been admonished about it by the diocesan and metropolitan. Wilkins's ally William Lloyd also referred to the comprehension scheme as Wilkins's "design," and Walter Simon, after considerable study, has concluded that Wilkins was indeed the "driving force" behind the 1668 movement.

Wilkins, though defeated, was not completely discouraged. Only a few months before his death in 1672, he was still encouraging nonconformist visitors "to live in hopes of Comprehension," and on his deathbed "took comfort in his healing Endeavors." Nor had Baxter given up. Not long after the passage of the Second Conventicle Act in 1670, he suggested to John Maitland, Duke of Lauderdale, that the government sponsor another conference on the 1668 model, with Wilkins or Reynolds representing the Church, perhaps assisted by other latitudinarians—Tillotson, Stillingfleet, Wallis, More, Whichcote, and Barlow. After Wilkins's death several of his disciples, including Tillotson, Lloyd, and Stillingfleet, continued the fight for comprehension and toleration, using his 1668 plan as the basis of their proposals.

It was probably as a result of his efforts on behalf of comprehension in 1668 that Wilkins contracted "a firm and familiar friendship" with Matthew Hale, although it is possible they had met many years earlier as students at Magdalen Hall. Wilkins became the only one of the busy Hale's many friends for whom he would take the time to dine and converse. The two men had much in common: an interest in science, a distaste for eloquent and rhetorical modes of discourse, and the experience of holding important positions under Cromwellian rule. Their religious views were almost identical. Hale, like Wilkins, tried to protect nonconformists from the severities of the law and enjoyed a cordial relationship with Richard Baxter. As latitudinarians both deplored animosity and contention over nonessentials and focused on natural religion in their own writings. Hale's attempt to counteract atheism and prove the attributes of God from the principle of natural reason, innate ideas of morality and conscience, and the evidence of Providence were very similar to Wilkins's *Principles and Duties of Natural Religion.* When Hale finished the manuscript of his *Primitive Origination of Mankind,* he sent it anonymously to Wilkins for "his judgment of it."

Wilkins, in addition to making a firm friend of Hale, cemented his ties with George Villiers, Duke of Buckingham. In some respects their relationship must have been a strange one, although they shared liberal views on religious matters. Wilkins was promoted to the episcopacy largely through Buckingham's efforts, but he, like most of his clerical contemporaries, must have been shocked at the Duke's profligate life. Buckingham was, as we have seen, a proponent of toleration and comprehension, and was considered the "head of all those parties that were for liberty of conscience." If his liberal policy was to succeed, he of course needed allies in the Church. He was instrumental in replacing Morley with Herbert Croft as Dean of the Chapel, and pushed Wilkins's interest whenever possible, to such an extent that Wilkins was called a "creature" of the Duke. The Duke, like Wilkins, was a latitudinarian and believed things unnecessary to salvation should not be legally imposed. In 1685 he wrote a short tract on natural religion. Buckingham's past association with the Interregnum government and his current liberalism made him, like Wilkins, suspect. He was referred to as

> a pocky peer
> that neither Roundhead is nor Cavalier.
> But of some Medley cut. . . .

Buckingham must have considered Wilkins more than his "creature," for he devoted considerable time to working on the universal language. He undoubtedly respected Wilkins's intellectual abilities as well as his political talent. Furthermore Buckingham, like so many noblemen, dabbled in science and became a founding member of the Royal Society.

Thus despite Buckingham's spotty reputation, it is not difficult to see how Wilkins could have fallen into his circle. Nor is it surprising that Wilkins was considered congenial by Buckingham, the King, and other members of the court. A man of wide culture and considerable experience, he was accustomed to the company of the high-born. He had, as Walter Pope put it, "been bred in the Court." His service with the Elector, Lord Saye, Lord Berkeley, who was now active in court circles, and with the Cromwells, had accustomed him to the ways of the governing classes. His talent and experience, as well as his "comely Aspect and Gentlemanlike Behavior," made him at home among a wide range of sophisticated and learned men. His association with the inner circle at court continued despite the failure of the comprehension plan, and he in fact became to some extent that circle's ecclesiastical spokesman.

Wilkins's position improved markedly after Clarendon's fall. By July 1667, he had become one of the King's chaplains, a sure mark of favor and probably a sign of his expected elevation to the bench of bishops. There were soon rumors of better things, and as early as May 1668, it was thought the King would "make him a Bishop upon the next opportunity." The death of Bishop George Hall of Chester in August provided the opportunity, although Wilkins's name was only one of several mentioned during August and September. Wilkins was the candidate of Buckingham, to a lesser extent of Lord Arlington and almost certainly of the King, who on September 26 finally sent the congé d'élire to the dean and chapter requesting his formal election as bishop. The patronage of the profligate Buckingham did not help Wilkins's reputation. Burnet reported, "It was no small prejudice to him, that he was recommended by so bad a man." *

While latitudinarians rejoiced at Wilkins's elevation, the High Churchmen did not. William Sancroft, writing before the decision had been made, thought that if the rumors of Wilkins's appointment were true, it "doth prognostick to the Church but ill." Sheldon also made his opposition clear. Wilkins's elevation, as Sheldon must have realized, symbolized a change in the religious policy of the Crown and government. It was perhaps for this reason that Wilkins, who would normally have been consecrated in the province of York, was granted special permission to have the ceremony performed in London. This move was unusual enough to require a search for precedents.*

Wilkins was consecrated in Ely Chapel on November 15, 1668, by the Bishop of Durham, assisted by the Bishops of Ely and Salisbury. Although John Evelyn noted that the Archbishop of Canterbury also officiated, another source indicated that Sheldon and the Bishop of London "stood behind the Curtaine all during the Ceremony" to express their displeasure. The event was quite a social occasion. Many bishops and "several of the Nobility and persons of Honour" were present. The ceremony was followed by "a most sumptuous dinner," attended by such notables as "the Duke of Buckingham, Judges, Secretaries of State, Lord Keeper, Counsell, Noblemen, & such an infinity of other Companie, as were honourers of this incomparable man, the most universaly beloved of all that knew him." During the elaborate dinner Wilkins had a conversation with Bishop John Cosin of Durham, in which he reiterated his moderate views and suggested the policy he would follow in his own diocese.

Bishop Wilkins promptly told his lordship, that for his part, it was his apprehension, that he who was by many (with ill nature enough) reflected on for his moderation, was in reality a better friend to the church than his lordship, who was for rigorously supporting the constitution. Bishop Cosins seeming surprised, Bishop Wilkins added this as the reason of his assertion. For while you, my lord, said he, are for setting the top on the piqued end downward, won't be able to keep it up any longer than you continue whipping and scourging; whereas I, says he, am for setting the broad end downward, and so it will stand of itself.

Wilkins appears to have consciously attempted to turn away the hostility of men like Sheldon, Morley, Cosin, and Hacket by assuming a conciliatory posture.*

Wilkins's friends were naturally pleased by his elevation. Unlike some of his Cambridge allies, Wilkins and many other latitudinarians recognized that teaching in the somewhat isolated halls of the university, and even writing and preaching for a broader public, could accomplish little without political power. Wilkins's bishopric would provide some opportunity, albeit on a modest scale and in a limited geographical area, to put his principles into practice.

Another mark of favor shown to Wilkins after he became Bishop of Chester was his regular selection as Lent Preacher to the King. Three of four sermons he delivered before the King in this capacity were published on the order of the monarch. The theme of the first, given in 1669, was that the practice of religion would contribute to happiness not only in the next world but also in this, and would produce health, riches, peace, pleasure, and honor. Perhaps because of the nature of his audience, he focused on honor, and attempted to show that true honor could only be attained through religion and virtue. The second, delivered the following year, was an attempt to show that religion was "the whole duty of man," and involved a discussion of the nature of man and religion. Irreligion, which he insisted deprived men of the peculiar qualities that separated them from the beasts and preserved all societies, was really Wilkins's target. His third Lenten sermon, preached on March 19, 1671, continued the argument of the one delivered a year earlier by trying to prove the "Reasonableness and Credibility" of a future state of rewards and punishments, "against the Infidels and Scoffers of this age." With a variety of arguments based on reason rather than Scripture, he attempted to show why the most "profane Atheistical persons" should recognize the existence of an afterlife, which was one of the fundamental truths of natural religion. Even if they did not, they would surely concede it was "a very politick invention," necessary to keep men from "secret mischiefs." Although his intention was to show that religion alone could secure man's future condition, there was more than a hint of Machiavellianism in his view of the political utility of religion, and perhaps an underlying suggestion that if government officials were not in fact religious, it would be advisable that they should seem so.

All three sermons were marked by the same desire to emphasize the court's need for moral reform and to show courtiers that their profligacy would not only harm themselves but would also subvert the government. Thus Wilkins speaks of those who engage in "open profaneness and contempt of Religion" as "the worst kind of Seditious persons." All three sermons also appealed to the self-interest of his audience. Religious duty and self-interest coincided. The theme of the "advantages" of religion, made popular by Wilkins and even more so by Tillotson, became a frequent one during the next decades. In style these sermons resembled moral or philosophical lectures. It was this quality that led Bishop Hacket, who always went out of his way to attack Wilkins, to say of his 1670 sermon, "what a pittiful sermon of his, preached in Lent, is commanded to be printed. Is it because the Court likes no sermons longer than a quarter of an hower?" And it was perhaps the appeal to self-interest that led him to say Wilkins was "a shallow man both in philosophy and divinity."

The bishopric, although it certainly added to Wilkins's prestige and influence, did not initially improve his still precarious finances, for Chester was not a rich see, and the expenses involved in becoming bishop could easily have equaled the £500 levied on an earlier Bishop of Chester. Perhaps as a special mark of favor, Wilkins was permitted to retain the Deanery of Ripon and the connected hospitals in order to increase his income. Although Chester was officially valued at only £499 a year, its annual income was actually considerably greater because of the rich living of Wigan held *in commendum* by the bishop. Furthermore, the episcopal properties in Chester do not seem to have been as severely damaged during the wars as many others were, and therefore did not require the enormous sums for repairs usually defrayed from the diocesan income. Nevertheless, Wilkins's will did not indicate he had amassed particularly large sums while Bishop of Chester, and he left his wife somewhat less than gossip expected.*

Wilkins's administration of the diocese was marked by two distinctive features: an effort to bring nonconformists into the Church, and singular leniency and good relations with those who remained outside. Chester was in many ways a problem diocese, for it was a stronghold of both Roman Catholicism and Presbyterianism. Wilkins continued his efforts to persuade nonconformists, and especially dissenting ministers, to join the Church. Several ejected ministers were "brought in" by his "soft interpretation of the terms of conformity." It was thought his success with two leading Lancashire Presbyterians might "be instrumental in bringing in many of the faction." The problem of reordination was, as we have seen, particularly troublesome, but Wilkins was able to bring over John Humphrey and reordained him himself. Later Humphrey wrote a book on the subject, which he presented to Wilkins for his approval. Wilkins evidently had considerable success, for John Rawlet reported in the summer of 1670 that several dissenters had conformed "overcome partly by the candour, partly by the arguments of our Bishop." *

Rawlet's frequent mention of Wilkins's "soft terms" suggests that Wilkins was not strictly fulfilling the demands of the law, and in fact may have been instituting something like comprehension in his diocese. There had, of course, always been considerable variation among the dioceses as to strictness of enforcement. Wilkins may have gone beyond leniency. Adam Martindale, a nonconformist minister, said that Wilkins, "having a good opinion of some of us, that he took to be moderate Non-conformists, he proposed terms to us, to which we returned a thankful answer;

showing our willingness to comply in anything that would not cross our principles, instancing, in particular what we could do." But before Wilkins's not quite legal scheme could really go into effect, the Archbishop of York "took all power out of his hands for a year, soon after which (if not before) this honest Bishop Wilkins died." The timing of Wilkins's plan is rather curious, for it seems to have developed about the same period the Declaration of Indulgence of 1672 was being drafted. Wilkins may actually have had some idea of bringing over the nonconformists rather than having them take out licenses, which would have meant an absolute separation from the national establishment.

Wilkins's proposals for a kind of surreptitious comprehension probably involved more systematic permission to engage in some of the evasions that he was already permitting in his own diocese on a piecemeal basis. One ejected minister, for example, was allowed to preach as a lecturer while the incumbent vicar read the prayer. On Wilkins's death John Tilsley, who "had done something to satisfy Bishop Wilkins" and kept his "publick station at Dean Church," was immediately ejected. Another ejected minister, who was on good terms with the neighboring conforming clergymen, got them to preach and even read divine service for him. Wilkins, quite aware of the evasion, allowed him to continue his ministry despite several attempts to remove him. Another dissenter received a license from Wilkins to preach in his own house although such licensing was not legal. Lancashire had many "conforming nonconformists," who subscribed but were not obeying required regulations.

In Wigan Wilkins was somewhat stricter than elsewhere, yet nonconformists in this Presbyterian stronghold thought well of Wilkins, who permitted open discussion of the relative merits of presbyterianism and episcopacy. Wilkins could not, of course, care personally for the needs of the extremely large parish of Wigan, although he preached there occasionally and lived there for rather extended periods of time. The parish duties were performed by John Rawlet, a protégé of Richard Baxter. Wilkins intervened occasionally to settle disputes over pews and seating in the nearby chapels, and he brought suit against John Dwight, the secretary of several successive bishops, for injuring the income of the rectors of Wigan.

The Declaration of Indulgence in 1672, which legalized licensed nonconformity, revealed the continued strength of dissent in Wilkins's diocese. One local commentator, who noted their overflowing congregations, added "our episcopal congregations look very thin." Wilkins could not, of course, hope to convince all the important dissenting clergy. With those he could not persuade, however, his relationship was more than cordial. There was "great joy" among them at his appointment, and it was said he found "places for those harried from neighboring counties." Adam Martindale, Henry Newcombe, Oliver Heywood, and John Angier were on good terms with the bishop and were rarely troubled by him. Wilkins's attempt to soften the terms of conformity, his leniency, and his friendly relations with dissenters naturally made him suspect. John Rawlet wrote to Baxter that the bishop should be "engaged to great caution: for some of our high flown Gentry are full of prejudice against him and would . . . be glad of an opportunity of venting their spleen."

Aside from his administration of the acts relating to conformity, we know very little of Wilkins's rule as bishop. His visitation of July 1671 seems to have been uneventful. He visited Manchester in July 1671, where he may have delegated some of his episcopal authority to Nicholas Stratford, then Warden of the Collegiate Church and later Bishop of Chester. For all practical purposes, Wilkins may have made him suffragan bishop. Stratford was sympathetic to many of Wilkins's views. He was lenient with the nonconformists and was involved in later years in comprehension schemes similar to those of Wilkins. The ecclesiastical jurisdiction was largely managed by the Chancellor, John Wainwright, and Wilkins probably had little to do with such matters. We know very little of his relationship with the Archbishop of York except the archbishop's displeasure over what seemed to him the circumventing of ecclesiastical legislation. Aside from some not very friendly correspondence over a troublesome vicarage in Whalley, there are few indications of the state of Wilkins's official relations with Sheldon.

On becoming bishop, Wilkins moved into the episcopal palace in Chester, which became his "constant residence." At Chester he was not so isolated from his scientific companions as one might have expected. John Ray and Francis Willoughby seem to have been frequent visitors, and Ray, who even lived with Wilkins for a time, was constantly moving between Middleton, where Willoughby lived, and the cathedral town. Wilkins himself frequently stopped at the Willoughby seat to break the long coach journey between London and Chester. He also seems to have received a number of other guests.

Once Wilkins was in a position of some power, he could use his position to assist others of a similar persuasion. Few vacancies occurred during his short tenure, but he was able to help his son-in-law Tillotson, who like himself was dispossessed when St. Lawrence was destroyed. Although it is not clear whether Tillotson received an official post, he did spend a considerable amount of time with Wilkins in Chester, preached occasionally at Wigan, and accompanied him on his tours of the diocese. Walter Pope, Wilkins's stepbrother, became Register of Chester in 1669. Wilkins filled the one canonry that fell vacant during his rule with Phineas Bury, a fellow of Wadham College, who according to Tillotson was also Wilkins's chaplain.* Wilkins was sought out for favors much in the same way he had, just a short time before, sought the assistance of Seth Ward. John Worthington, who was still unhappily situated in a remote country living, sought Wilkins's assistance in gaining the now vacant vicarage of St. Lawrence Jewry, where he had occasionally preached. Worthington's appeal seems to have resulted in some strain on the friendship between Wilkins, Worthington, and Whichcote, for it was Whichcote who finally obtained the post through Wilkins's efforts.

Whichcote, one of the Cambridge Platonists and a prominent

latitudinarian, was no stranger to the parish. He had not only preached there but performed other clerical duties as well. Wilkins had known Whichcote, who had also recently lost his London church, from the time he had been Master of Trinity and Whichcote Provost of King's College. Ideologically they had a great deal in common. Both were moderates who propounded a rational theology and emphasized the moral rather than doctrinal aspects of religion in a simple, colloquial style. Thus although Wilkins himself left St. Lawrence, his views would still be expressed from its influential pulpit by his increasingly famous son-in-law, who continued to lecture there, and his friend and successor, Benjamin Whichcote.

Wilkins's contemporaries did not think he would end his career merely as Bishop of Chester. Pepys, shortly after Wilkins had been raised to Chester, reported, "it is all the talk, I find, that Dr. Wilkins my friend, the Bishop of Chester, should be removed to Winchester, and be Lord Treasurer." Pepys recognized that "this be foolish talk," yet said, "I do gather that he is a mighty rising man, as being a latitudinarian and the Duke of Buckingham his great friend." Such gossip might not have been accurate, but it was symptomatic of the expectation that Wilkins would be given an important position in the Cabal government, and that his latitudinarianism might be reflected in government policy. Just a few days later Thomas Henshaw noted further talk of this kind. He had heard that Wilkins would succeed the infirm Lord Keeper. But Henshaw, like Pepys, discounted such a possibility and thought the gossip based "on no other ground than that he is a great favorite." Nothing came of these rumors. Wilkins's very important role in the Roos divorce bill, which was occupying Parliament at the time, was undoubtedly the basis for these speculations. A more likely possibility was that Wilkins would be promoted to a more important and more lucrative diocese. In 1670 it was rumored that he would be translated to Worcester through the influence of Buckingham. Buckingham, however, failed to get Worcester for Wilkins, and his rival the Duke of

Ormond obtained it for Walter Blandford. Early in 1672 Wilkins was being considered for the bishopric of Durham. The King, however, left the post unfilled for over two years in order to collect its revenues.

During the four years he was Bishop of Chester, Wilkins had an active but little-noted career in the House of Lords. Between November 1668 and his death in November 1672 he served on at least fifty committees, a remarkable number considering that Parliament was not in session during much of that period. No other bishop, with the possible exception of Ward, was so much a parliamentary "man of business" during this time. Wilkins's services were no doubt valuable to the government, which needed support in a house where few of the bishops were sympathetic to the Cabal. His presence gave them at least one ecclesiastical spokesman. Furthermore, there were very few members who could be counted on to attend parliamentary sessions and committee meetings with the regularity that Wilkins did.

Wilkins's role as active politician and committeeman drew upon his early talent for reconciling differing points of view and creating harmony among clashing personalities. At both Oxford and Cambridge, and during his later years, he had become accustomed to dealing with politicians. All his early patrons were participants in the game of high politics. In their service Wilkins no doubt picked up many of the tricks of the trade. He always got on well with laymen, much better, one suspects, than with the clergy. He rarely stood on principle, preferring to accomplish the work at hand as circumstances would allow. Perhaps more than most of his clerical contemporaries, he possessed the politician's sense of the possible.

There were only two occasions on which Wilkins emerged into the limelight in Lords. One was the sensational divorce case of Lord Roos, which caused "more ado than ever any act in this Parliament did." Wilkins was one of the chief promoters of the bill in Lord Roos's favor. Its political significance became apparent only in March 1669, when Lord Roos, who had obtained a divorce from a spiritual court on the grounds of adultery, brought a bill into the upper house that would allow him to remarry. Important issues were concealed in this seemingly unimportant private affair. First, there was the propriety of lay decisions on matters normally in the jurisdiction of ecclesiastical courts. This question and the doctrinal soundness of remarriage under these conditions most concerned the bishops, all of whom, with the exception of Wilkins, Cosin of Durham, and Reynolds of Norwich, were opposed to the bill.

There was an even more serious issue. If Roos were permitted to remarry, it was widely thought that the King might use the decision as a precedent for his own divorce and remarriage. This was said to be the hope of the bill's chief promoters, the Duke of Buckingham and George Digby, Earl of Bristol. It was believed that their aim was to divert the succession from the Roman Catholic Duke of York. The King's exact plans were not known, but it was widely believed that he intended "to put away the Queen." The Duke of York, who (probably correctly) took the case as a kind of trial balloon for an exclusion plot, spoke out vigorously against the bill, and spent considerable effort in "Browbeating the favourers of it and almost violently Halinge out Lords upon the division."

Debate in the House of Lords was heated and lengthy. The principal lay speakers in favor of the bill were the Earls of Anglesley and Essex, and Lord Ashley. Opposition speakers from the bench of bishops included the Archbishops of Canterbury and York and the Bishops of London, Rochester, and Salisbury. Only Wilkins and Cosin spoke for the bill. Wilkins was one of the major speakers on March 28. His arguments were largely Biblical, and he devoted considerable effort to refuting the opposition's Scriptural citations. A week earlier it was reported that Wilkins had urged the separation on the grounds that "divorce might be not only in case of adultery but alsoe of the immundicity of the womb, which is given forth to be the queen's condition." If this is an accurate statement of his position, it is clear he was concerned with the attempt, associated with Buckingham, to divert the succession. Charles strongly favored passage and came to hear the debates. The final vote resulted in the passage of the bill by a majority of two. In the end Wilkins was the only bishop voting in its favor, for Cosin, who had spoken so warmly for it, abstained from voting.*

Wilkins's participation in the Roos affair had two results. He had proven he was not only a valuable man of business but also an effective speaker and organizer. As a result the King felt, at least for a time, that he could rely on an able and pliable politician. That his activity was appreciated by the King and his chief ministers is suggested, as we have noted, by the rumors that Wilkins himself might soon be taking his place among them. The second result was to confirm the churchmen's dislike and mistrust of him. The bishops were incensed at Wilkins's defection and used this episode as further evidence that Wilkins did not have the welfare of the Church at heart.*

The poor opinions of his ecclesiastical colleagues were no doubt confirmed by Wilkins's actions during Parliamentary consideration of the Conventicle Act of 1670. As an advocate of religious moderation and leniency toward dissenters, Wilkins could naturally be expected to support and promote measures that advanced these goals. Opportunities were not as frequent, however, as Wilkins might have hoped. The only significant piece of ecclesiastical legislation to come before Parliament between the time he became Bishop of Chester in 1668 and his death was the Conventicle Act that Wilkins vigorously opposed. His activity is interesting because it shows that he was willing to press for moderation even at considerable risk to his own position. As one might expect, most of the bishops favored passage of the repressive measure, which, in addition to the penal provisions of the expired Conventicle Act, fined negligent magistrates and provided for a system of informers. Wilkins, contrary to the King's expectation, attacked the measure and displayed considerable independence in the face of the monarch's repeated attempts to persuade him to reverse himself.* His opposition went far beyond speaking and voting against the Act. He was probably responsible for managing the opposition in the Lords. Although he was not a member of the committee that initially considered the bill, he did become a member of the conference committee. Of the bishops, only Cosin, Edward Rainbowe, Bishop of Carlisle and Reynolds, who was absent because of illness, opposed the measure. Again the combination of bishops and a Cavalier Commons, this time with the support of the King, was able to ensure the continuation of persecution. Wilkins and such allies as Lords Ashley and Halifax who had argued strongly against the measure lost again.

Wilkins's opposition could not have endeared him to the bishops; his refusal to enforce the measure vigorously in his diocese, despite the Archbishop's orders, could not have helped matters. Although for a time there was considerable persecution, it varied considerably from diocese to diocese. In 1672, when the King issued his Declaration of Indulgence permitting licensed nonconformist services, repression was temporarily halted. Whether or not Wilkins played any role in promoting this measure is not known. Certainly he would have preferred a parliamentary solution to one based on the prerogative powers. Even dissenters were suspicious of the Indulgence, which in any event was withdrawn in 1673 under the pressure of an outraged Parliament.

In tracing Wilkins's ecclesiastical career from the Restoration through his elevation to the bench of bishops and his service in Lords, certain things are worthy of remark, and no less worthy because they have also been remarked in discussing Wilkins's earlier years. Indeed it is in part Wilkins's consistency that makes him such an exceptionally vital historical figure. First, we must note again his moderation, pursued at the level of doctrine in the latitudinarian movement, at the level of ecclesiastical practice in his diocese, and at the level of politics in the Buckingham circle and the House of Lords. Second, he continued to provide intellectual leadership, not so much by contributing new ideas but by crystallizing and nourishing new intellectual groups such as the latitudinarian clergy. Third, he was somehow always in the right place at the right time, or perhaps more precisely, always found the energy to make maximum use of his opportunities: Dean of Ripon but in London for the launching of the Royal Society and the London latitudinarian circle; holder of a prestigious London pulpit when it was most needed to communicate the latitudinarian message; recipient of Buckingham's patronage at the time of the Cabal; as a member of the House of Lords, the only active ecclesiastical opponent of the hierarchy, and a parliamentary leader of the moderate opposition to the High Churchmen. Wilkins was undoubtedly a busy man, but more important, he was a man who knew how to profitably invest his energies.

VII. The Royal Society

John Wilkins has been widely recognized as a key figure in the creation of the Royal Society and a vital participant in its early activities. The talent for recruiting and organizing that had put Wilkins at the center of the 1645 and Oxford groups finally bore permanent fruit in Restoration London, and it is to this culmination of his scientific career that we now turn.

The period between the decline of the Oxford group in 1658 and the historic meeting at Gresham College on November 28, 1660, represents something of a hiatus in Wilkins's scientific activities. "Set meetings" at Oxford ceased, and the focus of scientific activity shifted to London. Of the several informal London groups attracting those who flocked back to the capital, the most important was based at Gresham College. It included Wilkins and other important founding members of the Royal Society.

In spite of the generally confused conditions, the idea of formal organization was hardly novel in 1660. Not only the Oxford group but several foreign societies provided possible models. Plans for scientific organizations were offered about this time by Samuel Hartlib, William Petty, John Evelyn, and Abraham Cowley. It was perhaps fortunate for the Royal Society that these ambitious schemes all came to naught, for most of them envisioned elaborate collegial organizations involving considerable expense as well as teaching functions. An attempt to undertake such functions would surely have led to opposition from the universities, and, in view of the Society's later financial problems, it seems most unlikely that the large subsidies required would have been forthcoming.

Once the political situation had stabilized, and the London

group had been augmented with "diverse Eminent and Noble Persons" who had returned with the King, Wilkins and the virtuosi began to make plans. On November 28, 1660, following their "usuall custom," Wilkins and others met at Gresham after Christopher Wren's lecture. But on this occasion they discussed "a designe of founding a Colledge for the promoting of Physico-Mathematicall-Experimentall Learning," and a method for regularizing their meetings in accord with the practice in other countries. Wilkins, appropriately enough, was appointed to chair this historic meeting. For some time he had in effect been seeking state assistance for scientific research. Because of the recent political changes, however, others were now more useful in dealing directly with the government. Although not actually out of favor, Wilkins wisely permitted Sir Paul Neile and Sir Robert Moray, who had "the King's ear," to approach the monarch. Charles II, himself something of a scientific amateur, proved very receptive. Within the next few weeks things moved very rapidly. By December 5 Moray brought word of the King's approval and readiness to encourage the promotion of experimental learning. The following week constitutional arrangements regarding membership and officers were drawn up. On December 19 Wilkins was selected to serve on a committee to receive proposals for experiments. From that time on the program of the Society was well under way, meetings were regularized, and a continuous program of experiments initiated.

The membership was largely composed of participants in the old 1645 and Oxford groups, plus a significant number of returned Royalists. Conspicuous by their absence were Thomas Hobbes, who had engaged in conflicts with several of its leading members and whose views on religion were thought dangerous, and the indefatigable Samuel Hartlib. Few of Hartlib's circle, with the exception of Boyle and Oldenburg, who had become part of the Wadham group, were asked to join.

The 1645 and Oxford practice of excluding political and religious controversy from scientific discussion was continued, a policy perhaps even more important now that Royalist exiles were involved. Sounding like an echo of Wilkins, Thomas Sprat, the quasi-official historian of the Society, praised its "singular sobriety of debating, slowness of consenting, and moderation of dissenting." He contrasted the "yielding compliant" temperament of the scientists to that of "Bold, and haughty Asserters." The unusual politeness, "civility and moderation" of the Royal Society's meetings, which were noted by such foreign observers as the Grand Duke of Tuscany as well as by its own members, must have pleased Wilkins, who had always striven for precisely this tone in both religious and scientific intercourse. The Society also recognized that the international scientific movement should not be disrupted by religious differences or national borders. The members insisted that philosophers of all nations must join the war against "Ignorance, and False Opinion," and hoped that the Society would become "the general Banck, and Freeport of the World" in the realm of ideas. Foreigners and men of all religious persuasions were freely admitted to membership.

Socially the Society was a great meeting ground, where men of little social status, like Hooke, could mix relatively freely with members of the gentry and even the nobility. After meetings members frequently adjourned to nearby taverns to dine and continue their conversations. Evelyn and Pepys often found Wilkins at these convivial gatherings. On one occasion, Pepys noted, he, Wilkins, and some others met at a tavern at St. Clement's churchyard, where they discussed recent attempts to oust Lord Clarendon from political power as well as the Society's transfusion experiments. The circle seems to have included many high officials of the anti-Clarendon faction.

Not long after its founding, the new group petitioned the King for incorporation; in the summer of 1662, it officially became the Royal Society. On August 29, Wilkins was among those who went to Whitehall to thank the King. In the elections that followed incorporation, Wilkins received one of the two secretaryships, a post he held for several years. It was clear from the beginning that the position was primarily honorific, awarded in recognition of Wilkins's general contribution to the scientific movement. Henry Oldenburg, the second secretary, performed most of the secretarial duties, although Wilkins handled many of the dealings with the Society's printers.* There was considerable wisdom in not electing Wilkins president, although he had frequently held that office before the reorganization, when the post was rotated monthly. His earlier associations and his marriage would have made the group vulnerable to attack. In June 1663, however, Wilkins was elected vice-president and served in that capacity for several years. When the Society formed a Council, he became a member of this policy-making body and sat on it until his death, attending its meetings with great fidelity for a number of years. Thus while he was not given a post of great public recognition, he was able to continue his former guiding role.

Not only was Wilkins active in drawing up the initial charter, but when that was found to contain defects, he participated in redrafting its provisions for the new charter, issued in 1663. He also helped draft statutes for the group, and was on several occasions asked to audit the treasury reports. He performed other administrative chores, ranging from thanking Prince Rupert for his gift to the Society and planning a suitable program for the King's visit to advising on the proper salary for the group's "Operator." He was asked to investigate a disputed Gresham College election, which finally resulted in Robert Hooke's succession to a Gresham Professorship of Astronomy. He actively furthered Hooke's interest, not only proposing him for the curatorship of the Society, but nominating him to the Council. He was also involved in hiring other curators from time to time.

Like many modern scientific administrators, one of Wilkins's chief tasks was raising money to support scientific investigation. This became a serious problem for the Society, especially after the Irish revenues promised by the King failed to materialize and members became increasingly remiss in paying their subscriptions. Wilkins was particularly active in soliciting noblemen in the group to pay their arrears, and played a leading role in the Society's efforts to obtain Chelsea College. In 1667, Wilkins suggested that the members themselves try to raise money to build a college to house their laboratories, library, and meetings. A subscription campaign was soon under way, with Wilkins as usual expending much energy. Although they were never successful in obtaining the amount required, they collected £1075, of which Wilkins himself donated £50.

This scheme was connected with the negotiations for Chelsea, of which the Society finally took formal possession in the fall of 1667. Legal difficulties prevented even repair of its dilapidated buildings. Wilkins was sent to work out arrangements with the Treasury commissioners in January 1668, and soon after that to discuss the problem with the Queen's Lord Almoner. Despite the continuing difficulties, architectural plans were again made and a new fund-raising campaign launched. Wilkins was assigned to approach twelve prominent men, including the Duke of Buckingham and the Earls of Devonshire and Carlisle, as well as members of Parliament who belonged to the Society. For the next few weeks the Society optimistically discussed the alternative building plans of Wren and Hooke and poured over cost estimates. They sent Wilkins and Hooke to investigate the procurement of timber for the buildings, and Evelyn donated money to buy 50,000 bricks. But despite their very considerable efforts and great enthusiasm, legal complications and insufficient funds continued to plague them, and the college never materialized. But Wilkins's efforts to give the Society financial stability continued. When he died, he left £400, a considerable portion of his estate, to the group that had played such an important role in his life.

In addition to these important organizing and administrative functions, Wilkins made two major contributions. The first involved his active participation in scientific experiments. The second was his role in determining the group's literary policy and developing a universal, scientific language.

Wilkins's experimental interests were nearly as wide as the Society's. He dabbled in a large variety of subjects, concentrating for the moment on whatever struck his fancy. Curiously, astronomy no longer interested him greatly; he did not become a member of the Society's permanent astronomical committee. His activities in the field seem to have been limited to presenting the Society with Henry Power's instrument, which demonstrated "the fashionable hypothesis of Copernicus," and relaying whatever information he received on the New England comets. He did, however, become interested in the related problem of weather prediction, suggesting that continuous observation of meteorological phenomena would make prediction possible. It was Robert Hooke and Christopher Wren, however, who actually made some progress in this field. The latter recognized Wilkins's interest and sent him a detailed report of his weather clock. Although the great microscopic advances of the century are associated with the names of Hooke and Wren, Wilkins also made occasional forays into this field with their assistance. When for example, Wilkins reported his observations of deer hair, comparing them to the hair of other animals, it was Hooke who did further studies along these lines.

Wilkins also initiated several experiments involving vacuums and compression with Robert Boyle's air pump. He performed an experiment for the group that exhibited his new interest in air pressure and his older one in mechanical principles. It concerned the force or power that could be gained by "blowing with a man's breath." He succeeded in lifting "a fat boy of sixteen or seventeen years" seated on a stool about two inches from the floor, and in raising a weight of 110 pounds five or six inches. This experiment was considered suitable entertainment for the King's projected visit to the Society. After its first successful trial, the Society asked Wilkins to attempt it again, this time using "pipes of several bores." In view of his interest in underwater travel and submarine vessels, his participation in the Royal Society's diving experiments was to be expected. Wilkins himself proposed sinking glass-covered lamps underwater to see how long they would burn, and tried to devise a method of obtaining water from the bottom of the sea. He also worked on the group's unsuccessful attempts to compress water, and participated in the pendulum experiments that took place in St. Paul's Cathedral. He was present when several fellows climbed to the top of the cathedral's steeple to let down their 200-foot pendulum. He was also requested by the group to work on a universal standard of measure, a problem that he discussed at some length in his *Real Character*. Wilkins, William Brouncker, and Christian Huygens collaborated in attempting to pursue Wren's suggestion that such a measure could be derived from the motions of a pendulum.

More practical matters also engaged Wilkins. He worked on problems ranging from the acquisition of naval timber to rapid methods of roasting meat, and was a member of the committee preparing a history of trades. He continued to work with hearing devices, exhibiting his "engine for hearing" to the Society, and presenting his "Otocustick, or Instrument to help the hearing" to the Society's Museum. Soon afterward he participated in Wallis's experiment in teaching the deaf and dumb to speak. Agricultural problems, in which he had become interested at Wadham, continued to fascinate him. Not only was he a member of the "Georgicall" committee, which investigated soils, new crops, and agricultural implements, but he became particularly interested in the possibilities of widespread potato cultivation as a means of preventing famine. He reported on a new method of planting corn, and was requested to send to Oxford for the planting device itself. When interest was aroused again several years later in connection with a Spanish model, Wilkins told the group that their own Operator had devised one earlier, and that he himself had used it before loaning it to a gentleman in Surrey.

Wilkins took only an occasional interest in botany until he became involved in the problems of classification late in life, and even then he allowed those with more expertise to do most of the work for him. He was, however, interested in biology, especially the possibilities of spontaneous generation of insect life. Not longer after he proposed that the Society study the question, Wilkins was requested to try to produce maggots from "old cheese and sack." Wilkins also observed animal habits, and on one occasion reported on the feeding habits and skin changes of frogs he had kept for a year in a wire-covered tub, presumably at the vicarage of St. Lawrence Jewry. He gave the group three queen bees and presented his views on the differences between queens and drones.

In 1663 he proposed that skin grafting on dogs be attempted. Although many doubted that such an operation could succeed, it was performed several times by his friend Dr. Walter Charleton, once at Wilkins's house for "the better care of the Dog." When Wilkins suggested an attempt be made to remove kidney stones from dogs, Charleton again performed the experiment.

Wilkins's suggestion of May 17, 1665, that the blood of one dog be injected into the vein of another led to the Society's famous blood transfusion experiments. He was appointed to the committee designated to undertake the experiments and subsequently reported their procedures and results in detail. The Society moved on to transfusing the blood of sheep into dogs, and after Wilkins reported on French experiments with transfusing sheep blood into humans, to human transfusions as well. The latter experiment was performed twice before large, curious crowds. Wilkins was acquainted with the young man on whom the transfusion was performed, and told Samuel Pepys that Arthur Coga, who was probably a Bachelor of Divinity, had read for him in his church. Coga, whom Wilkins considered a "poor and debauched" man, survived the ordeal without ill effects, and immediately after the operation downed a glass of canary, took a pipe of tobacco, and went home. In view of Wilkins's initiation of these and other anatomical experiments, it is not surprising that he was one of the three nonphysicians elected to membership on the standing anatomical committee.

Wilkins also assisted in the Royal Society's efforts to gather botanical, biological, and practical information from all corners of the globe. He was requested to contact Lord Berkeley, himself a member of the Society and heavily involved with the East India and Levant Companies, for assistance. On another occasion Wilkins brought a traveler just leaving for Barbados to a Society meeting so he might receive the members' queries. He also proposed that John Ray and Francis Willoughby, then traveling on the Continent, be asked to make certain observations. Apparatus and directions were accordingly sent them. Wilkins's half-brother, Walter Pope, when traveling in Italy, sent Wilkins reports on items of interest which he then conveyed to the Society.

Mechanical devices continued to attract Wilkins, and he became a member of the "mechanical" committee, which was concerned with the improvement of inventions. He and Hooke were asked to develop a cheap, improved device for harpooning whales. Hooke, as usual, seems to have done the actual work on the project. Practical gadgets such as the waywiser again occupied Wilkins's attention. After the Society had viewed this contrivance, he was asked to donate it to their repository. Still another invention he described to the members was an instrument shaped like an "umbrella to be used instead of an anchor . . . or to stay a ship in a storm." Wilkins donated several of his contrivances to the Society's repository.

Wilkins had been interested in carriage improvement long before the Society took up the subject in 1665. He was working on the project when the plague emptied London and disrupted regular meetings. Before the fellows dispersed, the president requested that they continue their experiments and "give a good account of them on their return." Wilkins, unlike many of the fellows, did not go to Oxford, and initially planned to travel to nearby Nonsuch with Sir William Petty and Robert Hooke. Instead they settled at Durdans, near Epsom, at the seat of Lord Berkeley, taking scientific instruments with them in order to carry out a number of experiments on motion. Shortly after their arrival, John Evelyn, a frequent visitor at Durdans, found them hard at work, "contriving Chariotts, new riggs for shipps, a Wheele for one to run races in, & other mechanical inventions." He wrote that "perhaps three such persons together were not to be found elsewhere in Europe, for parts and ingenuity." They did not limit themselves to mechanical investigations, however, but planned "divers experiments of heat and cold, of gravity and levity, of condensation and rarefaction, of pressure, of pendulous motions and motions of descent; of sound, of respiration, of fire, and burning, of the rising of smoke, of the nature and constitution of the damp, both as to heat and cold, driness and moisture, density and rarity, and the like." Despite the Society's dispersal, communication between members was quite regular. The group of fellows at Oxford was in contact with Wilkins and Hooke at Durdans. Not only did Hooke and Boyle report faithfully to one another, but Moray, also at Oxford, corresponded with Hooke and Wilkins as well.

From the time of their meetings at Oxford many years earlier, Wilkins and the young, brilliant, and versatile Robert Hooke, who shared his temporary exile from London, had been close friends. Wilkins's early encouragement, his efforts in obtaining for Hooke the Society's curatorship and a Gresham professorship, as well as Wilkins's own very considerable achievements, led Hooke to a warm friendship and admiration for the cleric. A small token of his feelings was a gift of one of his newly invented balance spring watches. Another, more lasting tribute appears in Hooke's *Micrographia*, (appropriately, since it was Wilkins who had first advised Hooke to embark on this work):

That there is scarce any one Invention, which this Nation has produc'd in our Age, but it has some way or other been set forward by his assistance. My reader, I believe, will quickly guess, that is Dr. Wilkins that I mean. He is indeed a man born for the good of mankind, and for the honour of his country. . . . In a word, his zeal has been so constant and effectual in advancing all good and profitable Arts, that as one of the Antient Romans said of Scipio, That he thanked God he was a Roman; because where ever Scipio had been born, there had been the seat of the Empire of the World; so may I thank God, that Dr. Wilkins was an Englishman, for whereever he had lived, there had been the chief Seat of generous Knowledge and true Philosophy. To

the truth of this there are so many worthy men living that will subscribe, that I am confident what I have here said, will not be look'd
upon by an ingenious Reader, as a Panegyrick, but only as a real
Testimony.

Hooke's view, as he indicated, was shared by most members of
the Society.

When Wilkins and Hooke had returned to London and the Society met again, one of the first topics they turned to was the
causes and treatment of the plague. Wilkins reported on one
method of treatment and suggested the physician members who
had remained in London recount their observations. Soon after
they had reconvened, the president inquired into the activities of
the long recess. Wilkins and Hooke reported on "the business of
the chariots, viz., that after great variety of trials they conceived
that they brought it to a good issue, the defects found since the
chariot came to London being thought easy to remedy." Wilkins
added to Hooke's report that he himself had traveled in it and
thought "it would make a very convenient post-chariot." The
chariot aroused considerable public interest. Pepys and Lord
Brouncker made two special visits to see "Mr. Hooke and a new
invented chariott of Dr. Wilkins," "where the coachman sits
astride upon a pole over the horse, but do not touch the horse,
which is a pretty odde thing; but it seems it is most easy for the
horse, and as they say, for the man also."

Although the Great Fire had severe consequences for Wilkins's
clerical career and financial status, he continued to be quite active
in the Society's affairs in 1667 and 1668. When he became Bishop
of Chester, however, in November 1668, his participation dropped
off sharply, and he even relinquished the secretaryship. His now
intermittent residence in London partially explains his absence
from the Society's meetings, but his new preoccupation with clerical politics and administration was probably equally responsible.
Even after he became Bishop of Chester, however, he continued
to participate in the Society's affairs. He undertook such adminis-

trative tasks as the selection and payment of curators, and concerned himself with the recurrent problems of finance. The rise in
social status that accompanied his appointment as bishop gave
him more opportunity to cultivate the King on the Society's behalf, a task assigned most exclusively to those members with
connections at court. Wilkins still found time to serve on committees of the Society, including the one that arranged for experiments. This committee included John Locke, who may have been
somewhat influenced by Wilkins. Wilkins proposed further
anatomical experiments and was still involved in investigating
spontaneous generation of insects and in embryology.

Wilkins continued some of his scientific activities while in
Chester. John Ray reported that he had dissected a dolphin with
him there. He also worked with Ray and Willoughby on the classification of plants, insects, and animals, and, surprisingly, seems
to have been involved in some chemical experiments which he
discussed with the powerful local magnate, Lord Derby. Nevertheless, the period of his greatest service to the Society came to an
end in 1669. Despite his very active participation in the substantive
experiments of the Society, his greatest services had been organizational and administrative. These skills had been largely responsible for the success of the Society's principal forerunner in the
1650's, and for the Society's own success in its crucial early years.
Perhaps his greatest merit as a scientific administrator, and the
principal key to his success in this role, was his combination of the
interests and energies of an entrepreneur and organizer with a
genuine talent for scientific work. We have already noticed
Hooke's testimony, and even Anthony Wood said that Wilkins
"was a person endowed with rare gifts, . . . a curious critic in
several matters, an excellent mathematician and experimentist,
and one as well seen in mechanisms and new philosophy (of
which he was a great promoter) as any of his time." His reputation as a man of science was international. Christian Huygens, for
example, thought he had "a most elevated Judgement & a most
profound witt."

Wilkins brought his unique combination of talents to bear in handling the Society's publication program. Not only was he responsible for drawing up the regulations governing the Society's printers, but he seems to have been the group's principal agent in dealing with them. In several instances when Wilkins recommended publication of a work, printing was begun immediately. He was asked to read Evelyn's manuscript of *Sylva* and Boyle's *Hydrostatical Paradoxes* before publication, and helped prepare Hooke's *Micrographia* for press. He seems not to have been in any way connected with *Philosophical Transactions,* the scientific journal that developed from Oldenburg's voluminous foreign correspondence. Wilkins was deeply involved in the preparation of Thomas Sprat's *History of the Royal Society,* the principal source of information on the Society's early years. The first hint of such a project appears in May 1662, when following the suggestion of Seth Ward, "it was proposed to make a draught of the society's design, in order to be shown to such as might be benefactors." Wilkins was appointed to the committee charged with drawing up the report. The project may have lapsed for a time, although by mid-1663 it was well under way and Thomas Sprat had been selected as author.

Wilkins was almost certainly responsible for the selection of Sprat, who, although a promising literary figure, had no particular interest in science before or after writing the *History* and never undertook independent writing projects. Wilkins had known Sprat for many years before he proposed him for membership, having been his patron at Wadham. The author of the most complete analysis of Sprat's thought and writings has shown that Wilkins was the model by which he "shaped his early career and by which his later ideals were unconsciously measured." The two were both connected with the Duke of Buckingham, himself a member of the Society.

Almost immediately after Sprat's admission to the society on April 1, 1663, Wilkins began his direct and constant supervision of the *History.* Sprat himself noted "it is onely my hand that goes, the substance and direction came from one" of the Society's two secretaries. The Society's minutes leave no doubt to whom he referred. While the Council retained final control over the contents of the *History,* Wilkins exercised substantial discretion. For instance, when Sprat requested guidance on whether or not to insert the group's statutes in the manuscript, "it was thought proper, that Dr. Wilkins should be desired to peruse the said statutes, and so to abridge them," for inclusion. And when the sections describing the group's scientific activities were at issue, Wilkins selected representative examples of each type of activity.*

The actual writing, and therefore the cooperation between Sprat and Wilkins, took place over a period of several years, for the plague and fire delayed publication until 1667. When the work was completed, the members of the Society considered the finished product their own and not Sprat's. As the Society intended, this very successful account of its history, activities, and attitudes proved useful not only in fending off would-be attackers, but in spreading the knowledge and acceptance of science to an ever-increasing portion of English society. The volume had more mundane uses as well. Wilkins picked up half a dozen copies to be distributed to possible benefactors during one of the fundraising campaigns.

Although we can assume the *History* contained little that displeased Wilkins, it is less certain how much of the work can be directly attributed to him. One can point to many passages that might have been written by Wilkins. These include the sections approving latitudinarianism and the reconciliation of religion and science, those condemning religious and philosophical zealotry, the analysis of the relation between ancient and modern learning, and the defense of existing educational institutions. Although the *History*'s extreme utilitarianism and great adulation of Bacon are not echoed in Wilkins's own writings, we have already noted an increase in his utilitarian concerns after 1648, and his very considerable respect for Bacon.

Margery Purver has recently sought to especially emphasize the

Royal Society's debt to Bacon. She does so by attempting to save Bacon from the charges of vulgar empiricism frequently brought against him. Having shown that Bacon does indeed leave room in his philosophy for ultimate generalization based on empirical and utilitarian experimentation, she concludes that the Royal Society represents an essentially Baconian movement. If Bacon had enunciated highly substantive and specific ideas on scientific method and the formulation of scientific laws, it would be easy to test hypothesized influences by determining whether the works of the Society accorded with or contradicted various of his concrete presumptions. Unfortunately his ideas are vaguely stated and allow us to say little other than that Bacon believed in scientific generalization and so did the Royal Society. Such a conclusion does not lend itself to very confident statements about influence.

Where we do have more concrete data, the facts seem to suggest a lesser role for Baconianism than Miss Purver would claim. The Oxford group, to which she assigns the role of forerunner to the Royal Society, engaged in a wide variety of scientific activities, many of which can be traced to the works of earlier scientists. Exactly the same may be said of the Royal Society itself. At the level of actual experiments done, inquiries undertaken, works borrowed from and cited, in short at the one level amenable to firm demonstration, the virtuosi can be shown to have owed substantial debts to nearly all of their scientific predecessors, Bacon, of course, included, but only as one among many.

There remain the frequent encomiums to Bacon delivered by members of the Society and the inclusion of so much Baconian argument in the *History of the Royal Society*. What these rhetorical uses of Bacon's name and ideas would surely suggest is that in the intellectual climate of the day, Baconianism was a persuasive symbol behind which support for scientific activity whatever its intellectual origins might be mustered. Perhaps it is necessary to distinguish between the ideology and the practice of science. In the sphere of ideology it would be impossible to deny the preeminence of Bacon's name; in the sphere of practice Bacon's influence seems to have been largely confined to the Society's utilitarian experiments and construction of natural histories conducted as part of an overall scientific program much of whose theoretical, mathematical, observational, and experimental aspects must be traced to other sources.

The *History*'s famous comments on proper language and style should almost certainly be attributed to Wilkins rather than Sprat, who did not himself use the unadorned prose he recommended. To a very large extent Sprat simply described the stylistic aims of the Society. He noted that, in the virtuosi's efforts to make "faithful Records" of the works of Nature and Art, they have "indeavor'd to separate the knowledge of Nature, from the colours of Rhetorick, the devices of Fancy, or the delightful deceit of Fables." To avoid this

They have [made] . . . a constant Resolution, to reject all the amplifications, digressions, and swellings of style: to return back to the primitive purity, and shortness, when men deliver'd so many *things,* almost in an equal number of *words.* They have exacted from their members, a close, naked, natural way of speaking; positive expressions; clear senses; a native easiness: bringing all things as near the Mathematical plainness, as they can: and preferring the language of Artizans, Countrymen and Merchants, before that, of Wits and Scholars.

This was essentially a restatement of Wilkins's comments of a few years earlier. Sprat did not confine himself to scientific writing, and, in passages which again are little more than paraphrases of Wilkins, he roundly condemns intemperance of language in religious discourse as a cause of intemperance in religion itself.

The Royal Society had other linguistic concerns besides the promotion of the plain style. Several of its members worked toward "perfecting" the English language, and intended to form an Academy along French or Italian lines. There was also a committee "to improve the English tongue," particularly for philosophical purposes. It has been suggested that, although Wilkins's name was not included in the list of committee members, it was he who initially raised the matter in a Council meeting. In any event, Wilkins was asked to meet with the committee and to inform the Council of its proceedings. Although he was one of the very few members whose chief interest lay in this direction, others such as John Wallis and William Holder made important contributions to the study of language. It was obviously a subject that many virtuosi felt to be intimately connected with their scientific activities. This was particularly true of projects for the construction of a universal language, which had captivated Wilkins as early as 1641.

The Society's preoccupation with language, and even a universal language, was by no means unique. Seventeenth-century intellectuals everywhere in Europe developed a deep interest in their own and in artificial languages. It was the latter that especially attracted Wilkins. His *Mercury,* written in 1641, was not an important contribution, but by the 1650's he was working to create such a language. His new efforts corresponded to an important change of direction in the work of other European scholars that occurred about that time. Initial discussion had focused exclusively on creating a relatively simple core language that could be learned easily, into which existing languages could be rapidly translated. During the 1650's efforts shifted to the creation of a universal philosophical language, which, in addition to meeting the requirement of simplicity, would also be better suited to the communication of philosophical truth than any existing language. The concept of a philosophical language had been formulated as early as 1629, when Descartes mentioned it to Mersenne, insisting, however, there could be no such language until such time as the true philosophy had been established. Mersenne himself worked on a design for such a language and seems to have influenced Comenius, who took up the idea about 1640.

At this point two related problems occur. One concerns Wilkins's indebtedness to Comenius, who, it has been argued, was the first to seriously develop the concept of a philosophical language and influenced Wilkins through his disciples Cyprian Kinner and

Samuel Hartlib. The second problem concerns Wilkins's indebtedness to George Dalgarno, an Oxford schoolmaster and author
of a universal and philosophical language very similar to Wilkins's.* On closer examination, however, these problems largely
disappear, for in fact it seems to have been Seth Ward and the collective concern of the Oxford group and then the Royal Society
that principally motivated Wilkins's efforts.

Although Wilkins's *Mercury* was published about the time that
Comenius visited England, there is no evidence the two men ever
met. The manuscript of Comenius's *Via lucis,* containing his
views on the universal language, was available in manuscript no
earlier than 1642, too late to have influenced *Mercury,* which in
any event was little more than an elaboration of Bacon's suggestions in his *Advancement of Learning.* Like most of the efforts
Hartlib promoted in the 1640's, Wilkins's was then concerned
simply with a written character, not a philosophically based language. Both William Petty and Robert Boyle, then members of
the Hartlib circle, were enthusiastic about a universal character.*
It would consist solely of symbols, so that a single symbol would
mean "house," for instance, and could be substituted for its verbal
equivalents in all other languages. Such symbols would thus convey different verbal statements depending on the native language
of the reader, but statements of equivalent meaning.

The next English development in creating universal language
came from the Oxford scientific circle. As early as 1650, Seth
Ward and William Petty were working on a philosophical language, perhaps based on Cyprian Kinner's communication to
Hartlib. The university had by the 1650's become not only a scientific but a linguistic center. John Wallis frequently discussed linguistic questions with Archbishop James Ussher and Gerald
Langbaine at Oxford, as well as with his more scientific colleagues. In 1653 he published his *Grammatica lingua Anglicanae,* a pioneering work on the English language. Oxford also
became the center of the efforts to create a universal character.
Wilkins's work on it was "first undertaken" during the "vacancy

and leisure" he enjoyed at Oxford. Ward introduced him to the newer concept of a universal language. It was "from this suggestion of his," Wilkins said, "that I had any distinct apprehension of the proper course to be observed in such an undertaking." Wilkins traced his plan directly to the one Ward described in 1654 in the *Vindiciae academiarum*. Ward explained how such a philosophical language might properly be constructed along Cartesian lines:

But it did presently occurre to me, that by the helpe of Logicke and Mathematicks this might soon receive a mighty advantage, for all Discourses being resolved in sentences, those into words, words signifying either simple notions or being resolvable into simple notions it is manifest, that if all the sorts of simple notions be found out, and have Symboles assigned to them those will be extreamly few in respect of the other, (which are indeed Characters of words . . .) the reason of their composition easily known, and the compounded ones at once will be comprehended, and yet will represent to the very eye all the elements of the composition.

These characters would be "utterable, and the names be made up of the definitions of things, or a complexion of all those notions, whereof a Complex is compounded, every simple notion being expressed by one syllable, and the most complexe notions, consisting of as many syllables, as it doth of simple elementall notions."

In these passages we see a considerably elaborated version of the plan Wilkins later adopted. Ward's concern is no longer simply with a set of common symbols for simultaneous translation of conventional verbal usages in existing languages, but with the creation of a whole new language, each of whose words would refer to a single, scientifically observed phenomenon or philosophically constructed concept, without the penumbra of vagueness and imprecision introduced into conventional languages by varying usages and faulty observation.

Walter Charleton's comments indicate that the much-talked-of project for a universal character was drawing to completion about

1656. But it was only about this time that Wilkins and Dalgarno really became involved in it. Charleton writes that symbols similar to those used in mathematics were being worked out by the Oxford virtuosi to facilitate "discourse in Philosophy, Physick, and other parts of Learning," and that the group had already made very "considerable progress toward the invention of Symbols, or Signs, for every thing and notion." He was probably referring to Ward's efforts because he mentioned the *Vindiciae academiarum,* of which Ward rather than Wilkins was the principal author. Ward may, therefore, have done considerably more work on this project than most historians have suspected. Wilkins himself admitted it was "some considerable time" after his conversations with Ward, which probably predated the *Vindiciae academiarum,* that he "had any thought of attempting anything in this kind" himself.

The first occasion of it [was derived] from a desire I had, to give some assistance to another person, who was willing to ingage in this design of framing a real Character, from the Natural Notion of things; for the helping of whom in so worthy an undertaking, I did offer to draw up for him, the Tables of Substance, or the species of Natural Bodies, reduced under their several Heads; which I did accordingly perform, much after the same Method [as that in the Essay of 1668].

"Another person" was probably Dalgarno, for Cave Beck, with whom Wilkins was also involved, never worked on a philosophical language. Wallis corroborated Wilkins's statement about his relationship with both Ward and Dalgarno.*

Dalgarno seems to have begun work on the universal language about 1656. It is at this point, at least, that we begin to hear about him in connection with Wilkins. In 1657 Hartlib became involved more directly in the Oxford project. In the same year the work of Cave Beck, who had invented an older, nonphilosophical character, was nearing completion. If he was backed by Hartlib, as he probably was, some doubt is cast on the theory that the shift in interest to a philosophical language took place through Hartlib's influence. Rumors of Dalgarno's work filtered out of Oxford and soon reached Hartlib, who suspected him of "borrowing" from Beck, who was nearly ready to publish. Dalgarno therefore introduced himself to Hartlib, assured him he was not plagiarizing from Beck although he freely admitted having seen Beck's manuscript at Wilkins's quarters at Wadham, and indicated how substantially Beck's work differed from his own. This is the first clear evidence we have of Wilkins's association with Dalgarno. Dalgarno also indicated that Beck had given his manuscript to Wilkins "for his censure of it" and that Wilkins had dissuaded him from publishing, presumably because his language was not a philosophical one.* In submitting his work to Wilkins, Beck had indicated that he considered Wilkins, not Dalgarno, the leader in the field.

The confusion of overlapping projects now began to increase, for Dalgarno soon moved into Hartlib's house, and all parties were kept informed of one another's progress. Wilkins was now hard at work preparing his tables, which would encompass all knowledge, for Dalgarno's use, although he found the "doing of it" more time-consuming and difficult than he had anticipated. To his chagrin, however, Wilkins found that Dalgarno disapproved of his method for being of "too great a Compasse." Dalgarno therefore did not use Wilkins's tables, and the two evidently continued their work separately. Wilkins said "being myself convinced, that this which I had begun, was the only course for the effecting of such a work, and being withal unwilling to loose so much pains as I have already taken toward it, I resolved (as my leisure would permit) to go on with the other Tables."

Just a few months after Dalgarno joined Hartlib, Boyle wrote to Hartlib from Oxford, giving his opinion on what were now clearly two distinct projects. He was somewhat dubious about Dalgarno's, but said that "the Universal Character [of] Dr. Wilkins" was "now brought to that perfection that he is pleased to promise me sometime next week to show it to Dr. Ward and me together, that it may be jointly considered by us all." Boyle added that "if he be as wary in his affirmations of it as he used to be about other things, I make no doubt but it will be extraordinarily ingenious." Pell, now in Europe, was sent Boyle's letter by Hartlib, and he in turn passed on the information to the European Comenians, who were thus informed of both Wilkins's and Dalgarno's efforts. In January 1658 Hartlib tried to obtain more information on Wilkins's progress, particularly because "Mr. Comenius hath lately sent to Mr. Dalgarno his ideas of it." Unfortunately Comenius's comments were "so short and general" that Hartlib did not think them worth relating.

Dalgarno was the first to make his work public. Several very brief printed notices appeared in which he indicated his dissatisfaction with previous efforts and described the distinguishing features of his own work, which he said had the approval of several eminent university men. One undated three-page document included a letter to the "Right Worshipful and eminently learned Doctors" Wilkins and Ward, in which he thanked them for their "singular favors and civilities." In it Dalgarno sought to assure Wilkins that he would not "conceale from the world your labours and merits, in this present literary sphere," and freely admitted "that a great part of the work is your owne."

Wilkins was very quiet about his own efforts during the last two years of the decade. He did, however, discuss Dalgarno's work with Wallis, who was not particularly enthusiastic. In 1659 John Owen was convinced that Wilkins's effort would prove more successful than any other. Henry Oldenburg, too, was confident that Wilkins's system would prove superior to Dalgarno's, whose brief publications he considered little more than a statement of purpose.

Late in 1659 Dalgarno was almost ready to publish his work in full but was concerned that Wilkins might publish first. He told Hartlib that for nearly a year he had conversed daily with Wilkins, and added "If he published anie thing he deales neither ingenuously nor justly with me and I fear if he attempt anie thing on the subject he shall have small credit for it for besides that all he will doe wil be to discover another man's labours." Wilkins in fact continued to encourage his rival and did more than anyone else to ensure the completion and publication of his work. Dalgarno's *Ars signorum* appeared in 1661 with the backing of "divers Learned Men from both Universities." He thanked many of them, including Ward, Petty, Bathurst, Boyle, and Wilkins. Wilkins evidently was not satisfied with Dalgarno's efforts and continued his own.

The universal languages of Wilkins and Dalgarno were similar in many ways, perhaps because both derived from Ward's earlier work. Wilkins's final publication, however, differed from Dalgarno's in many respects besides his use of philosophical tables. Wilkins offered a fuller discussion of the nature of language, a different and more elaborate classification, and a different notation. Yet the two languages had the same purpose—they were designed for use in general international communication as well as in science. In the disputes over which system was superior, the verdict in nearly every instance went to Wilkins.

Wilkins's *An Essay towards a Real Character and a Philosophical Language* was ready for publication in January 1666, but its appearance was delayed when the Great Fire destroyed most of the manuscript and all but two copies of the portion of the work that had been printed. He immediately set out to improve his work, and asked Francis Willoughby and John Ray for help in the classification of plants and animals. Wilkins hoped to improve the new edition in other respects as well. He wrote Ray that if he could fully satisfy himself "in the methodical Enumeration of such things, I would put out the next Edition in *Folio,* with handsome Cuts." The project took a great deal of Wilkins's time both before and after the fire, although his multifarious activities in the Church and the Royal Society also required his constant attention. Fortunately Wilkins had great powers of concentration and could work steadily for very long periods of time. As one of his collaborators on the project said, "What he was in his Studies, I have reason to know, that have often been tired with him. He was indefatigable, and would have worn himself out, if he had not been relieved with multiplicity of business." *

The final revision of Wilkins's *Essay Towards a Real Character and a Philosophical Language* was completed in the spring of 1668. It was licensed by the Council of the Royal Society in April. The published volume was sent to the Council on May 7. The following week his dedication to the Society was read before the assembled group. The first portion of the *Essay* was devoted to a discussion of languages and alphabets and contained Wilkins's views on their origins, change, adoption, and diffusion. He argued that the creation of alphabets and writing followed that of languages, often being adopted by several language groups. He described the various types of writing and symbolic representation of words and the reasons for their early association with magic. Historical development rather than deliberate creation of language and writing, he insisted, meant that all languages contained defects. But because all men's minds operated in the same way and had a similar "apprehension of things," it was possible to develop a rational language and a character that would also express things and notions. It was only necessary to devise a method of expression on which all could agree. This would be the universal language and character. It was necessary, however, to classify all abstract notions and concrete things systematically, so that the names of things would actually correspond to the things themselves and reflect true philosophy. This classification of "Universal Philosophy," which was the second portion of the *Essay,* was composed of forty genera and many subspecies. His classification owed no small debt to the traditional Aristotelian distinction between genus and difference, and ranged from the most metaphysical concepts to the classifications of animals, plants, and insects, and even naval, military, ecclesiastical, and political relationships. The system is easiest to grasp in outline form. The forty genera are themselves grouped as follows:

1. Transcendental General
2. Transcendental Mixed
3. Transcendental Relation of Action
4. Discourse
5. God
6. World

Substance	*Quality*
7. Element	24. Natural power
8. Stone	25. Habit
9. Metal	26. Manners

Herb considered according to the { 10. Leaf, 11. Flower, 12. Seed-vessel }

27. Quality sensible
28. Disease

13. Shrub
14. Tree

Action

29. Spiritual
30. Corporeal
31. Motion

Animals { 15. Exanguious, 16. Fish, 17. Bird, 18. Beast }

32. Operation

Relation

33. Œconomical
34. Possessions

Parts { 19. Peculiar parts, 20. General parts }

35. Provisions
36. Civil

Quantity

21. Magnitude
22. Space
23. Measure

37. Judicial
38. Military
39. Naval
40. Ecclesiastical

Each genus is in turn broken down by differences. Stones (genus 8), for instance, may be differentiated as

Vulgar, and of no price	I
Middle priced	II
Precious	III

Each category within the genus can be further broken down by species. Thus vulgar stones (genus 8, difference I) are divided into the following species:

GREATER MAGNITUDES of Stone; used either about
Buildings; whether of
    Walls; chiefly, being of a
        Softer consistence; whether natural, or
        factitious.
          1.   FREE-STONE
                BRICK
        Harder consistences; not easily yielding to the
        Tool of the Workman, growing either in
        Greater masses;
          2.   RAGG
        Lesser masses; whether such as are for their figure
        More knobbed and unequal; used for the striking
        of fire, either the more common which is less
        heavy, or the less common which is more heavy,
        as having something in it of a metalline mixture.
          3.   FLINT
                MARCHASITE, Fire-Stone
        More round and even;
          4.   PIBBLE, Thunderbolt
        Roof or Pavement; being of a laminated figure, either
        natural, or factitious.
          5.   SLATE
                TILE
    Metals, either for the
    Sharpening or trying of them.
          6.   WHET-STONE
                TOUCH-STONE
    Polishing or cutting of them; being either of a more
    spingy and soft, or of a more hard consistence.
          7.   PUMICE
                EMRY
LESSER MAGNITUDES; either more, or less minute
          8.   SAND, Grit
                GRAVEL

Wilkins recognized the problems inherent in defining metaphysical concepts like God as genera but attempted to avoid any
definitions that involved "subtle disputes." The definition for the

genus quantity gave him little trouble—like most scientists of his day, he limited it to "motion" and "figure"—but the concept of quality was more difficult. He finally classified qualities as they were "commonly known," although he recognized new theories soon might explain their real causes.* His views of time, space, and motion were also confused. Wilkins's language would be only as scientific as the classifications, and these varied tremendously in their sophistication. Those concerned with biology and botany were particularly good. Others were more arbitrary. Stones, for example, are classified according to their value as well as their transparency and insolubility. However defective his definitions and classifications may appear in retrospect, they are based on the most advanced knowledge of his time.

To express the simple ideas of the classification in speech or discourse was the task of Part III, the "philosophical grammar," which contained a systematic discussion of parts of speech, syntax, orthography, and phonetics. The purpose of the "natural" or philosophical grammar, which was probably composed after the Restoration, was to abstract the necessary rules from existing languages, a task in which he thought he was breaking new ground. This was followed by the real character and philosophical language themselves, which were based on the classification and constructed according to the principles of the natural grammar. Each genus, difference, and species was represented by a mark that resembled a shorthand symbol. Actually two groups of symbols were provided, one to represent ideas and the other sounds, so that the language might be spoken as well as written. He thus provided a phonetic form of symbolic logic. As for the written language, the real character, he was anxious that the characters be easily formed, easily distinguishable from one another, graceful in appearance, and methodical. The spoken language should have a "pleasant and graceful sound." An alphabetical dictionary, which included English words, their symbols in the real character, and references to their proper place in the classification, was appended to the Essay.

To what extent the Essay was considered an official project of the Royal Society is not clear. Many of its members were interested and cooperative. Wilkins claimed to have been working under the Society's orders, and the *Essay* was printed under its auspices. Although Wilkins had asked that a committee be appointed to assist in improving the language, particularly in connection with the classification of natural bodies, no such committee seems to have been formed. A committee was appointed to report on the *Essay* soon after it was published, but no report seems to have been issued then or when the order was repeated. Although this may suggest doubt or even disapproval, the Society thought enough of the system to use it in classifying its repository.

Although Wilkins had not followed Comenius's dictum that only a "College of Wise Men" should attempt to create the universal language, he did seek the assistance of others. Seth Ward was credited with the basic conception. Francis Willoughby and his companion John Ray, both great naturalists, were responsible for drawing up the tables of animals, birds, fishes, and plants. Ray, although quite willing to oblige Wilkins, whom he very much admired, found that the classification system imposed by Wilkins actually hindered rather than promoted the scientific study of plants, and thus pointed to one of the defects of the scheme. Unless the classification system were subject to constant change, knowledge would become ossified and limited by Wilkins's structure. Ray's later classification of plants, based on structure rather than habitat, proved far superior. But despite their defects the botanical and biological classifications were superior to any yet available and Wilkins's initial prodding gave a tremendous impetus to the scientific classification of animals and plants and the creation of a scientific nomenclature. If Wilkins's work had yielded no other results, it would have been a major contribution in this respect alone.

Others may have been responsible for certain portions of the classifications, for Pepys, though unmentioned by Wilkins, reported that he had helped make up the table of "naval matters; the names of rigging, and the timbers about a Ship." Wallis made it quite clear that the portions concerned with the "Formations of Sounds in Speech" owed much to himself and his conversations with Wilkins. William Holder and Francis Lodowyck had also discussed problems of grammar and sound articulation with Wilkins. William Lloyd, whose skill in "Philological, and Philosophical matters" Wilkins so much admired, was almost wholly responsible for the "tedious and difficult task" of composing the dictionary. The Duke of Buckingham, though unmentioned by Wilkins, also helped work on the dictionary.

Wilkins felt his universal language and character would have several important uses. They would not only facilitate international scientific communication and international commerce, but "prove the shortest and plainest way for the attainment of real Knowledge, that hath been yet offered to the World." He was convinced that his classification of universal philosophy, reminiscent of Comenius's pansophia, would offer "a much better and readier course, for the entring and training up of men in the knowledge of things, than any other way of Institution" then available. And finally, the universal language would benefit the cause of religion. Not only could the universal language be second only to the Apostles' gifts of miracles and tongues in spreading "the knowledge of Religion," but it would "contribute much to the clearing of some of our Modern differences in Religion, by unmasking wild errors, that shelter themselves under the disguise of affected phrases; which being Philosophically unfolded, and rendered according to the genuine and natural importance of Words, will appear to be inconsistencies and contradictions."

Despite Wilkins's great enthusiasm for the benefits of the real character, he was not naïve enough to think it would be adopted immediately for common use. He thought the chance of adoption would be greatly improved if his work had the official approval of the Royal Society, which would provoke "at least, the Learned part of the World to take notice of it" and encourage it. When Christian Huygens, who admired the work, indicated he thought the problem of adoption was a difficult one, Sir Robert Moray, a

former president of the Royal Society and confidant of the King, replied that he was more hopeful. The King, he said, had already expressed a desire to learn Wilkins's language, and his example would be followed by others. Wallis was enthusaistic, but he too did not think the language "likely to obtain in Practice." Nevertheless, he and Wilkins corresponded in the real character and "perfectly understood one another as if written in our own Language." Wilkins's close friend Robert Hooke proposed that all scientific findings be communicated in Wilkins's universal language, "it being a Character and a Language so truly Philosophical, and so perfectly and thoroughly Methodical, that there seemeth to be nothing wanting to make it have the utmost perfection, and highest Idea for any Character or Language imaginable, as well for Philosophical as for Common and Constant use." *
The doubts Ray expressed about the scientific value of Wilkins's classification have led at least one recent writer to deprecate the value of Wilkins's work, and to suggest that his contemporaries were somewhat embarrassed by his efforts, and after his death quite willing to let the whole subject quietly drop. This does not seem in fact to have been true. Wilkins's treatment of the alphabet and phonetics, for example, were considered authoritative for many generations after his death.

Wilkins never considered the 1668 *Essay* a finished product. Long afterward he and others, including Ray and Willoughby, were working on an improved edition, which would be printed in Latin to ensure wider circulation. Wilkins on his deathbed was extremely troubled that "his Darling" was incomplete. Far from abandoning it at his death, John Aubrey, Robert Hooke, Andrew Paschall, Francis Lodowyck, and Thomas Pigot all continued to work on the project.* Other scientists, among them Christopher Wren, shared their enthusiasm. Even Ray, who had the most doubts about the language, felt it far excelled all similar works, and suggested that Aubrey's circle incorporate Willoughby's Table of Insects, intended for the Latin edition of the *Essay,* in their own efforts to improve the work. Pepys not only praised the *Essay* when it first appeared, but corresponded with John Evelyn about it as late as 1694. One of the few provincial scientific societies hoped to promote and improve on Wilkins's scheme.

Some of the greatest minds of the century received Wilkins's efforts warmly. Newton, who at one time had attempted a similar scheme, mentioned Wilkins's work in his correspondence. John Locke, too, was interested in Wilkins's work, and recommended his book on the subject in preference to Dalgarno's. Contemporaries such as Sir William Wotton even saw a connection between the work of Wilkins and that of Locke, and suggested that anyone wishing to pursue the subject of a universal character beyond Wilkins should consult Locke's *An Essay Concerning Human Understanding*. Leibnitz was very interested in a universal character, and was familiar with the work of both Wilkins and Dalgarno. One recent writer has suggested that they, rather than Leibnitz, should be credited with the important developments in symbolic logic that resulted from the search for a philosophic language. Wilkins's *Essay*, although written in English, quickly found its way abroad. Comenius was sent a copy by Oldenburg. Wallis sent one to the Italian physicist Giovanni Borelli. Huygens and Leibnitz obtained copies. The Elector Palatine, Wilkins's former patron, tried to obtain a copy, and Thomas Pigot, one of the Aubrey circle, was hopeful that the Elector would "be very instrumental" in promoting Wilkins's design in his domains. A Latin edition was prepared to make the work more widely available, but it was never printed. Efforts were undertaken to translate the *Essay* into French as well.

This should not suggest that all comments were favorable, although it was literary men rather than scientists who tended to be suspicious. Jonathan Swift and Sir William Temple were decidedly hostile, although Sir William Wotton, Temple's literary opponent, defended the *Essay*. He proclaimed it the best book of "philosophical grammar" published and insisted that those who studied it could "never commend [it] enough." Horace Walpole, however, ridiculed it in 1784. He claimed to have found a connection between Wilkins's art of flying and his universal language, "the latter of which he no doubt calculated to prevent the want of an interpreter when he would arrive at the moon." Nevertheless, the language received favorable notice in the *Athenian Mercury* and the *Athenian Oracle*.

Wilkins's *Essay* continued to attract serious attention in the nineteenth and twentieth centuries. Erasmus Darwin praised it, as did the pioneer anthropologist Lord Monboddo, in his *Origin and Progress of Language* (1809). The philologist A. J. Ellis, author of the *Alphabet of Nature* (1845), acknowledged his indebtedness to Wilkins. Max Müller, also writing in 1845, said that Wilkins's universal language provided the best solution to the problems with which it dealt presented up to that time. Roget, author of the still popular *Thesaurus,* expressed his indebtedness to Wilkins and modeled his classifications on those of his predecessor. More recently, Wilkins's work has come to the attention of those concerned with the development of symbolic logic and semantics. The *Essay* has also been recommended to librarians wrestling with the problem of classifying scientific documents. It has naturally enough attracted the notice of promoters of international languages. Solutions such as Ogden's Basic English, Interglossa, or Esperanto are perhaps less interesting and certainly no more successful.

It has recently been argued, as a result of scientific, linguistic, and logical studies, that Wilkins's failure was the result of attempting too much; that the effort to combine a simple international language with a scientific classification, necessarily requiring both precision and an infinite capacity for change, could not help but fail. If Wilkins and his associates had continued with their original plan for an international nonphilosophical language, based on the smallest number of radicals, their work might have had more practical effect. Nevertheless, linguistic perfection still lures philosophers; Bertrand Russell, for one, has discussed the properties of the "perfect language."

The overambitiousness of Wilkins's linguistic treatise is also the source of its peculiar virtues—virtues found not only in the universal language, but in all his scientific work, of which the language was an integral part. For Wilkins's principal scientific concern was not the discovery of new knowledge, but the organization and systematic communication of the activities and findings of the new philosophers. The Royal Society was founded to rationalize and coordinate scientific research. The universal language was to rationalize and coordinate the result of that research. Its principal goal was not improved international communication *per se,* but a uniform classification of knowledge that would enable the international scientific movement to work more efficiently. The organization of scientific societies, together with the adoption of the language, would create a perfect communications network among all active scientific researchers, and in addition contribute to public recognition and application of the new scientific knowledge. Wilkins's preoccupation with systematizing and communicating scientific knowledge may have led to the failure of the universal language, but it also contributed immeasurably to the success of the Royal Society.

VIII. Religion and Science

It is in his last philosophical and scientific writings and his post-humously published work on natural religion that the central role Wilkins played in relating science to religion in seventeenth-century England can be seen most clearly. Here we find an explicitly stated and highly developed body of thought, which from the standpoint of science formulated a moderate, nondogmatic religion compatible with scientific knowledge, and from the standpoint of religion elaborated an approach to the epistemology and methodology of science compatible with religious belief.

In view of the popularity of the hypothesis relating Puritanism and science, one of the most striking patterns to emerge from an examination of the thought of seventeenth-century English and Continental scientists, whatever their particular religious commitments, is an almost universal suspicion of religious disputes, accompanied by a pronounced desire for religious compromise and unity. Copernicus, for example, strove for an accommodation between Roman Catholics and Lutherans. Galileo and Kepler were religious men, but either unconcerned with dogmatic theology or hostile toward it. Campanella was an outspoken critic of religious zealotry. Simon Stevin, the Dutch mathematician who was so important in the development of mechanics, wrote a tract urging that religious disputes not be permitted to disturb the public peace. Bacon was unsympathetic to the quibblings of the theologians, and his advocacy of a moderate policy toward the Puritans may have stemmed as much from his distaste for persecution as from Puritan sympathies. Like Wilkins and the great majority of later scientists, he made it clear that "controversies of religion" could only "hinder the advancement of science."

Sir Walter Raleigh and the scientific circle that clustered around him have, along with Bacon, been enlisted in the Puritan cause. Raleigh "had no strong feelings about dogma," and opposed condemning even Brownists and Jesuits for their opinions. The Raleigh circle engaged in a wide range of religious speculation, most of which would have been beyond the limits of either Puritan or Anglican orthodoxy, and was willing to countenance a wide range of religious expression. Here again, moderation, not Puritanism, seems to be the recurrent phenomenon. There is also some doubt whether the Comenians are best characterized as Puritans. If as a group they possessed one distinguishing characteristic, surely it was their desire for religious unity and Protestant reunion, and a distaste for the religious controversies and warfare which were destroying both Europe and England.

We have already noticed the desire of the 1645 and Oxford groups to exclude religious topics from discussion, and their willingness to accept members of widely divergent political and religious affiliations. The scientists in these groups had no inclination to force their own views on others, and in fact wished for a settlement in which all could participate. There was an extremely high proportion of religious moderates in the Oxford circle. Wilkins himself is probably the most outstanding example, but he was hardly an isolated instance. Robert Boyle, William Petty, Jonathan Goddard, and Ralph Bathurst were all known for their dislike of religious controversy. There are, it must be admitted, two important figures in the Wadham circle who can hardly be described as moderates or latitudinarians. One of them, Seth Ward, was a staunch Anglican and became a persecuting bishop. If he was not a moderate, he certainly was not a Puritan. Although there can be no question of John Wallis's Puritanism and Presbyterianism during the earlier and middle years of his life, his later career exhibits a growing moderation and movement toward latitudinarianism. Wallis may not have begun his life as a moderate, but he surely ended as one.

At Cambridge, too, those who shared Wilkins's scientific interests shared his moderate religious predilections as well. The liberal and rationalist views of the Cambridge Platonists are too well known to require recounting here. Similar attitudes were expressed by Francis Willoughby, John Ray, and John Worthington, who tried so hard to create a chair in mathematics. The mathematician Isaac Barrow, an Anglican of strong conviction and of Arminian persuasion, was also a convinced latitudinarian.

It was thus no accident that the Royal Society and its predecessors excluded religious and political topics and included men of widely differing viewpoints. The moderate, tolerant policy established by Wilkins at Oxford was recognized by the virtuosi as indispensable to scientific progress. The policy was not motivated by expediency, but by the conviction that religious disputation was itself harmful, and that Christian ethics were more important than Christian dogma.

If many scientists were latitudinarians, of course not all latitudinarians were scientists. Nevertheless, as a group they were peculiarly receptive to the new philosophy. Lloyd and Tillotson did not themselves engage in scientific activities, but assisted Wilkins in his *Essay Towards a Real Character and a Philosophical Language*. Tillotson became a member of the Royal Society. Edward Stillingfleet, while not an active virtuoso, greatly admired Boyle's contribution to experimental philosophy. Simon Patrick, too, was enthusiastic about the new philosophy. Gilbert Burnet, another leading liberal clergyman, was not only a member of the Royal Society but learned his science from Boyle and Wilkins. Burnet, who together with Sir Robert Moray was one of the leading figures in the effort to obtain comprehension for Scotland in 1668, turned to the study of mathematics and chemistry when he was forced to withdraw from political life. Joseph Glanvill was a spokesman for both the new philosophy and moderate religion. Matthew Hale, a close friend of Burnet and Wilkins and one of the most noted latitudinarian laymen, collected mathematical instruments and engaged in scientific experimentation. In John Locke we again see the combination of liberal religion and scientific interests. He conducted medical experiments at Oxford and was a member of the Royal Society. Locke's patron, Lord Ashley, was also an active member of the Royal Society's council and one of the most powerful advocates of religious toleration. Patronage connections are revealing; it was surely no accident that Wilkins's last three patrons shared both his scientific interests and his latitudinarian predilections.

Thomas Sprat's official *History of the Royal Society* made perfectly clear the open alliance between liberal religion and scientific inquiry. In describing the necessary stance of the virtuosi, he might well have been describing the latitudinarians. It was "requisite" that the scientists "be well practis'd in all modest, humble, friendly, Vertues; should be willing to be taught, and to give way to the judgement of others," for able philosophers would never be produced by "high, earnest, insulting Wits, who can bear neither partnership, or opposition." It was the sin of pride that both groups found so distasteful.

Sprat, Glanvill, and Wilkins, among others, frequently noted the similarities between the moderate Christian and the scientific experimenter. They particularly emphasized consciousness of one's own and others' fallibility as the mark of the true Christian and the true scientist. Such consciousness not only bred a reluctance to accept traditional authorities but a hesitation to create new ones. Overconfident assertions blocked investigation by presenting hypotheses as unquestionable truths. One of the basic qualities of the scientific attitude was humility before an ever-increasing body of knowledge and a willingness to give way to the judgment of others. These were accompanied by an intense feeling that freedom to differ and investigate was the most important tool of the scientist. Sprat even suggested that scientific inquiry itself provided a remedy for religious dissension. "Spiritual frensies, . . . can never stand long, before a clear and a deep skill in nature." * Joseph Glanvill, who after Sprat was the Society's most important public defender, suggested that

by a generous and open Inquiry in the great Field of Nature, men's minds are enlarged, and taken off from all fond adherences to their private Sentiments. They are taught by it, That Certainty is not in many things; . . . By which means they will find themselves disposed to more indifferency toward those petty Notions, in which they were before apt to place a great deal of Religion; and to reckon that [it] lies, in the few, certain, operative Principles of the Gospel; in a Life suitable to such a Faith; not in doting upon Questions and Speculations that engender strife.

The Royal Society, Glanvill was certain, would "dispose men's Spirits to more calmness and Modesty, Charity and Prudence in the Differences of Religion, and even Silence Disputes there," for wherever scientific investigation prevailed "the Contentious Divinity loseth grounds."

The alliance between latitudinarianism and science, however, went deeper than a common core of practitioners and a shared distaste for dogmatism. For the two movements also shared a theory of knowledge, and members of both became the principal proponents of a rationalized religion and natural theology. Wilkins played a key role in the development of these ideas in both movements. In their respective areas, both scientists and theologians sought a *via media* between skepticism and dogmatism. On the scientific side this search for "certainty" resulted in an emphasis on hypothesis and a science without overt metaphysics. In spiritual matters it led to an emphasis on broad fundamentals and eschewing of any detailed, orthodox theology claiming infallibility.

It was Sebastian Castellio, writing nearly as century earlier, who had first attempted to deal with the problem of certainty in the terms adopted by Wilkins and his circle. Castellio suggested that while there was no way of eliminating all doubts concerning the validity of religious knowledge, it was possible to arrive at an adequate assurance about basic truths. This line of argument was elaborated by Hugo Grotius, whom Wilkins and Boyle much admired, and developed further by William Chillingworth. Henry Van Leeuwen has described the development of this approach to certainty in England from 1630 to 1690 and shown its importance in the evolution of scientific methodology and epistemological theory. He suggests that this formulation of the concepts was first introduced in the context of the Rule of Faith controversy between Protestants and Roman Catholics, and then secularized by such scientists as Wilkins, Glanvill, Boyle, Newton, and Locke. His examination of Restoration thinkers, however, suggests a simultaneous development of these notions by churchmen and scientists. Wilkins and Glanvill, for instance, were concerned with both religious and scientific methodology, making it unrealistic to rigidly distinguish religious and secular movements and assume a one-way flow of ideas from the former to the latter.*

Wilkins's treatment of the problem of certainty began with a typology of evidence. Simple evidence was based on either the senses or the understanding, mixed evidence on a combination of both. The understanding is that faculty that enables us to apprehend the objects of knowledge, "Generals as well as particulars, Absent things as well as Present; and to judge of their Truth or Falsehood, Good or Evil." The kind of evidence that related to the understanding arose from the "nature of things," that is, "Congruity or Incongruity betwixt the Terms of a Proposition" or deductions from propositions. Such evidence might either "satisfie the mind" or leave it in doubt. The testimony of others was evidence based on understanding, to be evaluated according to the "authority and credit of the Witness." Wilkins did not give absolute priority to either sense or understanding. In some cases the senses were superior, in others "the understanding power" would "correct the errors of our Senses and Imaginations." *

After laying out the types of evidence and their sources in sense and understanding, Wilkins suggested the several levels of certainty that might be derived from such evidence. There were two basic categories. The first, knowledge or certainty, was "that kind of Assent which doth arise from such plain and clear Evidence as doth not admit of any reasonable cause of doubting." The second was opinion and probability. Knowledge itself had three subcategories, physical, mathematical, and moral. The first was derived from sensory data, which yielded "the highest kind of Evidence, of which humane nature is capable." Physical certainty included information provided by the inward as well as the outward senses, that is, self-awareness as well as the awareness of objects. When it came to the actual "manner" or mechanism of sensation, however, Wilkins had to admit that it "was not yet understood." Mathematical certainty was not limited to mathematics alone, but extended to all "such *simple* abstracted beings, as in their own nature do lie so open, and are so obvious to the understanding, that every man's judgment (though never so much prejudiced) must necessarily assent to them."

The objects of moral certainty were "less simple" than either the physical or the mathematical, for they

are not capable of the same kind of Evidence . . . so as to necessitate every man's assent, . . . yet they may be so plain, that every man whose judgment is free from prejudice will consent to them. And though there be no natural necessity, that such things must be so, and that they cannot possibly be otherwise, without implying a Contradiction; yet may they be so certain as not to admit of any reasonable doubt concerning them.

The first two yielded "infallible" certainty, the last "indubitable" certainty. Even physical and mathematical certainty, it should be noted, were not "absolutely" infallible, for that was an attribute of God, who alone possessed an unerring judgment. Man was only capable of "conditional infallibility," which "supposes our faculties to be true, and that we do not neglect the exerting of them." Most things, however, were capable only of "indubitable certainty," that is a certainty which did not admit of any reasonable cause of doubt. This level of certainty arose from evidence derived "from the Nature of things" through testimony and experience:

I am from the nature of the things themselves *Morally* certain, and cannot make any doubt of it, but that a *mind free from passion and prejudice is more fit to pass a true judgment, than such a one as is byassed by affections and interests.* That *there are such things as Vertue and Vice.* That *Mankind is naturally designed for a sociable life.* That *it is most agreeable to reason and the common interests of those in society, that they should be true to their Compacts.* . . .

And as for the evidence from *Testimony* which depends upon the credit and authority of the Witnesses, these may be so qualified as to their *ability* and *fidelity,* that a man must be a fantastical incredulous fool to make any doubt of them. And by this it is that I am sufficient assured, That there was such a person as Queen *Elizabeth;* That there is such a place as *Spain.*

And so for the evidence of *Experience,* I am by that to a great degree assured of the succession of Night and Day, Winter and Summer. And have no such reason to doubt, whether the house wherein now I am, shall this next minute fall upon me, or the earth open and swallow it up, as to be in continual fear of such accidents.

Under certain conditions even indubitable certainty was unattainable. When the proofs are good, yet "not so weighty and perspicuous as to exclude all possibility of reasonable doubt and fear of the contrary," only opinion and probability resulted. Thus the senses and understanding, which might at times lead to the highest levels of certainty, at others led only to opinion and probability.

In addition to an analysis of knowledge and certainty, Wilkins provided several axioms and general rules for the pursuit of both religious and natural knowledge. First, he insisted that all truths were equally true. There was no hierarchy of truth itself. Yet all truths were not equally knowable, for they were not all capable "of the same degree of Evidence as to us." To insist on proofs "of which the nature of such a thing is not capable" was simply irrational. Citing Aristotle, he noted that different kinds of investigation required different kinds of proof. As a corollary one should be satisfied by "the best evidence" for a thing "which that kind of thing will bear, and beyond which better could not be expected." This of course implied a rejection of skepticism. Wilkins insisted at great length that the bare possibility that the contrary was true was insufficient reason for doubting weighty evidence. Where there was no certainty, the impartial judgment would "incline to the greater probabilities." If the probabilities on both sides were equal, it was appropriate to suspend judgment, although in this instance the least hazardous choice was justified.*

Wilkins was attempting to lay a philosophically sound groundwork for the truths of religion in expounding his theory of knowledge. Religious principles, however, belonged to the realm of moral certainty. In matters of faith and religion, it was only possible to render things "highly credible, so as an honest and teachable man may willingly and safely assent to them and according to the rules of Prudence be justified in so doing." To the unprejudiced, careful man the basic principles of religion would appear "unquestionable," and deductions from them "demonstrable." That religious principles could not attain the same level of certainty as mathematics or physical truth was to Wilkins a positive rather than negative consideration. If assent to religious principles were philosophically necessary rather than voluntary, there would be no place for faith or "the freedom of our obediance."

As an integral part of his theory of knowledge, Wilkins delineated certain basic principles of religion that could be known by means of reason "improved by Consideration and Experience, without the help of Revelation." The principles of natural religion are those of which we can acquire moral certainty through the same processes by which we acquire other knowledge. A considerable number of works on natural religion appeared during the Restoration period. Wilkins's was perhaps the most extended and systematic treatment, and certainly one of the most popular and influential. Natural theology itself, of course, was not new. It had been taught by the ancients, particularly the Stoics, to whom Wilkins was extremely indebted, as well as by Aquinas, Raymond Sabunde, and more recently Grotius, Chillingworth, and Lord Herbert of Cherbury. The revival was, however, stimulated by the scientific movement and by the search for common religious principles that would bind the wounds inflicted by the recent religious strife. Wilkins, like Tillotson, Stillingfleet, and the Platonists among the churchmen, and Charleton, Ray, Ward, Boyle, and Newton among the virtuosi, used natural religion to defend the harmony of reason and religion against real or imagined attacks. Although the writings of Wilkins and his associates often make it appear that they are fighting off hordes of skeptics and atheists of both the Epicurean and the Hobbesian variety, in fact there seem to have been few thoroughgoing materialists or philosophical skeptics during this period. One suspects that the proponents of natural religion were trying to make their views more palatable to religious conservatives by creating a straw man against whom they could display the comparative religiosity of their own doctrines.

Although Wilkins expressed most interest in natural religion in his later writings, his acceptance of the basic doctrines date from early in his career. The *Discourse Concerning the Beauty of Providence,* published in 1649, was essentially an essay on natural religion and could have passed as a model Restoration sermon. All his surviving sermons, in fact, are saturated with rational arguments, and are for the most part based on the principles of natural religion. His most systematic treatment appeared in his popular *Principles and Duties of Natural Religion,* written late in life and published posthumously. This work is typical of many of his writings. He did not propose original arguments but contented himself with "management of some of those old ones, which . . . seem most plain and convincing." * Here again Wilkins was the popularizer, who by an orderly and simplified treatment of what was being discussed in advanced intellectual circles, hoped to convey these ideas to a broader public. Natural religion for Wilkins consisted of three basic principles: a belief in the existence of a deity, recognition of his "Excellencies and Perfections," and "suitable affections and Demeanour towards him." Because Wilkins had placed religious principles in the realm of moral certainty, he could not of course absolutely prove the existence of God. Yet belief in the deity was not only "highly credible," but something in which "every sober man, who will not offer violence to his own faculties, must submit unto." Even if there was some doubt about the existence of a supreme deity, there certainly was no danger in believing in it. In this instance, one should accept the Pascalean wager and choose the position of least danger. Atheism was thus simply folly.

It is suggestive of the virtuosi's respect for Aristotle that Wilkins, who based much of his argument of the existence of God on common consent, referred to "the Philosopher" in employing this mode of proof. A belief became increasingly probable as the number of wise men who consented to it increased. A proposition that all men accept enjoys the highest degree of certainty attainable by propositions of that type. The fact that a few men did not believe in God's existence did not invalidate universal consent any more than prodigies disproved the regularity of natural law, and the substantial number of remaining polytheists and idolators was due to the prejudice of an education that prevented "impartial enquiry."

In the context of this discussion of common consent, Wilkins introduced the concepts of "Common Notions," "Seminal Principles," and "innate Law," which seem to have been of considerable scholarly concern at the time he wrote. It was generally agreed, Wilkins thought, that the acts of the mind were reducible to three types—simple apprehension, or the perception of single objects; judging, or "putting together such a single objections, in order to our comparing of the agreement or disagreement betwixt them"; and ratiocination or discourse, the "discerning of that connection or dependence which there is betwixt several Propositions, whereby we are enabled to infer one Proposition from another." "Natural" or "Common" notions sprang from all these types of mental operations, in the form of opinions that "have in them such a suitableness to the minds of men, as to be generally owned and acknowledged for true, by all such as apply their thoughts to the consideration of them." Natural notions, then, were not identical with innate ideas. Yet Wilkins was not entirely clear on the distinction between innate ideas and common notions, for he insisted that no "institution" or instruction could eradicate natural notions from the mind.

Nevertheless, natural notions were not present in all persons. One could not expect to find them in infants, among "dull sottish people," or those "destitute of all advantages of Education." It was necessary that men be "ready to exert and exercise their faculties to observe and consider the nature of things, to make use of that help which is to be had, by the instruction and experience of those with whome they converse." An idea was nonetheless natural for being "promoted" by experience and instruction. Wilkins thus defined common notions as those things which are "evident by *natural light,* which men of mature age, in the ordinary use of their faculties, with the common help of mutual society, may know and be sufficiently assured of." In this sense the notion of God was natural to the soul. This kind of argument prepared the way for Wilkins's assertion of the existence of a natural moral law. "All men have agreed that there is such a thing as the Law of Nature, whereby things are disginguished into good and bad; according to which, the actions of men are determined to be either virtuous or vicious." At the same time, however, he added that this law was "put into our natures" by God, who would enforce its observance. This, of course, suggests something like innateness. Thus Wilkins retains elements of the concept of innate ideas, but he is obviously moving in a Lockean direction. His work tends increasingly to view natural notions as shared learning based on common psychological operations, rather than readymade concepts implanted directly in each individual mind.

Wilkins moved from the proofs of God's existence based on common consent and natural notions to the conventional arguments from creation. More interesting is Wilkins's proof derived from a study of history and the beliefs of the "Barbarous Indians," for it suggests that comparative religion was beginning to have an impact on theological discourse. Wilkins was probably particularly receptive to the reports on native cultures that the Royal Society was collecting. He concluded from these data that it was "Not easie to imagine, how any such Tradition could arise so *early*, and spread so *universally*, if there were not a real ground for it." *

Like so many of the virtuosi Wilkins laid great stress on the argument for God's existence "from the admirable contrivance of Natural things." * Although this argument, too, was a very old one, it gained a new prominence in the mid-seventeenth century. Perhaps Wilkins's most important contribution in this area was his emphasis on the "Elegance and Beauty" to be found in nature. We have already noted that his appreciation of mountains added a new note to English aesthetics. Like Hooke, whom he encouraged, Wilkins appealed to the evidence of the microscope, which revealed

Whatever is *Natural* doth by that appear, adorned with all imaginable *Elegance* and *Beauty*. There are such inimitable gildings and embroideries in the smallest seeds of Plants, but especially in the parts of Animals. In the head or eye of a small Fly: Such accurate order and symmetry in the frame of the most minute creatures, a *Lowse* or a *Mite,* as no man were able to conceive without seeing of them. Whereas the most curious works of Art, . . . the most accurate engravings or embossments, seem such rude bungling deformed works as if they had been done with a Mattock or a Trowel.

In the course of relating the beauties they saw in nature to God, the virtuosi undoubtedly had a marked influence in changing aesthetic standards.

Wilkins also argued that the existence of God was to be proven by the "experience which we have of some Wise and Powerful Being who doth preside over and govern all things," that is, from Providence. He distinguished between common providence, which regulated the order of nature, and special providence, through which God guided human affairs. In the first realm God almost always operated by his "usual ways." It is not entirely clear whether Wilkins wished to suggest a similar automatic chain of second causes in human affairs or a greater measure of direct, divine intervention. The doctrine of providence found scientific as well as religious and political use. Particularly in the form of common providence, it provided a doctrinal middle ground that allowed virtuosi like Wilkins to emphasize both God's role in nature and the regularity and order of the cosmos. Natural laws, second causes, and providence operating in the "usual way" were often treated as almost identical. Such a conception of providence meant that God's direct intervention in the natural order could be increasingly deemphasized. It implied an almost, if not quite, totally mechanistic universe, in which God was little more than a first cause even though he was continually present in physical events.

There remained the problem of miracles, the occasions when God did intervene directly. Wilkins did not deny the possibility of miracles, for a denial would contradict God's omnipotence. But he felt the natural philosopher

in the Resolution of Natural Events should not fly into the Absolute Power of God, and tell us what he can do, but what according to the usual ways of Providence, is most likely to be done, to find out such Causes of Things, as may seem most easy and probable to our Reasons.

[A Miracle] often serves for the Receptacle of Lazy Ignorance; which any industrious Spirit would be asham'd of; it being but an idle way to shift off the Labour of any further search.

For all practical purposes, Wilkins limited miracles to Biblical times, and even Biblical miracles might be questioned if they conflicted with the findings of science, since scientifically accurate description was not the basic purpose of Scripture.

Whereas I have argued that the doctrine of providence, and particularly that of common providence, was helpful to the development of science, Richard Westfall has suggested an inherent, unresolved conflict between the doctrine and the mechanistic thrust of natural science. He argues that Wilkins's *Discourse*

Concerning the Beauty of Providence fails to confront this problem. For Westfall the crux of the matter is the miraculous, for as long as the seventeenth-century thinker as divine recognized miracles, he could not as scientist consistently espouse the regularity of the physical universe. Although Wilkins does not resolve this conflict, he does succeed in minimizing it. Emphasis on the "usual ways" of common providence increases the compatibility of providence with natural law, and the role of miracles is so reduced that for practical purposes they become irrelevant to scientific inquiry. The potential clash between providence and scientific regularity was further softened by the way Wilkins combined teleology and mechanism. Nature operated according to certain mechanisms and natural laws, but these laws themselves were due to God's will and were part of His purpose. Of course Wilkins was not alone in this effort at reconciliation. Pierre Gassendi and Charleton, for example, tried to combine mechanistic atomism with Christian concepts. By making God the author of the atom as well as the rest of nature, providence and mechanism could function in sufficient harmony to satisfy most seventeenth-century natural philosophers.

For all his emphasis on common providence and natural law, Wilkins did not absolutely minimize particular providence, for he was aware that a too abstract and distant concept of God would have "but a very flat and jejune operation upon our hearts." In the realm of nature God might be very distant, but in the realm of morals and religious practice he was still ever-watchful. For the most part the two competing conceptions caused him little difficulty. In a few instances, however, they jostled each other uncomfortably. As we noted earlier, for example, Wilkins thought the plague and Great Fire were in some sense the punishment of sinners visited by an angry God, yet at the same time he wished to investigate their natural causes. Unlike the Cambridge Platonists, Wilkins was not greatly concerned about the religious implications of mechanism and found their efforts to posit a divine principle in nature superfluous. Matter and motion provided a sufficient explanation of the operations of nature, and one safe from antireligious implications if it were remembered that both were created and guided by a deity rather than necessity or chance.

Having proved the existence of a deity, Wilkins turned to describing His attributes. He proposes the conventional ones—simplicity, unity, immutability, infiniteness, and the like. The relative weight he assigns each attribute, however, reveals much about his particular concept of the deity and man's relation to Him. Of all the qualities or attributes of God, goodness was the most important, and was, in fact, the basis of all religion and worship. Without goodness other divine attributes such as knowledge and power "would be but *craft* and *violence*." God would then simply "out-wit" men, "tyrannize over them and play with their misery." He found distasteful the "frightful and over-timorous notion of the Deity," which represented God as "austere and rigorous, easily provoked by every little circumstantial mistake." No doubt with the enemies of the latitudinarians in mind, he wrote that it was natural for "selfish and narrow men" to have such a view of God, since they made "themselves the rule and measure of perfection in other things."

Those that are of ill natures and of little minds, whose thoughts are fixed upon small and low matters, laying greater weight upon circumstance, salutes, addresses, than upon the real worth of persons, and substantial duties, being themselves apt to be provoked unto wrath and fierceness, upon the ommission of these lesser circumstances, . . . such men must consequently think themselves obliged to deal just so towards God, as they expect that others should deal with them.

Wilkins offers a rather perfunctory treatment of God's justice, perhaps the attribute most stressed by the Puritans. He says enough, however, to indicate how far he was from their view that if God were to judge men justly, he would consign them all to perdition, and that it was only by special grace some were saved.

He insists that God dealt "with his creatures according to the desert of their deeds." *

Although careful to distinguish man from God, particularly in their capacities for knowledge and perfection, Wilkins did not find an unbridgeable gulf between them. God provided "the Rule and Measure, from whom all created goodness is derived, and by conformity to whom is to be estimated." Some of God's goodness, wisdom, power, and immortality were communicated to man. Thus Wilkins opposes the traditional Calvinist view of man, and argues that God can indeed provide a measure for man. How far Wilkins had travelled from the rigors of predestinarian doctrine can also be seen in his belief that man was endowed with "natural principles" that "necessarily inclined" him "to seek his own well-being and happiness," that is, salvation. Man also possessed faculties that enabled him to judge things "as to their fitness or unfitness for this end," and "to chuse and prosecute such things as may promote this end." Man's salvation was thus in his own hands.

Wilkins argues that the acceptance of the existence of God and an understanding of his attributes would naturally lead men to the duties of religion, that is, adoration and worship of the deity. Natural worship was simply "the highest esteem and admiration of him in our minds, whereby we do continually bow down our souls before him, in the acknowledgement of his Excellencies; . . . together with such external services, as may be fit to testifie unto others that inward veneration which we have for him." It was as natural for men to establish public places and special times set apart for worship as it was for them to join civil societies. Even natural worship for Wilkins, required a special class of clergy-men, who were to "officiate in *Sacris,* assist the people in worship, to instruct, and to excite them to perform their duties." Natural worship was very similar in substance to Wilkins's conception of individual prayer, and involved "invoking of the Deity, returning thanks to him, and inquiring after his Will." Christianity was "a more rational and spiritual way of worship, whose *Precepts* were most agreeable to the purest and sublimist reason."

Man naturally had some "confused inclination towards God," but love of God required "choice and resolution." Of the two types of love, passion was based on the fancy and appetite, and led to "sudden impetus and transport of desire." Wilkins did not really approve of passion, which led to martyrdom. It was love derived from the rational part of the soul that produced the "full conviction, deliberate choice and full resolution" that were the central virtues of religion. Wilkins did not entirely slight the affections. He had insisted, for example, that preaching should move the affection as well as the reason. Wilkins and his fellow moderates repeatedly stressed the Stoic virtues of calm acceptance of worldly tribulations and modest, well-tempered pursuit of the good, rather than religious passion.

Wilkins sought to clearly distinguish natural principles from moral duties. Natural principles were those "impressions . . . originally stamped upon the nature of things, . . . the acts of which are necessary and under no kind of liberty of being suspended." The desire for salvation, for instance, was a natural principle, but man attained salvation through fulfillment of his moral duties. It was in this context that Wilkins attempted to show the "wisdom" of practicing the duties enjoined by natural religion. The development of this theme, also found in Tillotson's famous sermon *The Wisdom of Being Religious* (1664) on which he drew, was based on his concept of the nature of man. Following the traditional view, Wilkins noted that the form or essence of a thing was that which distinguished it from all other things. Reason, however, was not the essence of man for some animals possessed a natural sagacity very close to reason. It was "Reason as it is *determined* to actions of Religion" that separated man from the beasts, for no other creature possessed the capacity for worshipping and enjoying his creator. Without religion neither government nor society could exist. Invoking his usual teleological reasoning, Wilkins then insists that man will thus be driven to perfect his faculties in the direction of religion.

Religion would not only secure man's happiness in the next

world, but would produce honor, health, riches, and safety in this. These, however, were not moral rewards, but natural results. Wilkins emphasized religion's temporal rewards because "the generality of men are chiefly swayed" by worldly success. The seeming crassness of Wilkins's approach was mitigated by his definitions of riches and honor. He did not mean worldly honor, but only that honor due a virtuous and religious man. Riches did not mean great wealth but only freedom from the "want and necessity" that occurred when possessions were proportioned to social status. Worldly happiness would also be gained because "happiness of a good conscience" was a chief part of "that heaven which we enjoy on earth." Thus he concludes that the "generality of those who live most pleasantly in the world," that is, those who possessed inward peace and confidence, were "the most religious and virtuous part of mankind; such as know how to regulate themselves in the fruition of what they have, how to avoid the extremities on either hand to prevent those mixtures of guilt and fear." Wilkins's emphasis on the "advantages" of religion was not unique, although he and Tillotson were perhaps most responsible for the prominence of this theme in Restoration preaching.*

The question of salvation necessarily led Wilkins to the relationship of natural to revealed religion. For if mankind could reach salvation by following its natural inclinations and truths derivable from reason, Christianity would be superfluous. The thrust of Wilkins's thought was certainly in this direction, although he, like most virtuosi, preferred to emphasize the basic compatibility of natural and revealed religion. Reason led man to the principles of natural religion and morality, and thus natural knowledge alone enabled him to know and keep God's commandments. By the practice of natural morality men were "advanced into that state of happiness, wherein the perfection of our natures, and resemblance of the Deity doth consist." "In brief; That Salvation and Glory, which the Christian Religion doth so clearly propose to us, is, as to the nature and essence of it, but the very same thing with Religion; consisting in such a conformity of our minds to the nature of God, whereby we are made capable of the fruition of him in Heaven." It would thus seem clear that though Wilkins greatly admired Christianity, he did not consider revealed religion necessary for salvation, and held that all who obeyed the precepts of natural religion could expect to be saved.

Wilkins did not, however, consistently maintain this position. He was anxious to show that natural religion did not "derogate from the necessity and usefulness of Divine Revelation." Indeed he sometimes treated natural religion as only a preliminary to Christianity. The moral virtues were not quite identical with divinity, though "in the very next degree to it." Christians who possessed the means of grace were expected to "get above the morality of the Heathens," and for them natural morality alone was insufficient to attain true blessedness. At one point Wilkins suggests that although the moral virtues described by the heathen philosophers were the same as those in Scripture, Scripture enjoined them "in a far more eminent, sublime and comprehensive manner." But this may only mean, as Wilkins sometimes implies, that the Bible simply made particularly clear what every man might also know by his own devices. Christian doctrine was "so exactly conformable to the highest, purest reason, that in those very things wherein it goes beyond the rules of Moral Philosophy, we cannot in our best judgment but consent and submit to it." *

Wilkins ended his treatise on natural religion with a ringing affirmation of the necessity of Christianity. Not only were the merits of Christ responsible for the salvation of all those saved "in all ages and places," but none born under the dispensation of the Gospel who neglected its message would escape punishment. Wilkins's conception of Christianity, however, was sufficiently simple to bring it very close to natural religion. The end of Christianity was eternal blessedness, consisting of reconciliation to God and communion with him. It was to be attained through grace, which renewed and repaired men's corrupted natures and required faith in a mediator, together with "a hearty, constant and universal submission to the doctrine of the Gospel whereby men" were made "wise unto Salvation." Christian wisdom was "that habit of mind whereby a man is enabled to propose the true end of eternal blessedness, and to judge aright concerning such means as may be most fit for the attaining of this end," a definition that again brought Wilkins very close to natural religion.

Whatever the final compatibility of Wilkins's statements on the relationship between rational and revealed religion, it is clear that, compared with most earlier writings, the rational had tremendously increased in scope. Despite some of his more Christian pronouncements, the whole thrust of Wilkins's writings was in the direction of the sufficiency of natural religion. Revelation basically provided an added proof, a clearer statement, of the truths that the enlightened mind could attain independently.

Given the rationalism of his writings and sermons, it is not difficult to see why Wilkins was so often called a Socinian. Although he in no way rejected the divinity of Christ or his role as a mediator, he rarely even mentioned him. Wilkins's comments on the attributes of God, too, must have aroused suspicion. He and many of his latitudinarian associates so emphasized the unity of the Godhead in their argument against polytheism that they were accused of rejecting the Trinity. It was only after Wilkins's death, however, that Tillotson, Wallis, and others felt it necessary to openly reaffirm their belief in the Trinity.

Several aspects of Wilkins's thought are mutually reinforcing: his awareness of man's fallibility, his theory of knowledge and certainty, his desire to bypass the spiritual disputes of his day by focusing on the fundamentals of religion and his attitude toward nature. Thus it was Wilkins's theory of certainty and his natural theology which supported his latitudinarianism and enabled him to deemphasize traditional theological disputes. Most of these disputes were over matters that fell into a very low category of certainty, and in fact were usually to be placed only in the realm of probability and opinion. Overconfidence and dogmatism on such doubtful matters as the forms of church government and ceremony simply led to persecution over truths that might or might not be true, and could not in any event be established with a sufficient degree of certainty to justify coercive policies. Wilkins was thus quite willing to allow such controversies to be settled the Day of Judgment. Though he and his associates usually referred "the decision of all the Differences amongst good Christians" to Scripture, even here they recognized that often there was no certainty. The inevitable limitations on human certainty, which were so clearly operative and significant in science, were equally decisive in religion, and dictated a moderate and tentative stance on disputed points of doctrine.

Just as some scientific truths could be established with a high degree of certainty and thus become the foundation for further scientific investigation, so certain fundamental propositions of religion could be similarly established and similarly used to guide the conduct of religious life. There was a core of religious and scientific truth upon which rational agreement could be attained. Beyond that, the limits of certainty should establish the limits of dispute, particularly violent dispute:

It being utterly impossible . . . that we should always agree in the same apprehension of things. If upon every difference men should think themselves obliged to prosecute matters to the utmost height and rigour, such eager persons may easily from hence be induced to have recourse to Arms rather than such precious things as truth and justice shall suffer; and being once thus engaged, it will be impossible . . . to end their differences by any accommodation, they must fight it out to the last till one side be wholly subdued and destroyed. And thus would men grow wild and savage, the benefits of Society would be lost, and mankind destroyed out of the world.

It was thus an awareness of human fallibility, coupled with his theory of knowledge, that led Wilkins to especially emphasize natural religion as a core of established truth on which all men could agree, and which would be sufficient to guide their spiritual lives without attempts to settle insoluble questions that could only generate more heat than light.

More than any other quality, Wilkins's lack of sympathy for those who thought they had an infallible guide to minor religious questions separated him from the Puritans, in both their Interregnum and Restoration forms. His approach, with its emphasis on reason, was more congenial to Anglicans than it was to Puritans, who placed inordinate confidence in the infallibility of their authorities and dogmatic methods. The Anglicans had a long and relatively permissive tradition of rationalist thought. Indeed Wilkins's outlook has a great deal in common with that of Acontius, who, after insisting that no man was immune from error, and that the chief ally of Satan was spiritual or intellectual pride, concluded with the necessity of free inquiry. Acontius, like Wilkins, thought it best to "insist and urge only such points as tend to the confirmation of faith, to the extirpation of vice, to instil the fear of God, cherish pity, . . . to keep such as would be counted Christian brethern in brother love with a sweet harmony of affections."

Wilkins's relationship with the humanist Acontius raises a final question about Wilkins's significance in the development of English thought: to what extend did his fusion of rational religion and scientific thought fit into the tradition of Christian humanism? While the Cambridge Platonists and Anglican rationalists such as Falkland, Hales, and Chillingworth are generally admitted to belong to this tradition, Wilkins and the virtuosi are not, although the two groups obviously had much in common. If the basic aims of the humanist were to find a satisfactory union of Christianity and the classics and to exalt the moral and rational capabilities of man without denying his dependence on God, there is no question that the label is correctly applied to Wilkins. He and most of his associates shared the humanist conviction of harmony between "humane learning and Philosophy" and Religion, and were no less certain than the men of the Renaissance that secular knowledge would lead to both truth and piety. The fundamental compatibility of the ancient moralists and Christianity could not have been more strongly emphasized by Wilkins and his group. In fact, one of the most frequent complaints made against the latitudinarians was directed at their rationalism and dependence on non-Christian moralists. Wilkins repeatedly acknowledges his debt to the Stoics, especially the "divine Seneca," and despite his rejection of certain Aristotelian doctrines, Wilkins could still call Aristotle "the Philosopher." His friends Ralph Bathurst and Isaac Barrow were as famous for their classical scholarship as for their scientific endeavors.

Wilkins did, however differ in one respect from earlier humanists. Although he and his associates did not pit ancient learning against modern, but paid "a great Deference to Antiquity, yet they are not so fond of Error as to fall in love with it merely for his grey Hairs, but make use of his own Reason to judge the Reasonings of other Men." Basically, Wilkins's respect for the ancients was tempered by the doctrine of progress, but this doctrine was accepted by many seventeenth-century thinkers, humanist and nonhumanist alike.

It would not be inappropriate to compare Wilkins's outlook on many religious questions with that of Erasmus. Not only did he share the noted humanist's emphasis on the unity of piety and learning and on practical morality, but both men were intensely hostile to the bickerings over ceremonies and dogma that resulted in the neglect of true piety. Luther's criticism of Erasmus could surely have been made by Wilkins's critics as well: "He is thinking of peace, not of the cross." Erasmus wrote, "I merely want to analyze and not to judge, to inquire and not to dogmatize. I am ready to learn from anyone who advances something more accurate or more reliable." And Luther replied, "Not to delight in assertions is not the mark of a Christian heart. Indeed one must delight in assertions to be a Christian at all." The same exchange might well have occurred between Wilkins and his opponents.

In the crucial areas of religion, morals, and the reconciliation of Christian and classical learning, Wilkins was basically at one with earlier humanists. Furthermore, both humanists and scientists were vociferous in their rejection of scholasticism. Why, then, have such eminent scholars as Herschel Baker, Douglas Bush, and Basil Willey been drawn toward the conclusion that the scientific group in which Wilkins was so important was inimicable to the humanist tradition? I would suggest that as literary historians, they have been led astray by their preoccupation with style. Similarly the substitution of prose for verse is likely to strike the literary historian as a particularly sharp break with tradition. It must be admitted, of course, that Wilkins and his associates did abandon eloquence, one of the trademarks of the Renaissance scholar, and cultivated a simple prose style as their major mode of expression. Nevertheless, the basic issue is not stylistic, but the compatibility of science and humanism as substantive bodies of thought. Herschel Baker argues that the seventeenth-century change from a sacramental to a secular view of nature signaled the end of Christian humanism, that when nature was stripped of its theological implications and the universe seen as a fundamentally mathematical rather than moral structure, humanism could no longer survive. Even if we grant the general logic of Baker's arguments, Wilkins and the virtuosi can hardly be identified as opponents of humanism. For Wilkins and his fellow members of the Royal Society, nature was simultaneously moral and mathematical. Through their concept of providence they managed to provide for both an ordered cosmos regulated by second causes and an ever-watchful deity. If in the end the two concepts proved incompatible, they did not appear so to Wilkins's generation. Furthermore, the mechanism of the virtuosi was tempered by a strong dose of teleology, which at every point led back to a purposeful God. The continuous awe before the works of the Great Mechanic was by no means simply perfunctory. Mechanism to Wilkins did not mean secularism, but implied precisely the opposite, leading men to an appreciation of God through an appreciation of his magnificent creation. And if mechanism to some extent replaced morality in the physical world, moral philosophy was not yet mechanized and made into a science. The morality of Wilkins had advanced little beyond that of the humanists, though certain hedonistic and egoistic notes suggest what was to come. If Wilkins became involved in detailed psychological and epistemological investigations, these experiments implied no fundamental change in his basic view of man. And he, like the earlier humanists, was convinced that the world was made for man.

The change in cosmology and the addition of a scientific sphere of interest should not be allowed to obscure the fact that Wilkins shared the ideals and general outlook of the humanists, and that he and his followers kept alive that tradition for at least another generation, if not considerably longer. Wilkins himself surely felt that the development of science could only help to ensure the continuation of that tradition. If his attempts to combine the new concepts of scientific investigation with traditional morality and religion did not prove to be extremely long-lived, they at least enabled the seventeenth-century scientist to come to terms with the humanism of the day and the traditionally educated Englishman to accept the scientific revolution.

Wilkins's last writings thus display most of the characteristic intellectual themes to which he devoted his life. Here again is an attempt to synthesize ideas current in advanced scientific and philosophic circles and systematically present them in a form and language calculated to make them available to the broad strata of the literate. Once again we recognize the undeviatingly moderate, rational, and pragmatic substance and tone of Wilkins's writing, consistently aimed at reducing the heat of debate to the level of tentative and cooperative progress toward greater, but never perfect, truth. The repeated alternation of religious and scientific themes in Wilkins's work reflects his conviction that if the cooperative and tentative attitudes of the scientists could be carried over to the sphere of religious discourse, the temperature of religious debate might be considerably reduced. As his last work so clearly demonstrates, Wilkins refused to separate science and religion. Both sought the truths of creation and thus both were avenues to better understanding of God and man. To be sure, religious dogmas were not to stand in the way of scientific inquiry, but more important was Wilkins's insistence on the mutually reinforcing elements of latitude, moderation, and modest, tentative rationality in both the religious and scientific spheres. Not only was science a haven from religious dogmatism and conflict, but the methods of science, if instilled in the public mind, could improve the tenor of religious life. In the end, he hoped, science and a moderate, latitudinarian, natural religion might serve as the twins pillars supporting an intellectual life in which the calm, friendly, and pragmatic pursuit of truth and goodness replaced dogmatic, abstract debate and ideologically motivated civil strife.

Notes

All notes are keyed to the text by page and line number. Asterisks indicate the more important notes.

P. 1, l. 15

On treatment see Robert Hooke, *Diary*, eds. H. W. Robinson and W. Adams (London, 1935), pp. 12–14. On visits see William Lloyd, *A Sermon Preached at the Funeral of John Wilkins* (London, 1675), pp. 51–52; John Aubrey, *Brief Lives*, ed. O. L. Dick (Ann Arbor, 1957), p. 325; Oliver Heywood, *Life of John Angier* (Manchester, 1937), p. 102. On "Great Experiment" see Bodleian Library, Lister MSS, 34, f. 76v.

P. 1, l. 21

H.M.C. Reports, Thirteenth Report, Pt. VI, pp. 273, 274; Lister MSS 34, fols. 69v–70v, 76v; Lister MSS 25231, fols. 193, 195; C. E. Raven, *John Ray, Naturalist* (Cambridge, 1942), p. 116. The day after his death the Royal Society began investigating its cause.

P. 2, l. 7

"The Ross-Wilkins Controversy," *Annals of Science*, III (1938), 155.

*P. 5, l. 4

Wilkins's reputation was the subject for debate during his lifetime and after his death. The issues were always the same, his easy acceptance of the Interregnum and Restoration political and religious establishments and the question of his latitudinarianism. See Lloyd, *Funeral Sermon*, pp. 53–54.

Many of the defenses of Wilkins were produced as a direct result of the publication of Anthony Wood's *Historia et antiquitates universitates Oxoniensis* (Oxford, 1674). John Fell, however, was responsible for many of the most offensive comments. See Anthony Wood, *History and Antiquities of the University of Oxford*, ed. J. Gutch (Oxford, 1792–1796), Preface. John Aubrey, who cooperated with Wood in gathering biographical materials for this volume and the later *Athenae Oxoniensis* (ed. Phillip Bliss [London, 1813–1820]), thought Wilkins "was abused." He denied the charge that Wilkins had ever been a Presbyterian but said it "came from J. F.'s [John Fell's] quiver." Bodleian Library, Wood MSS, F. 39, n.p. Aubrey to Wood, May 22, 1680. Peter Pett also indicated Fell was responsible for the "low poor diminishing Character of the Talents of Bishop Wilkins" and attempted to redress Wood's view. Thomas Barlow, *Genuine Remains* (London, 1693), Preface by Peter Pett.

A modern reader of *Historia* or even the later English revision by Wood (Gutch) does not find it particularly offensive. Nevertheless, it aroused the great ire of Wilkin's associates who saw it as a vicious party attack. Bodleian Library, Aubrey MSS, 12, f. 107; Wood MSS, F. 39, f. 337; Wood MSS, F. 39, f. 327. Walter Pope, *Life of Seth Ward, Bishop of Salisbury,* ed. J. B. Bamborough (Oxford, 1961), p. 186; A. Clark, ed., *The Life and Times of Anthony Wood Antiquary, 1632–1695,* (Oxford, 1891–1900), II, 52; IV, 224, 296–297. Wood MSS, F. 39, f. 327.

Tillotson was also indignant of the

> very slight, and . . . unjust Character given [Wilkins] in a late Booke entitled *Historia & Antiquitates Universitatis Oxoniensis;* whether by the Author of that Book, or by some other Hand, as variously reported. . . . The former part . . . is chiefly made up of invidious reflections upon his carriage, and the circumstances of his conditions in the late Times. . . . The latter part of it consists of flat and ill-flavoured commendations. . . . Upon the Whole, it hath often been no small matter of wonder to me, . . . that so great a Man, and so great a lover of Mankind, who had the inclination, the skill, and the opportunity to oblige so very many, and was so highly valued and reverenced by all that knew him, should yet have the hard fate to fall under the heavy displeasure and censure who knew him not: And that he who never did any thing to make himself one personal enemie, should have the ill fortune to have so many. (John Wilkins, *Sermons Preached upon Several Occasions* [London, 1682]. Preface by John Tillotson.)

Wood himself admitted that many of the "great men of the church of England . . . did malign him." *Athenae,* III, 969. Some of the more complimentary statements must have been added by editors. They are taken from works published after the first edition. Nevertheless, James Harrington in a letter to Wood indicated that the Archbishop "will not let Wilkins' life come out entire," and added, "It was the complaint against the late Bishop of Oxford [Fell] That he put some Characters into your book; tho I find that your Complainants think it no Crime to put others out." Bodleian Library, Wood MSS, F. 42, f. 137.

Gilbert Burnet thought the *Athenae* to be a "despicable Book" which reproached "all the greatest men of our Church." E. D., *Vindication of the Historiographer* (London, 1693), pp. 18, 19, 22, 26.

Thus, if historians must rely on Wood's valuable collections, extreme care must be taken particularly if the individuals or events were likely to fall under the censure of High Churchmen. It was Wood's partisan accounts which have led many later students to label Wilkins a Puritan too easily.

P. 5, l. 31

Robert K. Merton, "Puritanism, Pietism and Science," *Sociological Review,* XXVIII (1938), 1–30; Robert K. Merton, "Science, Technology, and Society," *Osiris,* IV (1938), 360–630; Dorothy Stimson, "Puritanism and the New Philosophy," *Bull. of the Inst. of the Hist. of Medicine,* III (1935), 321–334. See also R. F. Jones, *Ancients and Moderns: A Study in the Background of the Battle of the Books* (St. Louis, 1961); R. F. Jones, "Puritanism, Science and Christ Church," *Isis,* XXXI (1939), 65–67; George Rosen, "Left Wing Puritanism and Science," *Bull. of the Inst. of the Hist. of Medicine,* XV (1944), 375–380; Christopher Hill, "Intellectual Origins of the English Revolution," *Listener* (May-June 1962), 943–946, 983–986; Christopher Hill, "Puritanism, Capitalism and the Scientific Revolution," *Past and Present,* XXIX (1965), 88-97; Christopher Hill, *Intellectual Origins of the English Revolution* (Oxford, 1965). For critiques of the Puritanism-science thesis see Mark Curtis, *Oxford and Cambridge in Transition* (Oxford, 1959); L. S. Feuer, *The Scientific Intellectual* (New York, 1963); M. M. Knappen, *Tudor Puritanism* (Chicago, 1939); P. H. Kocher, *Science and Religion in Elizabethan England* (San Marino, Calif., 1953); T. K. Rabb, "Puritanism and the Rise of Experimental Science in England," *Cahiers d'histoire mondiale,* VII (1962), 46–67; H. F. Kearney, "Puritanism, Capitalism and the Scientific Revolution," *Past and Present,* XXVIII (1964), 81–101; James W. Caroll, "The Merton Thesis on English Science," *Amer. J. of Economics and Sociology,* XIII (1954), 427–432; A. Rupert Hall, "Merton Revisited, or Science and Society," *History of Science,* II (1963), 1–16; H. Kearney, "Puritanism and Science: Problems of Definition," *Past and Present,* XXXI (1965), 104–110; T. K. Rabb, "Religion and the Rise of Modern Science," *Past and Present,* XXXI (1965), 111–126; T. K. Rabb, "Science, Religion and Society in the Sixteenth Century," *Past and Present,* XXXIII (1966), 148; L. Solt, "Puritanism, Capitalism, Democracy and the New Science," *A.H.R.,* LXXIII (1967), 18–29; B. J. Shapiro, "Latitudinarianism and Science in Seventeenth Century England," *Past and Present* XL (1968), 16–41. H. Burstyn and R. Hand, "Puritaniam and Science Reinterpreted," *Actes du XIe congres international d'histoire des sciences* (Warsaw, 1965), pp. 139–143.

P. 5, l. 34

Max Weber, *The Protestant Ethic and the Spirit of Capitalism,* trans. Talcott Parsons (London, 1930); R. H. Tawney, *Religion and the Rise of Capitalism* (London, 1926).

P. 6, l. 20
His conclusion rests on a classification of the whole spectrum of Protestantism, with the exception of Lutheranism, as Puritan. *Osiris,* IV, 416, 473, 487–490.

P. 6, l. 23
Stimson, *Bull. of the Inst. Hist. of Medicine,* III, 327.

P. 7, l. 9
Ibid., p. 325. Merton, *Osiris,* IV (1938), 467–469; Merton, *Sociological Review,* XXVIII (1938), 9.

P. 8, l. 2
Christopher Hill, *Past and Present,* XXIX (1965), 96. Christopher Hill, *Society and Puritanism in Pre-Revolutionary England* (London, 1964), p. 28. See also Hill, *Past and Present,* XXIX, p. 90; only here does he add the additional concept of "radical."

*P. 8, l. 6
Historians of Anglicanism have tended to focus on High Churchmen. There have been few studies of the Low Church tradition.

P. 8, l. 24
Hill, *Society and Puritanism,* p. 29.

P. 9, l. 20
Hill, *Past and Present,* XXIX (1965), 95, 96–97.

*P. 12, l. 8
Wilkins was almost certainly not born at Fawsley, Northamptonshire, although Anthony Wood, John Aubrey and Francis Sanders, author of the *D.N.B.* article on Wilkins, suggest that he was: Wood, *Athenae Oxoniensis,* ed. Phillip Bliss (London, 1813–1820), III, 967; Aubrey, *Brief Lives,* ed. Oliver L. Dick (Ann Arbor, Michigan, 1957). Actually the date and place of Wilkins's birth have troubled his biographers from the very beginning. Aubrey told Wood, who was gathering biographical information on his contemporaries, that Wilkins was born "somewhere in Northamptonshire at which place his mother went to lye in with him. I can know more from his brother W. Pope." In October 1673 Aubrey visited Wilkins's sister hoping to gain information. Bodleian Library, Wood MSS, F. 39, fols. 147, 231. Thomas Sprat told Aubrey he was writing a life of Wilkins but indicated he did not know where Wilkins was born (f. 231). Nevertheless, the editor of the 1898 edition of Aubrey's *Brief Lives* added "[Fawsley, near Daventry]" (ed. Andrew Clark [Oxford, 1898], II, 300). The fact that Wilkins's name does not appear in the Fawsley parish register, coupled with the fact that Dod did not come to Fawsley until 1624, ten years after Wilkins's birth, bothered Sanders, although his uneasiness is not reflected in his

article. *Dictionary of National Biography,* ed. Leslie Stephen (New York, 1885), XXI, 264; Chester Cathedral MSS, F. Sanders, "Materials for the Lives of Bishops of Chester." It seems fairly certain that Wilkins was not born in Fawsley. He may have been born at Canons Ashby, Northamptonshire, where his grandfather lived in 1614. The parish register has not been preserved for the period in question. John's father Walter Wilkins served as constable and later as member of the Common Council. I owe the information on Walter Wilkins's marriage to the Rev. Gordon High.

P. 12, l. 12

Timothy Wilkins seems to have been a man of no fixed profession. During the civil wars he served on first the Parliamentary and then the Royalist side. He became bedell of divinity at Oxford through the influence of his brother. Andrew Clark, ed., *The Life and Times of Anthony Wood, Antiquary of Oxford, 1623–1695* (Oxford, 1891–1900), I, 215, and II, 231; Thomas Hearne, *Remarks and Collections* (Oxford, 1884), V, 338; John Wilkins, *Mercury; or the Secret Messenger* (London, 1641), Preface, in *Mathematical and Philosophical Works* (London, 1708).

P. 12, l. 15

The will was proved December 6, 1623, in the Oxford Consistory Court. John was left £40. The other children each received £20. Bodleian Library, MSS Oxfordshire Wills, Series II, V, 78.

P. 12, l. 25

Aubrey, *Brief Lives* (Ann Arbor, Michigan, 1957), p. 319.

*P. 13, l. 11

For Sylvester see Wood, *Athenae,* II, 895. Wood, Aubrey, and the anonymous author of the life of Wilkins prefixed to his *Mathematical and Philosophical Works* do not mention Dod's role in Wilkins's early education. Although it is not impossible that Wilkins remained in Northamptonshire with Dod after his birth, it is more likely that he returned to Oxford with his parents in 1615. William Lloyd, however, indicated Wilkins had been trained by Dod. *A Sermon Preached at the Funeral of John Wilkins* (London, 1675), pp. 46–47. Wilkins's half brother, Walter Pope, however, was educated by Dod. A. B. Dugan, "Walter Pope, 1628–1713: A Study of His Life and Work," unpubl. B. Litt. thesis, Oxford, 1935.

P. 13, l. 28

Aubrey, *Brief Lives,* p. 294. Aside from his views on baptism, Tombes seems to have held typically Puritan views.

P. 14, l. 5

Anthony Wood, *History and Antiquities of the University of Oxford,* ed. J. Gutch (Oxford, 1792–1796), I, 365.

P. 14, l. 13
Ibid., II, 376. See also G. Hamilton, *Hertford College* (London, 1903), p. 111.

P. 14, l. 24
Robert B. Gardiner, *Register of Wadham College* (London, 1889), I, 170. Wood indicated that June 11 was the proper date. *Athenae,* II, 474.

P. 14, l. 34
Mathematical Magick, Preface. His *Discovery of a New World; or A Discourse tending to Prove, That ('tis Probable) there may be another Habitable World in the Moon* was published shortly after he left the university (London, 1638).

*P. 15, l. 17
For university science see *Oxford and Cambridge in Transition, 1558–1642* (Oxford, 1959), p. 231. See also pp. 227–260; Christopher Hill, *Intellectual Origins of the English Revolution* (Oxford, 1965), pp. 301–314. For Magdalen Hall see F. P. Verney and M. H. Verney, *The Verney Family Memoirs* (London, 1925), I, 75.

*P. 16, l. 2
See Hill *Intellectual Origins of the English Revolution,* pp. 14–74. H. F. Kearney, "Puritanism, Capitalism, and the Scientific Revolution," *Past and Present,* XXVIII (1964), 81–101. The movement from Gresham professorships to the Savilian chairs began as soon as the latter were established and continued throughout the civil war and Restoration periods.

P. 16, l. 11
John Ward, *The Lives of the Professors of Gresham College* (London, 1740), p. 81. John Greaves, *Miscellaneous Works,* ed. Thomas Birch (London, 1737), I, ii.

P. 16, l. 23
F. R. Johnson, *Astronomical Thought in Renaissance England* (Baltimore, 1937), pp. 213, 249.

*P. 16, l. 33
Henry Isham Longdon, *Northamptonshire and Rutland Clergy from 1500* (Northampton, 1938–1952), IV, 107. See also *D.N.B.,* XV, 145; George Baker, *The History and Antiquities of the County of Northamptonshire,* (London, 1822–41), I, 388; G. C. More Smith, ed., *Extracts from the Papers of Thomas Woodcock* (Camden Miscellany, 3d Series, Vol. XI: London, 1907), p. 55. It was reported that Laud did not think Dod "worthy of a liveing; but his son [sic] Wilkins was allowed the vaccarige of fawsley and Mr. Dod to be his curate," p. 55.

It is possible that Wilkins did not immediately succeed Dod, who had considerable difficulties with the ecclesiastical authorities. Fawsley was a "decayed" village. Dod and Wilkins had few parishioners outside the Knightley family. Their position may not have been very different from that of a chaplain. Wilkins was instituted June 2, 1637, and ordained priest at Christ Church Cathedral, Oxford, on February 18, 1638. MSS Oxford Diocese Papers, e. 13, fols. 376, 399.

*P. 17, l. 13

Baker, *Northamptonshire*, I, 388. For the Knightleys and Puritanism in Northamptonshire see G. B. Tatham, *The Puritans in Power* (Cambridge, 1913), p. 18; Christopher Hill, *Economic Problems of the Church* (Oxford, 1956), pp. 18, 56, 142. The Knightleys protected John Dod, John Preston, and other Puritan preachers. William Haller, *The Rise of Puritanism* (New York, 1957), p. 218. Secret political meetings of the parliamentary opposition were frequently held at Fawsley. Noble, *Cromwell*, II, 95.

P. 17, l. 30

Lloyd, *Funeral Sermon*, pp. 47–48. Thomas Fuller, *The Church History of Britain* (London, 1842), III, 478. On Royalism see David Lloyd, *Memoirs . . . of those that suffered . . . in our late Intestine Wars* (n.p., 1668), p. 129.

P. 18, l. 12

Haller, *Rise of Puritanism*, pp. 56–57, 61, 120–121. Samuel Clarke, *A General Martyrology* (London, 1677), p. 172. John Wilkins, *Ecclesiastes: or, A Discourse of the Gift of Preaching* (London, 1646).

*P. 19, l. 24

John Aubrey's traditional story about Wilkins's first meeting with Lord Saye supposedly backed by the authority of Wilkins himself (*Brief Lives*, p. 319) leaves several puzzles. The account suggests that Wilkins was introduced to the Lord in question while still considering an academic career, that is, prior to his Fawsley appointment in 1637. Wilkins may, however, have been considering an academic career as late as 1639 when he was encorporated M.A. at Cambridge. Joseph Foster, *Alumni Oxonienses, 1500–1714* (4 vols., Oxford, 1891–1892), IV, 1633. Aubrey himself was uncertain whether Wilkins's reference was to Lord Saye. It seems more likely that it refers to Knightley, although he was not a Lord or "great person." Nor did Wilkins obtain a really "good benefice" from Lord Saye as the account indicates. If the story refers to an event of 1639 rather than 1637, it is even possible that the "Lord" was Berkeley, although he received only a chaplainship from him. Dod may have had some part in introducing Wilkins to Saye, for he had at one time been a prominent preacher in Banbury, Oxfordshire, an area where Saye's influence was very great.

P. 20, l. 2

D.N.B., XVIII, 434. Wood, *Athenae,* III, 546. Secret political meetings were held at Broughton. Saye's career has recently been investigated by Robert Papstein of Marymount College, Los Angeles, California.

P. 20, l. 19

Wilkins's *Mercury* (London, 1641) notes, "I do here once more present your Lordship with the fruit of my leisure Studies . . . ." It is thus likely that *A Discourse Concerning a New Planet* (London, 1640) which bore no dedication was written when Wilkins was a member of Berkeley's rather than Saye's household.

P. 20, l. 35

Lloyd, *Memoirs, Actions, Sufferings,* pp. 126-127. *D.N.B.,* IV, 347; Vicary Gibbs, ed., *The Complete Peerage* (London, 1912), II, 139-140.

P. 21, l. 23

Reginald J. Fletcher, *Pension Book of Gray's Inn, 1569-1800* (London, 1807), pp. 355n, 357. For Savoy see Samuel Palmer, *Calamy's Nonconformist Memorials* (London, 1775), p. 302; *D.N.B.,* XXI, 1260. See also Robert Somervill, *The Savoy* (London, 1960), pp. 58-59, 60, 209, 247. Thomas Fuller, a friend of Dod, Berkeley, and Wilkins, also preached regularly at the Savoy.

P. 21, l. 34

On the appointment see *D.N.B.,* XXI, p. 264. Wilkins, *Mathematical Magick,* Dedicatory Letter. On the Elector see Sir John Clapham, "Charles Lewis, Elector Palatine 1617-1680, An Early Experiment in Liberalism," *Economica,* New Series, VII (1940), p. 385; Lewis Feuer, *The Scientific Intellectual: The Psychological and Sociological Origins of Modern Science* (New York, 1963), p. 173.

P. 22, l. 21

Sir George Bromley, *A Collection of Original Royal Letters* (London, 1787), p. 119. C. V. Wedgwood, *The King's Peace, 1631-1641* (London, 1955), p. 346; C. V. Wedgwood, *The King's War, 1641-1647* (London, 1958), pp. 68-69, 86-87, 88-89. Eva Scott, *Rupert, Prince Palatine* (New York, 1899), p. 208. Clapham, *Economica,* VII (1940), 387. If there was a plan to divert the succession the Elector was a likely candidate. Once Charles was deposed and his issue rejected, the Elector, after his mother the Queen of Bohemia (daughter of James I), would have been the next legitimate heir.

P. 22, l. 31

Christopher Wren, *Parentalia, or the Memoirs of the Family of Wren* (London, 1750), pp. 183, 140.

P. 23, l. 20
Wood, *Athenae*, III, 971. See also Aubrey, *Brief Lives*, p. 319.

P. 24, l. 10
It has been suggested by J. C. Crowther that Wilkins was engaged by Lords Saye and Berkeley and the Elector as tutors for their children. *Founders of British Science* (London, 1960), p. 31. Saye's children, however, were older or the same age as Wilkins himself. The birthdate of Berkeley's eldest son is unknown but he was ordained in 1649. His second son Charles was born in 1649. *D.N.B.*, IV, 347; Gibbs, *Peerage*, II, 140. The Elector married after leaving England for the last time.

P. 24, l. 24
Biographia Britannica (London, 1747–1763), IV, 4266. Harcourt Brown, *Scientific Organization in Seventeenth Century France* (Baltimore, 1934), pp. 270–271. Prince Rupert had similar interests and became a member of the Royal Society. Their sister was interested in Cartesian philosophy. Clapham, *Economica*, VII (1940), 395.

P. 24, l. 32
Wilkins, *Mathematical Magick*, p. 115.

P. 25, l. 34
John Wallis, "Account of some Passages of his own Life," written in 1696 and printed in Thomas Hearne, *Works* (Oxford, 1725), I, clxii–clxiii. Miss Margery Purver has suggested that Wallis's description, written long after the 1640's, was inaccurate and based on a list of modern scientific discoveries drawn up by Joseph Glanvill in *Plus Ultra* (London, 1668). She concluded that the club engaged in little original research and that its purpose was "the collection, discussion and dissemination of information on discoveries made by others." *The Royal Society: Concept and Creation* (Cambridge, Mass., 1967), pp. 170, 171. If Wallis's account is worthless as evidence, however, we are left with no real idea of what the group did. It does not seem permissible to argue that Wallis's account is not to be trusted and then on the basis of that account to suggest that the group devoted its time to discussion and dissemination of scientific ideas rather than experiment.

P. 25, l. 35
Hearne, *Works*, I, cixii. See John Wallis, *A Defence of the Royal Society* (London, 1678), p. 7.

P. 26, l. 14
The term "1645 group" refers to the group described by Wallis. See Charles Gillespie, "Physick and Philosophy: A Study of the Influence of the College of Physicians of London upon the Foundation of the Royal Society," *Journal of Modern History*, XIX (1947), 210–226;

F. R. Johnson, "Gresham College: Precursor of the Royal Society," *Journal of the History of Ideas,* I (1940), 414–438; Margery Purver and E. J. Bowen, *The Beginning of the Royal Society* (Oxford, 1960); Dorothy Stimson, "Comenius and the Invisible College," *Isis,* XXIII (1935), 373–388; R. H. Syfret, "The Origins of the Royal Society," *Notes and Records of the Royal Society,* V (1948), 75–137; G. S. Turnbull, "Samuel Hartlib's Influence on the Early History of the Royal Society," *Notes and Records of the Royal Society,* I (1953), 101–130; R. F. Young, "The Visit of Comenius to London in 1641– 1642 and Its Bearings on the Origins of the Royal Society," *Notes and Records of the Royal Society,* III (1941), 159–160. The most recent discussion of the Society's origins is to be found in Purver, *Royal Society,* which discounts the importance of the 1645 group.

P. 27, l. 2
See R. F. Young, *Comenius in England* (London, 1932); Benjamin De Mott, "Comenius and the Real Character in England," *P.M.L.A.,* LXX (1955), 1068–1081; Joseph M. Batten, *John Dury, Advocate of Christian Reunion* (Chicago, 1944); J. A. Comenius, *Natural Philosophie Reformed by Divine Light* (n.p., 1651). Stimson, *Isis,* XXIII, 373–388; Turnbull, *R. S. Notes and Records,* I, 101–130; G. H. Turnbull, *Hartlib, Dury and Comenius: Gleanings from Hartlib's Papers* (London, 1947); Young, *R. S. Notes and Records,* III, 159–160. Barnett, *Haak, passim;* Syfret, *R. S. Notes and Records,* V. 75–137; A. C. S., "Notes on the Foundation and History of the Royal Society," *R. S. Notes and Records,* I (1938), 32–36; Marie Boas, *Robert Boyle and Seventeenth Century Chemistry* (Cambridge, 1958), pp. 5–7, 14–15, 23–24, 31; Hill, *Intellectual Origins of the English Revolution,* pp. 44–55, 100–109, 128–129, 295. Purver, *Royal Society,* pp. 193–234. The Comenians however were more appreciators than activists in the scientific field. See Turnbull, *R. S. Notes and Records,* I, 103, 130, 135.

*P. 27, l. 22
Boyle was not mentioned by Wallis as a member of the 1645 group. Boyle and Oldenburg did not move out of Hartlib's circle into Wilkins's Oxford group until the mid 1650's. As early as 1642, however, John Wallis was enthusiastic about Comenian ideas. See *Truth Tried* (London, 1643), p. 2. On exchange of views see Royal Society, MSS Boyle Letters, VII, 2. Wilkins's *An Essay Towards a Real Character and a Philosophical Language* (London, 1668) was sent to Comenius by the Royal Society. Royal Society, MSS Early Letters, O. I. 68. Benjamin De Mott, in attempting to show similarities between the Comenians and scholars interested in a real character, inadvertently showed that the religious views of the Comenians and

Wilkins did not coincide. Comenians were somewhat mystically inclined and attracted to Renaissance Neoplatonism and Rosicrucian-
ism. *P.M.L.A.* LXX, 1070–1075. Wilkins was very unsympathetic
to these movements. Comenius was deeply indebted to the mystic,
Jacob Boehme, whom Wilkins found very unappealing.

*P. 28, l. 1

Haak is mentioned by Wallis as the originator of the 1645 meetings
in one (the 1696), but not the other, account of the Society's origin.
Miss Syfret has suggested that Haak provides the link between the
Comenian group of the late 1630's and the 1645 group. *R. S. Notes
and Records*, V, 89. Turnbull, however, rejects the linkage. *R. S.
Notes and Records*, I, 105. Haak's most recent biographer has de-
emphasized his role in the foundation of the Royal Society. Barnett,
Haak, pp. 77, 120–124. See also Stimson, *Isis*, III, 379; Wallis, *A
Defense of the Royal Society*, p. 8.

*P. 28, l. 8

Thomas Sprat, *The History of the Royal Society*, ed. Jackson I. Cope
and Harold W. Jones (St. Louis, 1958), pp. 53–57. Both Sprat and
William Holder suggested that the society originated at Oxford
under Wilkins's leadership. Syfret, *R. S. Notes and Records*, V. 78.
See also Purver, *Royal Society, passim.*

P. 28, l. 28

Purver, *Royal Society*, pp. 165, 170, 178.

P. 31, l. 1

*The Discovery of a New World, or a Discourse Tending to Prove that
'tis Probable There May Be Another Habitable World in the Moon*
(cited hereafter as *Discovery*). *A Discourse Concerning a New
Planet: Tending to Prove that 'tis Probable Our Earth is One of the
Planets* (cited hereafter as *Discourse*). *Mathematical Magick, or
the Wonders that May Be Performed by Mechanical Geometry;
Mercury, or the Secret Messenger: Showing How a Man with
Privacy and Speed Can Communicate His Thought to His Friend
at any Distance.* All in *Mathematical and Philosophical Works*
(London, 1708).

*P. 31, l. 8

Lawrence Stone, "The Educational Revolution in England, 1560–
1640," *Past and Present*, XXVIII (1964), 41–80; Douglas McKie,
"Men and Books in English Science (1600–1700)," *Science and
Progress*, CLVIII (1958), 608. Almost 12 percent of all works
published between 1475 and 1640 dealt with scientific subjects. R. P.
Stearns, "The Scientific Spirit in England in Early Modern Times,"
Isis, XXXIV (1943), 297.

P. 31, l. 27
Wilkins, *Mathematical Magick,* p. 168; Wilkins, *Discovery,* Preface to the Reader; Wilkins, *Discourse,* pp. 270, 271, 273-274.

*P. 32, l. 21
Wilkins, *Mathematical Magick,* pp. 3, 131. Galileo was also convinced of the importance of publicity. Among the ancients Wilkins felt only Aristotle had recognized that publication was as important as discovery itself. See also Wilkins, *Mercury,* p. 90.

P. 32, l. 30
Ibid., To the Reader.

P. 33, l. 33
See Grant McColley, "The Seventeenth Century Doctrine of a Plurality of Worlds," *Annals of Science,* I (1936), 385-430; Alexander Koyré, *From the Closed World to the Infinite World* (Baltimore, 1957).

P. 34, l. 14
Wilkins, *Discovery,* pp. 2, 9, 20, 23; Wilkins, *Discourse,* p. 200.

P. 34, l. 35
Wilkins, *Discovery,* pp. 32-33, 37-41, 63-65. See Marjorie Nicolson, *Mountain Gloom and Mountain Glory: The Development of the Aesthetics of the Infinite* (Ithaca, New York, 1959).

P. 35, l. 10
Wilkins, *Discovery,* p. 113, 135. Galileo refused to commit himself on the question of lunar inhabitants. Marjorie Nicolson, *Voyages to the Moon* (New York, 1960), p. 27.

P. 35, l. 25
Ray, *Wisdom of God Manifested in the Works of the Creation* (London, 1691), p. 57. Ray recommended that his readers consult both Wilkins and Fontenelle; for Huygens see Nicolson, *Voyages,* pp. 60-62; for Langrenus's map see Wilkins, *Mathematical and Philosophical Works,* p. vii. In 1669 Wilkins was ridiculed in Robert South's Oxford oration against the Royal Society: "and when he should obtain a domine in the world of the Moon, he would make an Archbishop of Cuckoo." To this it was replied "that the seat was not vacant, There was a Bishop upon (it) already, called the Man in the Moon. . . ." Royal Society, MSS Early Letters, W. I, 94. John Wallis to Henry Oldenburg. For a slightly different version see Bodleian Library, Additional MSS, D. 105, f. 37. For literary influences see Nicolson, *Voyages, passim;* Nicolson, "Cosmic Voyages," *E.L.H.,* VII (1940), 83-109; Nicolson, *Science and the Imagination* (London, 1956); Archibald Geike, *English Science and Its Literary Caricaturists in the Seventeenth and Eighteenth Centuries* (n.p., 1914); Norman Davy, ed., *British Scientific Literature in the*

Seventeenth Century (London, 1953), pp. 220, 226. Robert Shackel-
ton, *Fontenelle* (Oxford, 1953), pp. 14–16; *Bulletin du Bibliophile,*
14th Series (Paris, 1859–1860), 1485.

P. 35, l. 35

Wilkins, *Discourse,* pp. 270. Wilkins expected serious scholars to
consult Copernicus, Rheticus, Galileo, and Kepler. F. R. Johnson,
Astronomical Thought in Renaissance England (Baltimore, 1937),
pp. 250–257.

P. 36, l. 12

Wilkins, *Discourse,* pp. 152–153.

P. 36, l. 19

He scarcely bothered to refute Alexander Ross, whom he thought
"did scarce understand anything in Astronomie." *Ibid.,* p. 214.

P. 36, l. 35

On convenience, *ibid.,* pp. 214–215. He argued against the Tychonic
as well as the Ptolemaic system. On harmony, *ibid.,* pp. 218, 219.
See also p. 248.

P. 37, l. 8

Ibid., pp. 221–227.

P. 37, l. 21

Ibid., pp. 253–254. See also p. 215. Of course God could make the
heavens spin as fast as He liked, but it is the duty of Philosophers,
"in the Resolution of Natural Events, not to fly into the Absolute
Power of God, and tell us what he can do, but what according to the
usual way of Providence, is most likely to be done, to find out such
Causes of Things, as may seem most easy and probable to our
Reason." *Ibid.,* p. 248.

P. 37, l. 34

The *Discovery* was printed again in 1684, 1707, and 1802. The *Discourse* appeared in 1640, 1684, 1708, 1802. See H. M. Lord, "A
bibliography of John Wilkins," unpubl. thesis, Library School,
University of London, 1957; Grant McColley, "The Second Edition
of the Discovery of a World in the Moon," *Annals of Science,* I
(1936), 330–331.

P. 38, l. 10

Marjorie Nicolson, "English Almanacs and the 'New Astronomy,'"
Annals of Science, IV (1939), 18. See also Grant McColley, "Milton's
Dialogue on Astronomy: The Principal Immediate Sources," *P.M.-
L.A.,* XII (1937), 128–162; Grant McColley, "The Astronomy of
Paradise Lost," *Studies in Philology,* XXXIV (1937), 209–247.

P. 38, l. 25

Le monde dans le lune (Rouen, 1656). Trans. Jean de la Montagne.
Bulletin du Bibliophile, pp. 1484–1485. Shackleton, *Fontenelle,* pp.
14–16. *Vertheidigter Copernicus oder curiousei und grundlicher*

Bewiss der Copernicanisher Grundsatzel ed. and trans. J. Doppel-mayer (Leipzig, 1713), Preface.

P. 39, l. 13

H. E. Hodgson, *The History of Aeronautics in Great Britain* (London, 1924), p. 10; Alexander F. Magoun and Eric Hodgins, *A History of Aircraft* (New York, 1931), p. 11.

P. 39, l. 35

Wilkins, *Discovery*, pp. 121–122.

*P. 40, l. 17

Ibid., pp. 31, 116–117. For a pseudo-serious discussion about con-struction materials for enchanted castles, see *Discourses,* pp. 250–251. Wilkins's traveler "shall scarce find any Lodgings by the Way. No Inns to entertain Passengers, nor any Castles in the Air (unless they be enchanted ones to receive Poor Pilgrims, or Errant Knights." *Discovery,* p. 117. The Duchess of Newcastle, author of *Description of a New World, Called the Blazing World* (London, 1666), was said to have questioned Wilkins about his space voyagers. "But where, Sir shall they be lodged, since you confess there are no inns on the Way?" Wilkins replied, "Surely, Madam, you who have written so many romances will not refuse my mariners rest and re-freshment—in one of your many castles in the air." Quoted in Nicolson, *Voyages,* p. 122. See also B. Granger, *Biographical Dictionary* (2nd ed., London, 1824), pp. 15–16, citing *Oxford Almanac* (1737–38). Ben Jonson's masque, "News from the New World Dis-covered in the Moon," also included a discussion of lunar inns and taverns.

P. 40, l. 24

Wilkins, *Mercury*, p. 19.

*P. 41, l. 10

Wilkins, *Mathematical Magick,* pp. 113, 114, 117, 118. For a descrip-tion see p. 113. Wilkins recognized the problem of inadequate mus-cular strength and suggest that the legs rather than the arms be utilized. *Ibid.,* p. 121. Leonardo da Vinci recommended artificial wings attached to the arms and legs in his unpublished notebooks.

*P. 41, l. 14

Ibid., pp. 123, 125. See also *Discovery,* p. 133. While he did not deny the difficulty of applying sufficient force to move particularly large and heavy bodies, he considered the basic problem to be one of proportion. *Mathematical Magick,* pp. 114, 123, 125.

P. 41, l. 27

Ibid., p. 115.

P. 42, l. 7

Margaret 'Espinasse, *Robert Hooke* (London, 1956), p. 106; Carson
S. Duncan, *The New Science and English Literature in the Classical
Period* (Menasha, Wisconsin, 1913), p. 102. G. S. Turnbull, "Samuel
Hartlib's Influence on the Early History of the Royal Society,"
Notes and Records of the Royal Society, X (1953), 113n (Petty to
Hartlib, December 16, 1650). Christopher Wren and Hooke were
the major contributors to the Royal Society discussion. Nicolson,
Voyages, pp. 117, 170. Robert Hooke, *Diary 1672–1680,* eds. Henry
W. Robinson and Walter Adams (London, 1939), pp. 202–203.
Hodgson, *Aeronautics,* pp. 79–80; 'Espinasse, *Hooke,* pp. 106, 109,
129.

P. 42, l. 11

Bodleian Library, Aubrey MSS, 13, f. 141. Potter to Aubrey, April
10, 1651.

P. 42, l. 26

Joseph Glanvill, *Scepsis scientifica* (London, 1665); Thomas Powell,
Humane Industry or a History of Most Manual Arts (London,
1661); Nicolson, *Voyages,* pp. 137, 145, 185; A. N. Wilkins,
"Robert Paltock and the Bishop of Chester," *Notes and Queries,*
CCIII (1958), 438–440. Hodgson, *Aeronautics,* p. 66; Robert G.
Laurence, "Dr. Johnson and the Art of Flying," *Notes and Queries,*
New Series, IV (1957), 348–351; G. W. Kolb, "Johnson's 'Dissertation of Flying' and John Wilkins' 'Mathematical Magick,'" *Modern
Philology,* XLVII (1949), 24–31.

*P. 42, l. 35

Quoted in Nicolson, *Voyages,* pp. 120, 122–124. "The Philosophers
of King Charles's reign were busy in finding out the art of Flying.
The famous Bishop Wilkins was so confident of success of it, that
he does not question but in the next age it will be usual to have a
man call for his wings when he is going on a journey, as now to
call for his boots." *Guardian,* July 20, 1713, p. 111. Wilkins's discussion of flight attracted the notice of foreign as well as English
readers. Fontenelle adopted many of Wilkins's arguments as his
own. Hodgson, *Aeronautics,* p. 71. In the eighteenth century an
Italian romance utilized the character of "Giovanni Wilkins *erudito
Vescuvo Inglese"* as his voyager to the moon. Nicolson, *Voyages,*
p. 212.

*P. 43, l. 9

Wilkins, *Mathematical Magick,* pp. 2, 5–6, 7. Mechanical knowledge
was of "honorable Parentage, being produced by *Geometry* on the
one side, and Natural Philosophy on the other," *ibid.,* pp. 5–6. It was

a "Species of Mathematics" because it dealt with the quantifiable aspects of natural phenomena. Scholarly treatments of simple machines were not unusual among the disciples of Archimedes. See Boas, *Scientific Renaissance*, pp. 212, 215; Galilei Galileo, *On Motion and On Mechanics*, eds. I. E. Drabkin and Stillman Drake (Madison, Wisconsin, 1960). A French translation by Marin Mersenne appeared in 1634 under the title *Les méchaniques de Galilee*. An English 1636 translation circulated in manuscript form.

P. 43, l. 22
Wilkins, *Mathematical Magick*, pp. 54, 60.

P. 44, l. 31
Ibid., pp. 87, 92. Wilkins suggested movable sails for a chariot constructed so that "the Wind from any Coast will have a force to turn them [the Wheels] about. . . ." *Ibid.*, p. 95. Difficulties such as the uneven surface of the earth which would jolt the carriage and thus hinder the motion of the sails, might be overcome if the gentry, especially those who lived "near great Plains," should pursue experiments on the carriage. Besides, "what could be more delightful, or better Husbandry, than to make use of the Wind (which costs nothing and eats nothing) instead of horses?" *Ibid.*, p. 96. On artificial images see *Ibid.*, pp. 96, 101. Simple sounds duplicated by tones could easily imitate bird and animal sounds. Human sounds might be reproduced by copying the physical operations of tongue, lips, throat. *Ibid.*, pp. 104-105. See also Powell, *Humane Industry*, p. 32. On submarines see Wilkins, *Mathematical Magick*, p. 105. Wilkins admitted that there were many problems but when overcome men could travel "to any Coast of the World, invisible, without being discovered. . . ." Safety from the uncertainties of tides, storms, and ice, not to mention from pirates, was an obvious virtue. In addition to military use the craft would be "of unspeakable Benefit for Submarine Experiments and Discoveries," and for underwater fishing and sunken treasure retrieval. Only reluctantly, Wilkins admitted that he was uncertain "whether Experiment would fully answer to these Notional Conjectures." *Ibid.*, pp. 105-111. For his indebtedness to Mersenne see *Ars navigandi super et sub acquis* (Paris, 1634); Mersenne *Questions inouyes*, pp. 84-89, 95-96.

P. 45, l. 6
Bodleian Library, Aubrey MSS, 13, f. 142; Robert C. Fox, "Dr. Johnson, Bishop Wilkins and the Submarine," *Notes and Queries*, CCIII (1958), 364, 368.

P. 45, l. 16
Wilkins, *Mathematical Magick*, p. 130. Wilkins discusses methods which utilized chemicals, magnetism, and gravity. He was more

willing than most of his contemporaries to give serious consideration to the possibility of perpetual motion. Stevinus, Galileo, and Mersenne denied the possibility. Dugas, *History of Mechanics,* p. 128; Mersenne, *Questions inouyes,* pp. 76–78; Galileo, *On Motion* and *On Mechanics,* p. 148n.

P. 45, l. 25
See Albert E. Lownes, "Two Editions of John Wilkins' Mathematical Magick, London 1648," *Papers of the Bibliographical Society of America,* XLIII (1949), 195; G. J. Gray, "Bishop Wilkins' Mathematical Magick," *Booklore,* VI (1887), 113–115. It was reprinted in 1680, 1691, and 1708. Lord, "Wilkins Bibliography," p. 29. F. E. Manuel, *A Portrait of Isaac Newton* (Cambridge, Mass., 1968), pp. 39, 48–49. R. T. Gunther, *Early Science in Cambridge* (Cambridge, 1937), p. 76; E. G. R. Taylor, *The Mathematical Practitioners of Tudor and Stuart England* (Cambridge, 1954), p. 218.

P. 45, l. 30
James Harrington, *Politicaster* in *The Works of James Harrington,* ed. John Toland (London, 1771), p. 558; Fox, *Notes and Queries,* CCIII, 364, 368; Kolb, *Modern Philology,* LXVII, 24–31; Lawrence, *Notes and Queries,* New Series, IV, 348–351; Gwin J. Kolb, "A Note on Tristram Shandy, some New Sources," *Notes and Queries,* CXCVI (1951), 226–227.

P. 45, l. 35
Wilkins, *Mathematical Magick,* pp. 131, 133. Wilkins, *Mercury,* p. 67; Wilkins, *Discovery,* pp. 66–67.

P. 46, l. 8
Wilkins, *Mercury,* Preface.

P. 46, l. 17
Ibid., p. 31.

P. 46, l. 33
Ibid., p. 2.

P. 47, l. 4
Ibid., p. 56.

P. 47, l. 12
Ibid.

P. 47, l. 24
Ibid., p. 57. The character writing of the Orient attracted most seventeenth-century writers on a universal character.

P. 48, l. 2
Ibid.

*P. 48, l. 20
Discovery,* p. 99; *Discourse,* p. 143. The testimony of learned men was not useless but could not serve as a final arbiter because all

human testimony was subject to error. *Ibid.,* pp. 145, 150. In seeking philosophical truth it was essential to maintain a "philosophical liberty," to weight all the evidence and to make conclusions when all the evidence was in.

P. 48, l. 23
See R. F. Jones, *Ancients and Moderns: A Study of the Background of the "Battle of the Books,"* (2nd ed.; St. Louis, 1961).

P. 49, l. 18
Wilkins, *Discourse,* pp. 144–146; *Discovery,* p. 16. See also pp. 113–114.

P. 49, l. 25
Wilkins, *Discovery,* Preface.

P. 50, l. 14
Wilkins, *Discourse,* pp. 153, 201–202. Wilkins, *Discovery,* pp. 15. See also p. 26. Cf. Galileo, *Dialogue Concerning the Two Great World Systems,* pp. 50, 51, 110.

P. 50, l. 31
Herschel Baker, *The Dignity of Man: Studies in the Resistance of an Idea* (Cambridge, Mass., 1947), pp. 205, 207.

*P. 51, l. 12
Grant McColley, "The Ross-Wilkins Controversy," *Annals of Science,* III (1938), 165, 166. Calvin, however, also provided one of the principal arguments for his opponents, that of the accommodation of the Holy Ghost to the level of his audience. Wilkins, *Discourse,* pp. 171–172. See Edward Rosen, "Calvin's Attitude Toward Copernicus," *Journal of the History of Ideas,* XXI (1960), 431–441.

P. 52, l. 7
McColley, *Annals of Science,* III, 175–176, 179–180; Herschel Baker, *The Wars of Truth* (Cambridge, Mass., 1952), pp. 319–320.

*P. 52, l. 11
The controversy intensified when Copernicanism came to be considered an explanation of the actual operation of the universe rather than merely a convenient hypothesis. The observations of Galileo also contributed to this trend. Ross initially attacked Philip Landsberg, a Copernican, in his *Commentum de terrae motu* (London, 1634). His *The New Planet, No Planet* (London, 1646), was directed specifically against Wilkins.

*P. 52, l. 29
McColley, *Annals of Science,* III, 172–173, 183. It has been suggested that Wilkins wrote primarily to answer Roman Catholic authorities. Dorothy Stimson, "Dr. Wilkins and the Royal Society," *Journal of Modern History,* III (1931), 542. Grant McColley has

correctly shown that the literalism-science dispute had a long history. To insist that this was a Protestant-Catholic controversy, or even a Puritan-Anglican one, would simply obscure the fact that defenders and attackers could be found in all religious camps. Christopher Hill, however, still insists that astronomical disputes paralleled the political and that Royalists advocated the Ptolemaic and Parliamentarians the Copernican view. *Listener,* June 7, 1962, p. 985. See also Grant McColley, "The Debt of Bishop John Wilkins to the 'Apologia pro Galileo' of Tommaso Campanella," *Annals of Science,* IV (1939), 150–168. Most of Wilkins's arguments center on the intentions of the Holy Ghost and on His accommodation to the capacity of the average man. To His penmen He gave only what knowledge it was necessary for them to have. They obtained their knowledge of nature by study and instruction like all other men. Since scientific knowledge was not very far advanced in Biblical times, there was simply a great deal they did not know. Wilkins, *Discourse,* pp. 148–150. The Holy Ghost omitted philosophical secrets because it was better that "Time and future Discovery might with leisure settle them in the Opinion of others. . . ." *Ibid.,* p. 161. Indeed philosophical instruction emanating from the Holy Ghost would have been positively harmful to the cause of religion, for men would have been so intrigued by natural philosophy that they would have neglected their religion. Nevertheless, Wilkins felt it necessary to explain away Biblical passages that seemed to contradict Copernicanism. See Wilkins, *Discourse,* pp. 160, 168, 172–173, 189–199; Wilkins, *Discovery,* pp. 18–20.

*P. 53, l. 13
Wilkins, *Discourse,* pp. 271–272. Improving astronomical knowledge, he was convinced, "Make[s] us better Men." *Ibid.,* pp. 272–273. His enthusiasm led Wilkins far beyond traditional theological views. Man's eyes, unlike those of other creatures, did not turn downward to the ground: "Would you know why Man was not created so too," Wilkins asked rhetorically, "why it was, that he might be an Astronomer." *Ibid.,* p. 271.

P. 53, l. 23
Ross, *The New Planet, No Planet,* p. 13. See also p. 117.

*P. 54, l. 31
Mathematical Magick, pp. 2, 5–6. See also *Discourse,* p. 271. Mechanics had two aspects. The first which was rational and clearly liberal included the "principles and fundamental notions." The second included such manual tasks as making instruments and performing experiments. Because Wilkins was anxious that mechanics not be neglected as an exclusively illiberal science, he emphasized that it was essentially a species of mathematics. Some types of mathematics were "pure," such as geometry and arithmetic;

others were "mixed." Astronomy was mixed because it included "quantities of heavenly motions," that is, of specific things. *Mathematical Magick,* pp. 5–6. Using Wilkins's earlier classification of divine, natural and artificial, mechanics must be placed in both the natural and artificial classifications. The anlysis of its "principles" belonged to the first category, its "practices" to the second.

P. 55, l. 28
Wilkins, *Discourse,* pp. 145, 153, 146.

P. 56, l. 3
Ibid., p. 140. Cf. "Soft words and hard arguments being the most effectual way to convince . . ." Wilkins, *Ecclesiastes,* p. 16.

P. 56, l. 19
Wilkins, *Discourse,* pp. 145, 146, 158, 160, 221, 222, 271. Wilkins, *Discovery,* pp. 48, 106. He also noted that the senses are "altogether unfit to decide any Philosophical Doubt, which cannot be well explained without Discourse or Reason." Wilkins, *Discourse,* p. 147.

P. 56, l. 27
Dugas, *Mechanics,* p. 80.

P. 57, l. 7
Ralph Blake, C. J. Ducasse, and E. H. Maddan, *Theories of Scientific Method: The Renaissance Through the Nineteenth Century* (Seattle, 1960), pp. 50–103, 119–141.

P. 57, l. 21
Wilkins, *Discourse,* pp. 153, 211. Wilkins, *Mathematical Magick,* p. 115. See also pp. 114, 130.

P. 58, l. 10
On Baconianism see J. C. Crowther, *Founders of British Science* (London, 1961), p. 44; Jones, *Ancients and Moderns,* p. 78. Purver, *Royal Society,* passim. See Wilkins, *Mathematical Magick,* pp. 2, 87.

P. 58, l. 17
Wilkins, *Discovery,* p. 120; Wilkins, *Mercury,* p. 6.

P. 61, l. 7
Ecclesiastes (London, 1646). Unless otherwise noted this edition is cited. *Providence* (London, 1649). I have cited from the 1680 edition. *Gift of Prayer* (London, 1651).

P. 62, l. 11
For Wilkins's Calvinism see George Bridgeman, *History of the Church and Manor of Wigan* (Manchester, 1886–1890), III, 506; Harold Fisch, "The Puritan and the Reform of Prose Style," *English Literary History,* XIX (1952), 247; John Tulloch, *Rational Theology and Christian Philosophy in England in the Seventeenth Century* (London, 1874), II, 442. On Covenant theologians see Wilkins,

Gift of Prayer, pp. 105, 158, 176, 226. Wilkins frequently refers to the works of "practical divines" who adopted the Covenant position in his *Ecclesiastes.*

P. 62, l. 21
Wilkins, *Gift of Prayer,* p. 224.

P. 62, l. 29
Ibid., pp. 137, 178. See also pp. 130, 139.

P. 63, l. 12
Ibid., pp. 10–11, 14.

P. 63, l. 15
Ibid., pp. 94–95, 162–163.

P. 63, l. 34
John Wilkins, *Discourse Concerning a New Planet* (London, 1708), p. 146. John Wilkins, *The Discovery of a New World* (London, 1708), p. 17. Wilkins, *Ecclesiastes,* p. 8.

*P. 64, l. 10
Wilkins, *Discovery,* p. 66. John Wilkins, *Sermons Preached upon Several Occasions* (London, 1682), p. 31; see also p. 9. He did not approve of allegorical or mystical interpretations of Scripture. This was one of the points on which he differed from the Cambridge Platonists. On one occasion, however, Wilkins adopted a literalist position. His influential digression on Noah's ark contained in his *Essay Towards a Real Character, and a Philosophical Language* (London, 1668) explained how two of each species plus their food could have been accommodated in the ark given the dimensions provided in Scripture. Wilkins assisted Mathew Poole in his treatment of the problem of Noah's ark. Poole, *Synopsis criticorum aliorumque S. Scripturae interpretum* (London, 1669), I, vii, 83. See also Clark Emery, "John Wilkins and Noah's Ark," *Modern Language Quarterly,* IX (1948), 286–291.

P. 64, l. 29
Bodleian Library, Wood MSS, F. 31. f. 9; F. 39, f. 340; Anthony Wood, *Athenae Oxoniensis,* ed. Phillip Bliss (London, 1813–1820), III, 967.

P. 64, l. 33
P. A. Wright-Henderson, *Life and Times of John Wilkins* (Edinburgh, 1910), p. 62.

P. 66, l. 27
Thomas Birch, *The Life of the Most Reverend John Tillotson* (London, 1752), p. 408. J. T. Clarke, *Life of James II* (London, 1816), II, 439.

P. 67, l. 18

Walter Pope, *Life of Seth Ward, Bishop of Salisbury,* ed. J. B. Bamborough (Oxford, 1961), pp. 46, 48, 50.

P. 68, l. 24

William Lloyd, *A Sermon Preached at the Funeral of John Wilkins* (London, 1675), p. 48. For Wilkins on episcopacy see Gilbert Burnet, *History of My Own Time,* ed. O. Airy (Oxford, 1847–1900), I, 114–115.

P. 69, l. 31

London, 1649. It was reprinted in 1649, twice in 1659, and again in 1672, 1677, 1680, 1704, 1718, and 1720. There were several American editions.

P. 70, l. 7

Ibid., Preface to the Reader, pp. 143, 153, 154, 156, 158, 171.

P. 70, l. 11

Wilkins, *Providence,* pp. 168, 169; Wilkins, *Mathematical Magick,* p. 1. See Herschel Baker, *The Dignity of Man: Studies in the Resistance of an Idea* (Cambridge, Mass., 1947), pp. 308–309.

P. 70, l. 32

On prudence see Wilkins, *Sermons Preached upon Several Occasions,* p. 151. On Wilkins's prudence see Wood, *Athenae,* III, 968. Lloyd, *Funeral Sermon,* pp. 36, 41, 42.

*P. 71, l. 1

Ecclesiastes was published in 1646. It was reprinted in 1646, 1647, 1651, 1653, 1659, 1669, 1675, 1679, 1693, 1704, and 1718. H. M. Lord, "Bibliography of John Wilkins" (Library School thesis, University of London, 1957), pp. 24, 26. The volume changed considerably in successive editions and became a handy reference book whereby a minister could quickly refer to the appropriate writers on a large variety of subjects. Later editions provided indications of religious profession. All Englishmen, however, were simply designated English. Wilkins was assisted by William Crowe.

The Gift of Prayer was printed in 1651 (twice), 1653, 1655, 1667, 1674, 1678, 1690, 1695, 1704, and twice in 1718. Lord, "Bibliography," p. 51. It was the most popular work on prayer for several decades. A French translation appeared in 1665. It was occasionally associated with nonconformity. Anon., "Cabala, or an Impartial Account of the Nonconformists Private Designs," *Somers Tracts* (London, 1812), VII, 575. White Kennet, *An Historical Register and Chronicle of English Affairs* (London, 1744), p. 544; J. W. A. Smith, *The Birth of Modern Education: The Contribution of the Dissenting Academies, 1660–1800* (London, 1954), p. 212. Nevertheless, H. R. McAdoo's discussion of the *Gift of Prayer* suggests it was thoroughly consistent with traditional Anglican usage. *The Structure of Caroline Moral Theology* (London, 1949), p. 164.

P. 71, l. 18

Wilkins, *Ecclesiastes* (1660), Preface to the Reader, (1646) 42–43, 71, 49. Although "much cryed up and followed" of late, the mystics "do in the opinion of many sober and judicious men, deliver only a kind of Cabelisticall or *Chymicall, Rosecrucian* Theologie, darkening wisdom with words, heaping together a farrago of obscure affected expressions and Wild allegories, containing little of substance in them but what is more plainly and intelligibly delivered by others." *Ibid.,* p. 71.

P. 72, l. 9

Ibid., pp. 1–2. See K. G. Hamilton, *The Two Harmonies; Poetry and Prose in the Seventeenth Century* (Oxford, 1963).

P. 72, l. 27

Wilkins, *Ecclesiastes,* pp. 4–5. A sermon lacking in method was "a heap, full of confusion and deformity." *Ibid.* Wilkins rejected the view of Alsted and Perkins which advised concealment of organization and thought the congregation should be informed of "the general heads of matter."

P. 72, l. 33

Ibid., pp. 12–13. Although Wilkins provides formidable looking diagrams, they are really quite simple. Confirmation, for example, concerns proofs from either reason or Scripture as well as the resolution of any obvious or material doubts. The proper treatment of reason and Scripture are then further, but not elaborately, subdivided. The application is divided into the doctrinal and the practical, and each of these receives some subdivision, practical application for example being divided into exhortation and reproof, which in turn has two parts, the directive and the dissuasive. Explication, Confirmation, and Application are the most essential portions, but the external form such as the preface, transition, and conclusion should not be neglected. *Ibid.,* p. 7. Ambiguities were to be distinguished according to the proper meaning of the text. Scriptural tropes and figures were to be explained according to "their natural meaning." *Ibid.,* p. 12.

P. 73, l. 14

Ibid., pp. 12–13.

P. 73, l. 30

Ibid., p. 72.

P. 74, l. 11

Ibid. Wilkins, *Gift of Prayer,* p. 28. Prose and sermons "should be full, without empty and needlesse Tautologies which are to be avoided in every solid business, much more in sacred. Our expressions should not be so close, that they may be obscure, and so plain that they may not seem vain and tedious. To deliver things in a crude confused manner, without digesting of them by previous meditation, will nauseate the hearers, and is as improper for the edification of the minde, as raw meat is for the nourishment of the body." Wilkins, *Ecclesiastes,* p. 73.

P. 74, l. 20

Wilkins, *Gift of Prayer,* p. 48. Mystical phrases sounded well to "vulgar ears" but were usually meaningless when "reduced into plain English." *Ibid.*

*P. 74, l. 28

R. F. Jones, "Science and English Prose Style in the Third Quarter of the Seventeenth Century," *The Seventeenth Century: Studies in the History of English Thought and Literature from Bacon to Pope* (Stanford, California, 1951), pp. 75–100; "Science and Criticism in the Neoclassical Age," *Ibid.,* pp. 143–160. See also Carson S. Duncan, *The New Science and English Literature in the Classical Period* (Menasha, Wisconsin, 1913); George Williamson, *The Senecan Amble* (London, 1951); Harold Fisch, "The Puritans and the Reform of Prose Style," *English Literary History,* XIX (1952), 229–248; Lawrence Sasek, *The Literary Temper of the English Puritans* (Baton Rouge, Louisiana, 1961); W. Haller, *The Rise of Puritanism* (New York, 1957); W. F. Mitchell, *English Pulpit Oratory from Andrewes to Tillotson* (London, 1932); Perry Miller, *The New England Mind: The Seventeenth Century* (New York, 1939).

P. 75, l. 27

Anglican advocates of a plain style and logical method included John Jewel, George Herbert, Archbishop Ussher, Thomas Fuller, Edward Pococke, John Pearson, John Seldon, William Chappell, and Joseph Hall.

P. 76, l. 7

Jones, "Science and English Prose Style," *The Seventeenth Century,* p. 91.

*P. 76, l. 23

See W. S. Howells, *Logic and Rhetoric in England, 1500–1700* (New York, 1961); Miller, *The New England Mind,* p. 328. When seventeenth-century scientists adopted the scientific method as the proper means of investigating nature, they did not throw traditional logic overboard. They rejected it for scientific investigation, but not in all areas of thought. See Thomas Sprat, *History of the Royal Society,* ed. Jackson I. Cope and H. W. Jones (St. Louis, Missouri, 1958), p. 326. Wilkins, Ward, and Wallis also defended logic.

*P. 77, l. 4

Williamson, *Senecan Amble,* pp. 112–114, 250–255. He suggests that Wilkins echoes the Senecan statement "if it were possible (that a man) might understand that which I think, I had rather express it by signs, than by Words." *Ibid.,* 253. He thus associates the Royal Society's stylistic program with Senecan brevity. *Ibid.,* 287, 294. W. F. Mitchell has noted that Senecanism received its strongest support from Calvinist episcopalians and moderate Puritans. *English Pulpit Oratory,* pp. 108–109.

P. 77, l. 18

Kenneth Hamilton, *The Two Harmonies, passim.*

P. 78, l. 7

Edmund Gosse, *History of Eighteenth Century Literature, 1660–1760* (London, 1889), p. 76. Louis G. Locke, *John Tillotson: A Study in Seventeenth Century Literature* (Copenhagen, 1954), p. 130.

P. 78, l. 21

Lloyd, *Funeral Sermon,* p. 38.

*P. 78, l. 28

Glanvill, *An Essay Concerning Preaching* (London, 1678); Glanvill, *A Seasonable Defense of Preaching and the Plain Way of It* (London, 1673); Parker, *A Free and Impartial Censure of the Platonick Philosophy* (London, 1666), p. 41; Edward Fowler, *Principles and Practices of Certain Moderate Divines* (London, 1670), pp. 41, 104, 105, 112, 116–117. Burnet, *History,* I, 339–340; A. T. Hart, *William Lloyd, 1627–1717* (London, 1952), p. 222. Burnet's *Discourse of Pastoral Care* (1692) also restates Wilkins's views.

*P. 79, l. 8

C.S.P.D., 1661–1662, p. 517. R. F. Jones, "The Attack on Pulpit Eloquence in the Restoration," *The Seventeenth Century,* p. 115. Eachard, *The Grounds and Occasions of the Contempt of the Clergy and Religion Enquired into* (London, 1670), 38–40, 66ff. James Arderne, *Directions Concerning the Matter and Style of Sermons* (1671), ed. with Intro. by John Mackray, Luttrell Reprints, No. 13 (Oxford, 1952), pp. xxi. Arderne was a member of the Royal Society. George Bull's *Charge to the Clergy* (1714) still recommended Wilkins's *Ecclesiastes* to young preachers, though he added that they should use Tillotson as their actual model (p. 45). In the colonies Cotton Mather found it useful. T. J. Holmes, *Cotton Mather, a Bibliography* (Cambridge, Mass., 1946), II, 631. It was discussed seriously as late as 1800 although by then it was thought to be too scholastic and analytical. Edward Williams, *The Christian Preacher,*

Discourse on Preaching by Several Eminent Divines (Halifax, 1800), pp. vii–viii.

P. 79, l. 20

Burnet, *History*, I, 340–341. Gerald Cragg, *Puritanism in the Period of the Great Persecution, 1660–1668* (Cambridge, 1957), pp. 204, 207, 208. Caroline F. Richardson, *English Preachers and Preaching, 1640–1670* (New York, 1928), p. 43.

*P. 81, l. 13

The Elector may have sought the post for Wilkins, or Parliament may have appointed him as a complimentary gesture to Charles Louis. The Parliamentary committee concerned with reforming the universities included Lord Saye, Lord Berkeley, and Richard Knightley. Their recommendation could easily have been all that was needed.

P. 82, l. 26

Anthony Wood, *The History and Antiquities of Oxford*, ed. J. Gutch (Oxford, 1792–1796), II, 503–504, 516–517. The lay-controlled appeals committee included Knightley, Berkeley, and Saye and his sons. C. H. Firth and R. S. Rait, *Acts and Ordinances, of the Interregnum* (London, 1911) I, 937.

*P. 83, l. 5

Montagu Burrows, *The Registers of the Visitors of the University of Oxford, 1647–1658* (Westminister, Camden Society, 1881), p. lxxxv. The reaction of the colleges and halls depended on their religious and political composition. Magdalen Hall, which had remained anti-Laudian throughout the 1630's, offered no opposition and many of its members were rewarded with vacant positions. Three of its alumni, including Wilkins, were raised to the position of heads of other colleges. Sidney G. Hamilton, *Hertford College* (London, 1903), pp. 114–115.

P. 83, l. 24

Robert B. Gardiner, *Register of Wadham College* (London, 1889), I, 170. Anthony Wood, *Athenae Oxoniensis*, ed. Phillip Bliss (London, 1813–20) IV, 113–114. On All Souls see Charles E. Mallet, *The History of the University of Oxford* (London, 1924), II, 377. On Wadham see Wood, *History and Antiquities*, II, 570; John Rushworth, *Historical Collections 1680–1701* (London, 1721), VII, 1065.

P. 83, l. 34

Burrows, *Registers*, p. 22; Wood, *History and Antiquities*, II, 574, 576–578.

P. 84, l. 8

Anon., *The Lord Have Mercy* (Pembroke and Montgomery, ie. Oxford, 1648), p. 7. Anon., *Pegasus* (n.p., 1648), p. 10.

P. 84, l. 14
The Elector left in January or February 1649 after the execution of his uncle Charles I. Wilkins left with the Elector. Although Aubrey thought Wilkins remained there "not above a yeare," he was probably gone no more than a few months. John Aubrey, *Brief Lives*, ed. Andrew Clark (Oxford, 1898), II, 300. On March 5, 1649, Wilkins was granted a dispensation from the requirement that the Warden take the degree of Doctor in Divinity within a year after accepting the post. It indicated that "Mr. Wilkins . . . is at this tyme in attendance on the Prince Elector, and cannot in regard of that service have tyme to doe his exercise and all other things necessary unto that degree. . . ." Burrows, *Registers*, p. 222.

P. 85, l. 19
Wood, *History and Antiquities*, II, 623, 629; Bodleian Library, MSS, Convocation Register, f. 79; Burrows, *Registers*, p. 274n and lxxxviii; Wadham College, MSS Early Letters, f. 8, 83; Wood, *Athenae*, III, 967. Wilkins subscribed again when he became Master of Trinity College, Cambridge.

P. 85, l. 28
Mallet, *Oxford*, II, 386.

P. 86, l. 31
Walter Pope, *Life of Seth Ward, Lord Bishop of Salisbury*, ed. J. B. Bamborough (Oxford, 1961), p. 42. Wood, *History and Antiquities*, II, 635. Burrows, *Registers*, pp. xlv-xlix.

P. 87, l. 30
Bodleian Library, MSS Convocation Register, f. 57, 72, 234; Pope, *Life of Seth Ward*, pp. 19-21. Ward had been recently ejected from Cambridge for refusing the Covenant. Wood, *Athenae*, II, 124.

P. 88, l. 2
Bodleian Library, MSS Convocation Register, fols. 96, 97, 101-102, 104.

P. 88, l. 9
Bodleian Library, MSS Convocation Register, fols. 73, 97, 226. MSS English History, c. 310, f. 81; Anthony Wood, *The Life and Times of Anthony Wood*, ed. Andrew Clark, (Oxford, 1891-1900), IV, 61.

P. 88, l. 26
Bodleian Library, MSS Convocation Register, f. 198; Wood, *Athenae*, IV, 169.

P. 89, l. 2
On letters see *Calendar of State Papers, Domestic Series*, 1650, p. 427; *C.S.P.D.* 1656-57, p. 389; *C.S.P.D.* 1657-58, p. 130. On the press see Falcolner Madan, *Oxford Books: A Bibliography of Printed Works Relating to the University and City of Oxford* (Oxford, 1895-1931), III, 405; Madan, "Oxford Press 1650-75: The Struggle for a Place in the Sun," *Library*, 4th Series, VI (1925),

135–147. On canonists see Burrows, *Registers,* p. 398. On beggars see Wood, *Life and Times,* I, 155, 166. Wood, *History and Antiquities,* II, 646, 668. On the City of Oxford negotiations see Gerald Langbaine, *The Answer of the Chancellor* (Oxford, 1678); Bodleian Library, MSS Convocation Register, fols. 72, 73, 89, 96, 108, 110, 114, 130, 225; Wood, *History and Antiquities,* II, 625, 626, 654; Wood, *Life and Times,* I, 155.

P. 89, l. 16

Wood, *History and Antiquities,* II, 593; Burrows, *Registers,* pp. 140–141. Wilkins was on the continent when this rebellion occurred. At Wadham nine out of thirteen fellows, nine of fourteen scholars, and all but three of the fourteen commoners or battelers had been expelled. Burrows, *Registers,* pp. lxxvii, 212–213; J. Wells, *Wadham College* (London, 1898), p. 60. Wells's estimates differ slightly from Burrows's. See pp. 60–61n.

P. 90, l. 3

Wells, *Wadham,* p. 60; Wadham College, Early Letters, fols. 90, 93, 94, 99, 103, 105, 107, 109, 111; Burrows, *Registers,* pp. lxxviii, 362, 369, 369n, 398; Wood, *History and Antiquities,* II, 561–562; G. Broderick, *Memorials of Merton College* (Oxford, 1885), p. 105.

P. 90, l. 31

Wood, *History and Antiquities,* II, 663–665.

P. 91, l. 6

Ibid., II, 666.

P. 91, l. 30

Ibid., II, 378; Burrows, *Registers,* p. ci. Initially the colleges had thought conditions would be improved if more Visitors were themselves resident academics. Now they held that their presence was an aggravating factor and that they be limited to deciding appeals. The colleges also wished to return to the original disinterested Visitors of great public stature. Many of the current Visitors were heads of houses and therefore both parties and judges in the same cases. Wadham and New College therefore requested that Nathaniel Fiennes be made their Visitor. They also wished to reserve alteration of the college statutes to Parliament. Wood, *History and Antiquities,* II, 679. On party strife see Pope, *Life of Seth Ward,* pp. 48, 49, 50.

P. 92, l. 2

Bodleian Library, Additional MSS, D. 105, fols. 10–11.

P. 92, l. 14

Bodleian Library, Wood MSS, F. 35, f. 232. Wadham College, MSS Early Letters, fols. 94, 95; Burrows, *Registers,* pp. 234–235, 309, 390–392, 395.

P. 92, l. 23
   Wells, *Wadham,* pp. 24-25.

P. 93, l. 18
   S[imon] P[atrick], "A Brief Account of the New Sect of Latitude
   Men: Together with some Reflection upon the New Philosophy,"
   Phoenix (London, 1707-1708) p. 516.

P. 93, l. 32
   For the Puritan association with the vernacular see R. F. Jones,
   *Ancients and Moderns: A Study of the Background of the "Battle
   of the Books,"* 2nd ed. (St. Louis, 1958), p. 105, and his, *The Triumph of the English Language* (Stanford, California, 1935). On
   Latin requirements see Burrows, *Registers,* pp. 249-250, 266, 312,
   320.

P. 94, l. 15
   For the contemplated revisions see Wood, *Life and Times,* I, 155;
   Burrows, *Registers,* pp. xciii, xciv; Wadham College, MSS Early
   Letters, f. 90, 102; Bodleian Library, MSS Convocation Register, f.
   141. On Wadham's statutes see T. G. Jackson, *Wadham College
   Oxford* (Oxford, 1893), pp. 56-57, 64. On Stokes see Wells, *Wadham,* p. 32. Yet in 1651 Wadham received an order requiring students to attend public lectures, sermons, and chapel worship, and
   directed to remedy what the Visitors thought to be evasions of religious services. Wells, *Wadham,* Wadham College, MSS Early Letters, f. 89; Jackson, *Wadham* pp. 65-66. See also Wood, *History and
   Antiquities,* II, 655; Burrows, *Registers,* p. 372; Wadham College,
   MSS Early Letters, fols. 108, 109.

P. 94, l. 24
   Bodleian Library, Rawlinson MSS, E 199, fols. 82, 83v.

P. 95, l. 18
   John Wilkins, *Sermons Preached upon Several Occasions,* ed. John
   Tillotson (London, 1682), pp. 255, 259-260, 261; William Lloyd,
   Funeral Sermon, pp. 44-45; Gilbert Burnet, "A Sermon Preached at
   the Funeral of John Tillotson," in J. P. Wood, *Funeral Sermons by
   Eminent English Divines, 1650-1760* (London, 1831), pp. 325-326;
   Gilbert Burnet, "The Life and Death of Mathew Hale," in Mathew
   Hale, *Works, Moral and Religious* (London, 1805), p. 38.

P. 96, l. 6
   Quoted in Burrows, *Registers,* p. lvii.

P. 96, l. 27
   Wood, *History and Antiquities,* II, 536, 577, 635, 668-669; Owen,
   Works, I, 133, 150n.

P. 97, l. 3
   Pope, *Life of Seth Ward,* pp. 36, 37, 42.

P. 97, l. 13

Quoted in Burrows, *Registers,* p. cv.

P. 98, l. 7

Wood, *History and Antiquities,* II, 657. James Bass Mullinger, *The University of Cambridge* (Cambridge, 1884–1911), III, 471. J. B. Conant, "The Advancement of Learning During the Puritan Commonwealth," *Proceedings of the Massachusetts Historical Society,* LXVI (1936), 26–27. For 1659 see Wood, *Life and Times,* I, 292–293.

P. 98, l. 19

William Dell, *The Works of William Dell* (London, 1817), II, 34, 52, 55–56, 219.

*P. 99, l. 21

For the critics see Dell, *The Stumbling Stone* and *Trial of Spirits* in *Works;* Webster, *The Saint's Guide* (London, 1653); *Academiarum examen* (London, 1654); Webster, *Judgement Set,* (London, 1654); Solt, *Saints in Arms* (Stanford, Calif., 1959), pp. 92, 94. For the defenders of the university and a learned ministry see Joseph Sedgwick, *A Sermon Preached May 1, 1653* (London, 1653); Thomas Hall, *Histrio-Mastix* (London, 1655); T. Hall, *Vindiciae literarum* (London, 1655); T. Hall, *A Whip for Webster* (London, 1654); Edward Leigh, *A Treatise of Religion and Learning* (London, 1656); Edward Waterhouse, *A Humble Apology for Learning and Learned Men* (London, 1653); John Gauden, *Hieraspistes* (London, 1653); Robert Boreman, *The Triumph of Learning over Ignorance* (London, 1652); Edward Reynolds, *A Sermon Touching the Use of Humane Learning* (London, 1658); John Hall, *The Advancement of Learning,* ed. A. K. Croston (Liverpool, 1953). Leigh and Waterhouse became members of the Royal Society. For modern discussion see Conant, *Proceedings of the Mass. Hist. Soc.,* LXVI, 3–31; Richard Schlatter, "The Higher Learning in Puritan England," *Hist. Mag. of the Prot. Episcopal Church,* XXIII (1954), 167–187; R. F. Jones, "The Humanistic Defense of Learning in the Mid Seventeenth Century," *Reason and the Imagination,* ed. J. A. Mazzeo (New York, 1962); V. A. L. Vincent, *State and School Education, 1640–1660* (London, 1950); Foster Watson, "State and Education During the Commonwealth," *Eng. Hist. Rev.,* XV (1900), 58–72. For the American colonies see Charles Chauncy, *God's Mercy* (Cambridge, Mass., 1655); Perry Miller, *The New England Mind: The Seventeenth Century* (New York, 1939), pp. 76–86.

P. 99, l. 28

Jones, *Reason and the Imagination,* p. 79.

P. *101, l. 13*
Owen, *Works*, I, 132.

P. *101, l. 19*
[Joh]N. [Wilkin]S. and [Set]H. [War]D., *Vindiciae academiarum*
(London, 1654). See also John Wilkins, *Ecclesiastes: Or, a Discourse
Concerning the Gift of Preaching* (London, 1646), p. 202.

P. *102, l. 8*
Vindiciae academiarum, p. 3; see also p. 4.

P. *102, l. 14*
Ibid., pp. 3, 5.

P. *103, l. 8*
Wilkins, *Sermons Preached upon Several Occasions*, pp. 174, 176, 184.

P. *103, l. 14*
Ibid., pp. 184, 186.

P. *103, l. 33*
Ibid., pp. 186, 169, 193. Knowledge concerned speculation about
nature. Wisdom concerned practical affairs. Knowledge could not
rectify "crooked natures or save souls." It was thus possible to have
"learned heads and unsanctified hearts." *Ibid.*, pp. 171, 182, 190, 191,
194.

P. *104, l. 15*
Vindiciae academiarum, p. 50.

*P. *105, l. 17*
Ibid., p. 64. They agreed with many of Dell's ideas on reforming
elementary education. They agreed that the magistrates should "take
great care for the education of youth," that more schools should be built
in the greater towns and villages, and that godly instructors should
staff them. They also believed that children should be taught to read
in English and that schools in the larger towns should provide Latin,
Greek, and Hebrew instruction. They felt that more mathematics
should be taught. Nevertheless, Wilkins thought Dell was an "angry
fanatick man" who attacked the university because he lacked academic training. *Ibid.*, p. 7. On Webster see *Ibid.*, pp. 6, 9. Wilkins
noted, "I should have been apt to have conjectured him to be some
obscure person, whose peevish malcontent humour had brought him
into the gang of vulgar Levellers. . . ." *Ibid.*, p. 5.

P. *106, l. 2*
Ibid., pp. 1–2; also pp. 39, 46. See also Walter Charleton, *Immortality
of the Humane Soul* (London, 1657), p. 8.

P. 106, l. 17

Vindiciae academiarum, p. 2. For the public exercises see Thomas Severn, *Sive theses quadrangelsimiles* (Oxford, 1651).

P. 107, l. 9

Webster, *Examen*, pp. 45, 68, 70; see also p. 41. *Vindiciae academiarum*, pp. 2, 28, 29, 31, 36.

P. 107, l. 21

Webster, *Examen*, pp. 24, 25, 28, 74. *Vindiciae academiarum*, p. 5. Boehme was very popular with the sects.

P. 107, l. 28

Webster, *Examen*, pp. 24–25. *Vindiciae academiarum*, p. 5.

P. 108, l. 21

Ibid., pp. 3, 24, 25. For John Wallis's defense of logic, see W. T. Jackson, "Dr. Wallis' Letter Against Maidwell," in *Collectanea* Ist Series (Oxford, 1885), p. 315.

P. 109, l. 12

Christopher Hill, "Intellectual Origins of the English Revolution," *Listener*, LXVII (1962), 985.

P. 109, l. 33

R. E. W. Maddison, "Studies in the Life of Robert Boyle, Pt. VI, The Stallbridge Period 1645–1655," *Notes and Records of the Royal Society*, XVIII (1963), p. 119. He discovered that the criticisms were unjustified. *Royal Society*, MSS Early Letters, B. I., 62.

P. 110, l. 6

Owen, *Works*, I, 132.

*P. 110, l. 28

Vindiciae academiarum, p. 59. See also pp. 6–7. Wilkins's civil tone and his view that Hobbes was a person of "good ability and solid parts," though "otherwise highly magisteriall" and too willing to cast "unworthy reflections" on others (*Ibid.*, pp 6–7), led Hobbes to attack Ward and Wallis with greater violence than Wilkins. See Thomas Hobbes, *The English Works*, ed. Sir William Molesworth (London, 1839), VII, 337. Wilkins urged Wallis and Ward to write against Hobbes again in 1656. See Ward and Wallis, *In Thomae Hobbei philosophiam exercitatio epistolica* (Oxford, 1656), Prefactory letter to Wilkins. See also Samuel Mintz, *The Hunting of the Leviathan* (Cambridge, 1962), p. 47.

P. 111, l. 13

Mark Noble, *Memoirs of the Protectorate House of Cromwell* (London, 1784), I, 161n; *Mercurius politicus*, July 29, 1656.

P. 111, l. 23

C.S.P.D., 1657–58, p. 115; *C.S.P.D.*, 1658–59, p. 352.

P. 111, l. 31
Robert Boyle, *Works,* ed. Thomas Birch (London, 1744), V, 282; *C.S.P.D.,* 1656–57, p. 51.

P. 112, l. 28
John Evelyn, *Diary,* ed. E. S. de Beer (Oxford, 1955), III, 165. Pope, *Life of Seth Ward,* p. 47. John R. McGrath, *Flemings in Oxford, Being Select Documents of Oxford, 1650–1700* (Oxford, 1904–1924), p. 51. *C.S.P.D.,* 1656–57, p. 5. Robert Boyle wrote, Wilkins's marriage was "publicke enough to have been proclaimed in the markett-place." Thomas Warton, *Life and Literary Remains of Ralph Bathurst* (London, 1761), pp. 163–164. Owen was replaced by John Conant.

P. 113, l. 7
Bodleian Library, Tanner MSS, 314, f. 50. Pope, *Life of Seth Ward,* p. 47.

P. 113, l. 16
Quoted in Crowther, *Founders,* p. 46.

P. 113, l. 28
Wood, *Athenae,* III, 967. The dispensation was granted January 20, 1652. The colleges's statutes were also amended. Wadham College, MSS Early Letters, f. 102.

*P. 113, l. 33
Elizabeth French later married John Tillotson. There is no mention of a child in the wills of either Wilkins or his wife. Nevertheless, P. A. Wright Henderson suggested that a son Joshua Wilkins became Dean of Down. *The Life and Times of John Wilkins* (Edinburgh and London, 1910), p. 78. The matter is discussed in *Notes and Queries,* Series 13, Vol. 156, pp. 113, 356, 449. One contributor thought they had a son who died in early manhood.

P. 114, l. 14
Gilbert Burnet, *History of My Own Time,* ed. Osmond Airy (Oxford, 1897–1900), I, 142.

*P. 114, l. 22
Ibid., pp. 114–115, 332. Wilkins also discussed the matter with the Scots Presbyterian Sharp. He told him that he thought only episcopacy could maintain religious order in England.

P. 115, l. 24
Evelyn, *Diary,* III, 165. William Harris, "Memoirs of Thomas Manton," in *The Works of Thomas Manton* (London, 1870), I, xiv. The massacre occurred in April 1656.

P. *116, l. 11*

Evelyn, *Diary,* III, 166–167, 169–170, 172–173; Warton, *Bathurst,* p. 164.

*P. *117, l. 5*

See P. Zagorin, *A History of Political Thought in the English Revolution* (London, 1954), p. 143; H. R. Russell Smith, *Harrington and his Oceana* (Cambridge, 1914); James Harrington, *Works* (London, 1771); Mathew Wren, *Considerations on Mr. Harrington's Commonwealth of Oceana* (London, 1657); M. Wren, *Monarchy Asserted* (London, 1660). Harrington wrote that Wilkins and his Wadham scientists were "good at two Things, at diminishing a Commonwealth and multiplying a Louse." Wren answered that his opponents had "unjustly taken up against Universities and Mathematiques, and some particular persons who have an interest in both," obviously a reference to Wilkins. *Ibid.*

P. *118, l. 6*

T. G. Jackson, *Wadham College Oxford* (Oxford, 1893), p. 115; Pope, *Life of Seth Ward, Bishop of Salisbury,* ed. J. B. Bamborough (Oxford, 1961), p. 30.

P. *118, l. 23*

Pope, *Life of Seth Ward,* pp. 28–29. Anthony Wood, *The Life and Times of Anthony Wood, Antiquary,* ed. Andrew Clark (Oxford, 1891–1900), III, 587–588; Thomas Birch, *History of the Royal Society of London* (London, 1756), II, 460.

*P. *119, l. 27*

Mathew Wren, *Considerations on Mr. Harrington's Commonwealth of Oceana* (London, 1657), Dedicatory Letter. Wilkins "had nothing of Bigotry, Unmannerliness, or Censoriousness, which then were in the Zenith, amongst the Heads, and Fellows. For which Reason many Country Gentlemen of all Persuasions, but especially those then stiled Cavaliers and Malignants, for adhering to the King and the Church, sent their sons to that College, that they might be under his Government." Pope, *Life of Seth Ward,* p. 29.

P. *119, l. 34*

William Lloyd, *A Sermon Preached at the Funeral of John Wilkins* (London, 1675), pp. 48–49.

P. *120, l. 7*

Thomas Barlow, *The Genuine Remains* (London, 1693), Epistle to the Reader; William Orme, "Memoirs of his life and writing," in John Owen, *Works,* ed. Thomas Russell (London, 1826), I, 19.

P. *120, l. 21*

Jackson, *Wadham,* p. 212; Mallet, *Oxford,* II, 256; Wadham College, MSS Bursars Accounts, fols. 27, 36; Wadham College, MSS Convention Book, II, 2. For the waterworks see Robert Plot, *The Natural History of Oxfordshire* (Oxford, 1677), p. 235. For Hooke see R. T. Gunther, *Early Science in Oxford* (Oxford, 1920–1945), VIII, 355–356. On hollow statue see John Evelyn, *Diary,* ed. E. S. de Beer (Oxford, 1955), III, 110.

P. 121, l. 3

G. C. M. Smith, *Extracts from the Papers of Thomas Woodcock* (London, 1907), pp. 81–82.

P. 121, l. 25

For music at Oxford see Charles Burney, *A General History of Music* (London, 1789), III, 423. See also Pamela Willets, "Music from the Circle of Anthony Wood at Oxford," *British Museum Quarterly,* XXXIV (1961), 71–75; Anthony Wood, *The Life and Times of Anthony Wood, Antiquary,* ed. Andrew Clark (Oxford, 1891–1900), I, 205; Gardiner, *Wadham Register,* I, 187, 204; Jackson, *Wadham,* p. 117; W. Huddlesford and T. Warton, eds., *Lives of Those Eminent Antiquaries John Leland, Thomas Hearne, and Anthony Wood* (Oxford, 1772), II, 123–124, 127. On Baltzar see Anthony Wood, *Athenae Oxoniensis,* ed. Phillip Bliss (London, 1813–1820), I, xxxii.

P. 122, l. 7

Notes upon Parnassus (London, 1658). Contributors included Samuel Austin, Sylvanus Taylor, Gilbert Ironsides, Henry Langley, Nicholas Lloyd, and Thomas Sprat. Samuel Lee, *Orbis miraculum or the Temple of Solomon* (London, 1659), Dedicatory Letter.

P. 122, l. 19

S. J. Rigaud, *Correspondence of Scientific Men of the Seventeenth Century* (Oxford, 1841), I, 202. Evelyn, *Diary,* III, 105–106. See also pp. 104–105.

P. 123, l. 3

Burrows, *Registers,* pp. 390–391, 394, 396–397.

P. 123, l. 20

Pope, *Life of Seth Ward,* p. 46.

P. 124, l. 6

H. A. L. Fisher, "The Real Oxford Movement," *Pages from the Past* (Oxford, 1939), pp. 134–135. See Margery Purver, *The Royal Society,* pp. 100–142.

P. 125, l. 5

Robert Boyle, *Works,* ed. Thomas Birch (London, 1744), V, 630; R. E. W. Maddison, "Studies in the Life of Robert Boyle, Part VI," *Notes and Records of the Royal Society,* XVIII (1963), 119. Henry Oldenburg also considered moving to Oxford. *The Correspondence of Henry Oldenburg,* ed. and trans. A. R. Hall (1966), I, 94.

P. 125, l. 13

Wood, *Athenae*, IV, 403. Brooke was the son-in-law of the Royalist mathematician William Oughtred who had instructed several members of Wilkins's scientific group.

*P. 125, l. 35

See Sir Eric Ashby, *Technology and the Academies: An Essay on Universities and the Scientific Revolution* (New York, 1958), p. 6. Robert K. Merton, "Science, Technology and Society in Seventeenth Century England," *Osiris*, IV (1938), 40, 487. Christopher Hill, *Intellectual Origins of the English Revolution* (Oxford, 1965), pp. 301–314. Purver, *Royal Society*, pp. 62–75. Mark Curtis, *Oxford and Cambridge in Transition, 1558–1642* (Oxford, 1959), pp. 227–260; Phyllis Allen, "Scientific Studies in the English Universities of the Seventeenth Century," *Journal of the History of Ideas*, X (1948), 219–253.

P. 126, l. 12

"Intellectual Origins of the English Revolution," *Listener*, LXVII (1962), 943–946. See H. F. Kearney, "Puritanism, Capitalism and the Scientific Revolution," *Past and Present*, XXVIII (1964), 81–101. John Greaves, Peter Turner, and Henry Briggs left Gresham to become Savilian professors.

*P. 126, l. 26

The group included Ralph Bathurst, Charles Scarborough, Thomas Willis, Mr. Highmore, and George Ent, several of whom were associated with the 1645 group, the Oxford scientific group of the 1650's, and later the Royal Society. Louis Chauvois, *William Harvey* (London, 1957), pp. 145–147. Harvey gave up the post when Oxford fell into parliamentary hands. A. H. T. Robb-Smith and H. M. Sinclair, *A Short History of Anatomical Teaching at Oxford* (Oxford, 1950), p. 13.

P. 128, l. 2

S. P., *A Brief Account of the New Sect of Latitude-Men* (1661) in *The Phoenix* (London, 1707–1708), p. 516.

P. 128, l. 25

John Aubrey, *Brief Lives*, ed. O. L. Dick (Ann Arbor, Michigan, 1957), p. 320; Thomas Sprat, *The History of the Royal Society*, ed. Jackson I. Cope and Harold W. Jones (St. Louis, 1958), p. 53. H. W. Robinson, "An Unpublished Letter of Dr. Seth Ward Relating to the Early Meetings of the Oxford Philosophical Society," *Notes and Records of the Royal Society*, VII (1949), 68. See also Purver, *Royal Society, passim*.

*P. 129, l. 3

For meeting places see John Wallis, "Account of some Passages of His Own Life," *The Works of Thomas Hearne* (Oxford, 1725), III, clxiv. Miss Purver, however, suggests that the meetings at Petty's lodgings were short lived. *Royal Society,* p. 198. When Wilkins left for Cambridge, the meetings shifted to Robert Boyle's lodgings. On membership see Sprat, *History of the Royal Society,* p. 55; Gunther, *Early Science in Oxford,* IV, 2–3. Ward indicated that in 1652 the club consisted of about thirty persons, and that, in addition to this "Great Clubb," there was a smaller group of eight persons "who have joyned together for the furnishing an elaboratory and for making cymicall experiments. . . ." Robinson, *R.S. Notes and Records,* VII, 69–70. For 1655 see Robert Hooke, *Postumous Works,* ed. Richard Waller (London, 1705), p. iii. For 1658 see Thomas Birch, *History of the Royal Society of London* (London, 1756) I, 2.

P. 129, l. 22

Gunther, *Early Science in Oxford,* IV, 2–3.

P. 129, l. 28

Wallis, *Defense of the Royal Society,* p. 8.

P. 130, l. 7

On science as outlet see Sprat, *History of the Royal Society,* p. 53. See also pp. 55–56. On Wilkins's moderation see Seth Ward, *In Thomae Hobbei philosophiam exercitatio epistolica* (Oxford, 1656), Dedicatory Letter.

P. 130, l. 20

Charleton, *Immortality of the Humane Soul,* (London, 1657), p. 50; Thomas Warton, *Life and Literary Remains of Ralph Bathurst* (London, 1761), 35n.

P. 131, l. 10

W. T. Jackson, "Dr. Wallis' Letter Against Mr. Maidwell, 1700," *Collectanea* (1st Series, Oxford, 1885), p. 320. Christian Huygens, *Oeuvres complètes* (La Haye, 1888–1939), *passim.* Charleton, *Immortality of the Soul,* p. 33.

P. 131, l. 24

Hill, *Intellectual Origins of the English Revolution,* p. 118. Charleton, *Immortality of the Soul,* p. 43. See also Thomas Severn, *Sive thesis quadrangelsimiles* (Oxford, 1651).

P. 132, l. 7

Turnbull, *R.S. Notes and Records,* X, 116; Charleton, *Immortality of the Soul,* p. 47; Hooke, *Postumous Works,* p. viii. Marie Boas, *Robert Boyle and Seventeenth Century Chemistry* (Cambridge,

1958), p. 36; J. C. Crowther, *Founders of British Science* (London, 1960), p. 144.

P. 132, l. 11

Turnbull, *R.S. Notes and Records*, X, 115; Charleton, *Immortality of the Soul*, pp. 47-48; Mathew Wren, *Monarchy Asserted* (London 1660), Dedicatory Letter.

P. 132, l. 26

Robb-Smith and Singer, *Anatomical Teaching*, pp. 12-13. Richard F. Watkins, *Newes from the Dead* (Oxford, 1651). It contained poems by Christopher Wren, Walter Pope, and Anthony Wood. *A Wonder of Wonders* also celebrated the event.

P. 133, l. 9

For Wren see Sprat, *History of the Royal Society*, p. 317. For experiments see John Summerson, *Sir Christopher Wren* (New York, 1953), pp. 30-33; Henry Stubbe, *The Plus Ultra Reduced to a Non Plus* (London, 1670), p. 117; Turnbull, *R.S. Notes and Records*, X, 139. For 1658 see *Ibid.*, p. 115.

P. 133, l. 18

Robinson, *R.S. Notes and Records*, VII, 69-70; see also *Vindiciae academiarum*, pp. 34-35; Gunther, *Early Science in Oxford*, I, 12.

P. 134, l. 4

For flying experiments see Turnbull, *R.S. Notes and Records*, X, 113n. Petty to Hartlib. For other experiments see Crowther, *Founders*, pp. 144-145. Crowther provides a list of projects that Christopher Wren worked on while at Oxford.

P. 134, l. 26

On Wilkins's collection see Evelyn, *Diary*, III, 110-111. On dials see Gunther, *Early Science in Oxford*, I, 109-110. On waywisers see John Wilkins, *Mathematical Magick* in Wilkins, *Mathematical and Philosophical Works* (London, 1708), p. 97. Wilkins contributed a way-wiser to the Royal Society. Nehemiah Grew, *Musaeum regalis societatis* (London, 1681), pp. 360-361.

P. 135, l. 2

On the plow see Boyle, *Works*, V. 270. See also V, 271. On other implements see Crowther, *Founders*, p. 144.

P. 135, l. 20

Ibid., pp. 144-145. On fortifications see Wood, *Life and Times*, I, 155; Wood, *History and Antiquities*, II, 625, 626; Bodleian Library, MSS Convocation Register, f. 72.

P. 135, l. 26

Christopher Wren, *Parentalia, or Memoirs of the Family of Wren* (London, 1750), p. 338. Wallis lectured publically on the subject in

1652 and 1653. Grew, *Musaeum*, pp. 361–362. Wilkins, Charles II, and the Royal Society were given replicas.

P. *136, l. 16*

Evelyn, *Diary*, III, 110; Samuel Hartlib, *Reformed Commonwealth of Bees* (London, 1655), pp. 45, 50–51. See also Turnbull, *R.S. Notes and Records*, X, 125; John Evelyn, *Diary and Correspondence*, ed. William Bray (London, 1875), III, 76; Plot, *Oxfordshire*, p. 263. On the Royal Society see Sprat, *History of the Royal Society*, p. 192; Grew, *Musaeum*, p. 271.

P. *136, l. 23*

Turnbull, *R.S. Notes and Records*, X, 114. It was expected that the mathematical instrument maker Ralph Greatorix would become the keeper of the college.

P. *137, l. 5*

On the catalog see Robinson, *R.S. Notes and Records*, VII, 69. On Hartlib's comment see Turnbull, *R.S. Notes and Records*, X, 114, quoting from Hartlib's *Ephemerides*. See also Purver, *Royal Society*, pp. 121–126.

P. *137, l. 26*

For Digby's remarks see John Wallis, *Opera mathematica* (Oxford, 1693–1699), II, 764, 809. Theodore Haak handled foreign correspondence for the 1645 group, Henry Oldenburg for the Royal Society. John Wallis may have performed this function at Oxford. See Huygens, *Oeuvres, passim*. Petrus Gassendi, *Opera omni* (Stuttgart-Bad Canstaat, 1964), VI, 534, 540.

P. *137, l. 33*

Wood, *History and Antiquities*, II, 633–634.

*P. *138, l. 18*

Boyle, *Works*, V, 300. Oldenburg, a close associate of Hartlib's, does not seem to have been involved, for he wished to be informed of the progress of the plan. Royal Society, MSS Early Letters, O.B. 3. Oldenburg indicated that £12,000 for the purchase of confiscated Irish land might be given to such a group.

P. *138, l. 28*

On Evelyn see Boyle, *Works*, V, 396. He may have been referring to Wilkins's plan to build a college of experiments and mechanics in Oxford. On Hartlib *Ibid.*, V, 271–278.

P. *139, l. 1*

Ibid., V, 281, 282. Hartlib was not directly involved and had learned of the plans from a German correspondent. The proposed council had pansophic overtones which the Oxford group and the Royal Society did not share.

P. 139, l. 11
Ibid., V, 398 ff.

*P. 140, l. 11
Christopher Hill has suggested that the Restoration resulted in the ejection of science from Oxford, *Listener*, LXVII, 185. On the planned Oxford society see Royal Society, MSS Boyle Letters, V, 98.

P. 140, l. 32
Mark Noble, *Memoirs of the Protectorate House of Cromwell* (London, 1784), II, 314; Edmund Ludlow, *Memoirs, 1626–1672*, ed. C. H. Firth (Oxford, 1894), II, 61. See also Boyle, *Works*, V, 276.

*P. 141, l. 16
On the petition see Wood, *Athenae*, III, 968, 968n. But certain puzzles remain, for Wilkins and Seth Ward were incorporated at Cambridge at the same time and we hear nothing of Ward's preferment at Cambridge. Even the dating is confusing. The date of the petition was 1658 (that is, before mid-March) and it states that Wilkins was "put in by Richard Cromwell." *C.S.P.D.*, 1660–1661, p. 161. It would thus appear that Cromwell, either with or without the fellows of Trinity, initiated the appointment but that its confirmation was approved by Parliament after his retirement. This would explain why Wilkins was required to take the Engagement. On collegiate efforts to obtain Wilkins see Chester Cathedral, F. Sanders MSS, "Materials for the lives of the Bishops of Chester," citing Trinity College Bursars Accounts. On the 1660 petition see Public Record Office, State Papers 29/9 f. 96. The petition indicates that the appointment received the Great Seal and that when Parliament met and "excercise[d] the Supreme power," the college again requested Wilkins be kept in his post. *Ibid.*

P. 141, l. 30
On resignation see Wadham College, MSS Convention Book, I. He resigned September 3, 1659. Wallis noted "And though he did for some part of that year [retain] his title to Wadham Colledge, yet he was but little there in that year, save when he came to resign, and carry away his Goods." *Defense of the Royal Society*, p. 5. On bequests see Boyle, *Works*, V, 406. When he died he left Wadham College £200. On enemies see John Wilkins, *Sermon Preached upon Several Occasions* (London, 1682), Preface by John Tillotson.

P. 142, l. 10
Pope, *Life of Seth Ward*, p. 48. See also G. M. Trevelyan, *Trinity College* (Cambridge, 1943), p. 17; Aubrey, *Brief Lives*, p. 320; Trinity College, MSS Conclusion and Admonitions 1607–1673, f. 259.

P. 143, l. 5
Walter W. R. Ball, *Notes on the History of Trinity College Cambridge* (London 1899), pp. 97–98.

P. 143, l. 16
John Beardmore, "Memorials of John Tillotson" in Thomas Birch, *Life of the Most Reverend Dr. John Tillotson* (London, 1752), Appendix I. Vice Chancellor John Worthington, however, hoped to establish a mathematical professorship. Boyle, *Works*, V, 281.

P. 143, l. 35
The Theological Works of Isaac Barrow, ed. J. Napier (Cambridge, 1859), I, xi; P. H. Osmond, *Isaac Barrow: His Life and Times* (London, 1944), p. 98.

P. 144, l. 4
Gilbert Burnet, *History of My Own Time*, ed. Osmund Airy (Oxford, 1897–1900), I, 332–333.

P. 145, l. 31
Noble, *Cromwell*, I, 83n. Some evidence that Wilkins was a strong supporter of Richard Cromwell comes from Aubrey. The radical Henry Martin had made a motion in the House of Commons that "those that addressed to Richard Cromwell, Protector, to stand by him with their lives and fortunes," be punished and that all the addressers "might be turned out as enemies of the commonwealth of England and betrayers of their trust to bring in government by a single person." *Brief Lives*, ed. Andrew Clark (Oxford, 1898), II, 46. Aubrey noted that "Wilkins . . . was very instrumental in persuading persons of quality and corporations to addresse. . . ." *Ibid.* The small committee included Thurlow, St. John, Broghill, Pierrepoint, and Fauconbridge. François P. Guizot, *History of Richard Cromwell and the Restoration of Charles II* (1856), p. 217.

P. 146, l. 10
Ball, *Notes on Trinity*, p. 98.

P. 146, l. 34
For Pepys see Cooper, *Annals*, III, 476. For the proclamation see Mullinger, *Cambridge*, III, 554, citing *Parliamentary Intelligencer*, May 21, 1660. One verse is signed J. W. T. C. T. C. was the usual abbreviation for Trinity College. There were two men at Trinity other than Wilkins with the same initials; one was John Ray or Wray who signed his full name to another poem.

P. 147, l. 33
Public Record Office, State Papers, 29/9 f. 96. Parliament established the commission to hear and determine claims which might arise in connection with university appointments. Aubrey, *Brief Lives*, p. 320.

P. 148, l. 5
Walter Pope, *Life of Seth Ward, Bishop of Salisbury,* ed. J. B. Bamborough (Oxford, 1961), pp. 55-56.

P. 149, l. 26
John Wilkins, *Of the Principles and Duties of Natural Religion,* ed. John Tillotson (London, 1675), pp. 23-25, 267, 270; John Wilkins, *An Essay Towards a Real Character and a Philosophical Language* (London, 1668), p. 264; John Wilkins, *Sermons Preached upon Several Occasions Before the King* (London, 1680), pp. 4-5, 185. John Wilkins, *Sermons Preached upon Several Occasions,* ed. John Tillotson (London, 1682), pp. 47, 48, 431, 436, 450.

P. 150, l. 11
Wilkins, *Sermons Preached upon Several Occasions,* pp. 151, 199-200, 205, 207, 244, 277; William Lloyd, *A Sermon Preached at the Funeral of John Wilkins* (London, 1675), p. 36; Anthony Wood, *Athenae Oxoniensis,* ed. Phillip Bliss (London, 1813-1820), III, 969.

*P. 150, l. 14
There has been incredible confusion about the date Wilkins became Dean of Ripon. The *D.N.B.* indicated he probably became dean in 1660 but noted that others gave a 1668 date. The date was altered to 1668 in the *D.N.B.* addenda on the basis of Sloan, MSS 1326, F.40B. This, however, is simply a letter addressed to Wilkins as Dean of Ripon in 1663. Wood also confused the dates. *The Life and Times of Anthony Wood, Antiquary,* ed. Andrew Clark (Oxford, 1891-1900), II, 306; Wood, *Athenae,* III, 960. Wilkins was installed August 31, 1660, by Richard Marsh. Joseph T. Fowler, *Memorials of the Church of S.S. Peter and Wilfred, Ripon* (Durham, 1882-1908), II, 264, 266; George Bridgeman *History of the Church and Manor of Wigan* (Manchester, 1886-1890), III, 503.

Wood also suggested that Wilkins ceased to be dean when he became Bishop of Chester and that John Neale succeeded him. *Life and Times,* II, 337. Neale, however, did not become Dean of Ripon until 1673 or 1674. Wilkins was expected to give up the preferment when he became bishop to Thomas Lamplugh who even obtained the royal assent on October 14, 1668. Wilkins remained in possession until his death. *Calendar of State Papers, Domestic, 1668,* pp. 13, 19, 23, 24. *C.S.P.D.,* 1669, p. 190; *D.N.B.,* XXXII, 31-32. He also acquired the masterships of the hospitals of St. John the Baptist and St. Mary Magdalene which were associated with the deanery. Farrer, *Ripon,* pp. 95, 158, 161; *C.S.P.D.,* 1660-61, p. 209.

P. 150, l. 31
Lloyd, *Funeral Sermon,* p. 49.

P. 151, l. 6
Fowler, *Memorials of Ripon,* III, xiv–xviii. Public Record Office, State Papers, 29/9, f. 96. John Tillotson and Edward Stillingfleet were unsuccessful candidates. W. Farrer, *The History of Ripon* (Ripon, 1806), pp. 103–104.

*P. 151, l. 25
He was installed as prebend by the dean, Richard Marsh, in a private ceremony on September 4, 1660. York Cathedral, MSS Chapter Acts 1634–1700, f. 2v. Samuel Pepys, *Diary,* ed. Henry B. Wheatley (New York, 1893), I, 272. Oldenburg had the impression that Wilkins had become Dean of York. Oldenburg, *Correspondence,* I, 406. R. J. Fletcher, *The Pension Book of Gray's Inn 1569–1800* (London, 1801), I, 436. He held the post at Gray's Inn from January 1661 to June 1662. Joseph Foster, *Register of Admissions to Gray's Inn* (London, 1889), p. 298.

P. 152, l. 6
See R. S. Bosher, *The Making of the Restoration Settlement, 1649–1662* (New York, 1951); G. J. Cuming, "The Great Debate," *Church Quarterly Review,* CLXII (1962), 29–39.

P. 152, l. 16
Wilkins, *Sermons Preached upon Several Occasions,* pp. 417, 436; Mark Noble, *Memoirs of the Protectorate House of Cromwell* (London, 1784), III, 315.

*P. 152, l. 32
Anon., *Bishop Wilkins's Character of the Best Christian* (2nd ed., Dublin, 1759), pp. 4, 8. For his attempt to persuade John Howe, Samuel Lee, and Edward Calamy to conform, see Thomas Jackson (ed.), *Life of John Howe* (London, 1839), pp. 77–78; White Kennet, *An Historical Register and Chronicle of English Affairs* (London, 1744), p. 919; David Mountfield, *The Church and the Puritans* (London, 1881), p. 110.

P. 153, l. 22
H. C. Foxcroft, *A Supplement to Burnet's History* (Oxford, 1902), p. 46; Thomas Birch, *The Life of the Most Reverend Dr. John Tillotson* (London, 1752), p. 407; Norman Sykes, *From Sheldon to Secker: Aspects of English Church History 1660–1768* (Cambridge, 1959), p. 147.

P. 154, l. 11
Birch, *Tillotson,* p. 408.

P. 154, l. 32
For Lloyd see Gilbert Burnet, *History of My Own Time,* ed. Osmund Airy (London, 1897–1900), I, 337; A. Tindal Hart, *William Lloyd, 1627–1717* (London, 1952), pp. 22–23. For Burnet see Fox-

croft, *A Supplement to Burnet's History*, p. 463; Burnet, *History*, I, 335–337.

P. 155, l. 14
John Worthington, *Diary and Correspondence*, ed. James Crossley (Manchester, Chetham Society, 1947), II, Pt. 1, 142. See Jackson I. Cope, *Joseph Glanvill, Anglican Apologist* (Washington University Studies; St. Louis, 1956). Wilkins's pulpit at St. Lawrence Jewry was famous for its latitudinarianism. Anon., *Cabbala, or an Impartial Account of the Nonconformists' Private Designs*, in *Somers Tracts* (London, 1812), VII, 580.

P. 155, l. 26
Wilkins, Tillotson, Stillingfleet, Outram, and Patrick frequently discussed theology and the new philosophy in the home of painter Mary Beale. Elizabeth Walsh, "Mrs. Mary Beale, Paintress," *Connoisseur*, CXXXI (1953), 2–3; M. D. Whinney and O. Millar, *English Art, 1625–1714* (Oxford, 1957), p. 81.

P. 156, l. 7
Lloyd, *Funeral Sermon*, pp. 44–45.

P. 156, l. 14
Abraham Hill, "Some Account of the Life of Isaac Barrow," *The Works of Isaac Barrow*, ed. John Tillotson (London, 1687), I, unpaged.

P. 156, l. 32
Edward Fowler, *Principles and Practices of Certain Moderate Divines of the Church of England, Abusively Called Latitudinarians* (London, 1670) pp., 332–333. *Bishop Wilkins's Character of the Best Christian*, p. 6; Simon Patrick, "A Brief Account of the New Sect of Latitude Men," *Phoenix* (n.p., 1707–1708), II, 503–504. Burnet, *History*, I, 334.

P. 157, l. 8
Patrick, *Brief Account*, p. 503; *Bishop Wilkins's Character of the Best Christian*, p. 3; Wilkins, *Sermons upon Several Occasions*, pp. 335, 337.

P. 157, l. 15
Fowler, *Principles and Practices*, pp. 334–335.

P. 158, l. 3
For Wilkins's moderation see Wilkins, *Sermons upon Several Occasions*, pp. 364, 372–3, 380, 381, 386. For latitudinarian style see Fowler, *Principles and Practices*, pp. 42, 104, 116–117; Samuel Parker, *A Free and Impartial Censure of the Platonick Philosophy* (London, 1666), p. 73. See also Cope, *Glanvill*, pp. 144–166. For the Socinian charge see J. S. Clarke, *The Life of James II* (London, 1816), I, 439. See also Cope, *Glanvill*, p. 50.

P. 158, l. 11
Wilkins, *Sermons upon Several Occasions,* p. 63; Fowler, *Principles and Practices,* pp. 228-229, 239-240.

P. 158, l. 26
Wilkins, *Sermons upon Several Occasions,* pp. 77, 88, 89. See also Wilkins, *Natural Religion,* p. 205.

P. 159, l. 4
Wilkins, *Sermons upon Several Occasions,* p. 46. See also p. 57.

P. 159, l. 21
Ibid., pp. 400, 407-408; *Bishop Wilkins's Character of the Best Christian,* p. 6.

P. 160, l. 2
Wilkins, *Sermons upon Several Occasions,* pp. 77, 411, 419, 421, 452, 469. See also pp. 41, 42, 69, 409-11.

P. 160, l. 19
Fowler, *Principles and Practices,* pp. 8-9, 10. See also pp. 36-37.

*P. 160, l. 30
Wood, *Athenae,* III, 969; Patrick, *Brief Account,* pp. 500, 508. Wilkins "Thought it right and reasonable to submit himself to the powers in being, be those powers who they would, or let them be established how they would. And this making him as ready to swear allegiance to Charles II, after he was restored to the crown, as to the usurpers while they prevailed, he was charged with being various and unsteady in his principles, with having no principles at all, with Hobbism, and everything that is bad." Bridgeman, *Wigan,* III, 506 citing *Chalmer's Biographical Dictionary.*

*P. 161, l. 10
On preferments see Samuel Parker, *History of His Own Time* (London, 1727), pp. 36-37. The latitudinarians were Erastians; the dissenting ministers were still basically theocratic. On Roman Catholicism see Burnet, *History,* I, 335. Although the anti-Roman Catholic theme is weak in Wilkins's sermons, he is reported to have "often said if Dissenters were not taken in, popery would invade us." G. C. More Smith, *Extracts from the Papers of Thomas Woodcock* (Camden Miscellany, 3rd Series, London, 1907), XI, 63. Wilkins is supposed to have said, "we must on all occasions denie to papists any libertie within our realm until they abjure that constant threat to Christian freedom, the Bishop of Rome." Walter Simon, *The Restoration Episcopate* (New York, 1965), p. 118. Simon erroneously cites Pope, *Life of Seth Ward,* p. 15. See also John Tillotson, *The Rule of Faith* (London, 1666) and John Evelyn's correspondence with Wilkins concerning it. John Evelyn, *Diary and Correspondence,* ed. William Bray (London, 1875), III, 192.

*P. 161, l. 30

W. F. Mitchell, *English Pulpit Oratory from Andrews to Tillotson* (London, 1932), pp. 334–335. It was expected that Fuller would become a bishop through the influence of Berkeley. Dean B. Lyman, *The Great Tom Fuller* (Berkeley, Calif., 1935), pp. 110, 113, 133, 153. Wilkins held the Cranford post from December 10, 1661, to March 11, 1663. Guildhall Library, MSS Bishop of London Register 1660–1675, 9631/16, f. 25; MSS 9539A, f. 4.

P. 162, l. 22

[George Berkeley], *Historical Applications and Occasional Meditations on Several Subjects* (London, 1667), pp. 7, 61, 92–93. See also pp. 57, 97, 100.

*P. 162, l. 35

Pope, *Life of Seth Ward*, p. 55. Baxter erroneously suggested that Wilkins was chosen by the parishioners. *Reliquiae Baxterianae* (London, 1696), Part II, 437. He was presented by the King and formally confirmed by the vestry April 9, 1662. Guildhall Library, MSS St. Lawrence Jewry, Vestry Minutes 1656–1668, 2590, I, 553. Between 1294 and 1660 the right of presentation belonged to Balliol College. The vestry, however, had sometimes leased this right from the college. Whatever the legalities the King presented Reynolds, Ward, and Wilkins. Francis Bumpus, *London Churches Ancient and Modern* (London, n.d.), I, 329; Newcourt, *Repertoriam*, I, 385. When Wilkins assumed the post, they raised the salary from £150 to £180. Guildhall Library, MSS St. Lawrence Jewry, Churchwardens Accounts 1640–1697, 2593, fols. 384, 385, 369, 414.

P. 163, l. 15

Pope, *Life of Seth Ward*, p. 149. Anon., *Cabbala*, in *Somers Tracts*, VII, 580. For Baxter's role see Baxter, *Reliquiae Baxterianae*, II, 437; Pope, *Life of Seth Ward*, pp. 148–152.

*P. 164, l. 14

On Wilkins's influence see Louis G. Locke, *Tillotson: A Study in Seventeenth Century Literature* (Copenhagen, 1954), pp. 62, 113, 130; Burnet, *History*, I, 339; Birch, *Tillotson*, pp. 21–22. Several of Tillotson's biographers have concluded that Wilkins was responsible for Tillotson's appointment as Tuesday lecturer at St. Lawrence. Locke, *Tillotson*, p. 21; F. H., *Tillotson*, p. 21. The evidence does not fully warrant this conclusion. Tillotson began lecturing at St. Lawrence before it was known that Wilkins would become vicar. For the comparison see Gilbert Burnet, "A Sermon Preached at the Funeral of John Tillotson," *Funeral Sermons by Eminent English Divines, 1650–1760*, ed. J. P. Wood (London, 1831), pp. 325–326. On Hooke's suggestion see Crowther, *Founders*, p. 219. See also *The Moderate Man, the Best Subject in Church and State Proved from Arguments of Wilkins . . . with Archbishop Tillotson on the Same Subject* (London, 1712). Tillotson married Elizabeth French, Wilkins's step-daughter, on February 23, 1664. Wilkins performed the ceremony. There is a story, perhaps apocryphal, that she initially refused him and that Wilkins told her, "You shall have him Betty, for he is the best polemical divine in England." Locke, *Tillotson*, p. 21. Little is known about her except that she concocted home remedies which she frequently communicated to Robert Hooke. Crowther, *Founders*, p. 219.

P. 164, l. 23

Pepys, *Diary*, IV, 330; see also I, 272. Lawrence Echard, *The History of England* (3rd ed., London, 1720), p. 886. Wilkins, *Sermons upon Several Occasions*, Preface by Tillotson; Wood, *Athenae*, III, 968; Lloyd, *Funeral Sermon*, p. 39.

P. 165, l. 2

Wilkins, *Sermons upon Several Occasions*, pp. 231, 305, 309, 321, 323.

P. 165, l. 8

Pepys, *Diary*, III, 29; see also IV, 31.

P. 165, l. 14

Guildhall Library, MSS St. Lawrence Jewry, Churchwardens Accounts, 2593, fols. 397, 413, 427.

P. 165, l. 25

W. G. Bell, *The Great Fire of London* (London, 1920), p. 96.

P. 165, l. 35

For his papers see W. Derham, ed., *Philosophical Letters Between . . . John Ray and Several Correspondents* (London, 1718), p. 336. Pope, *Life of Seth Ward*, pp. 55–56. John Wallis thought it unlikely that Wilkins lost all his papers, because the fire took several days to reach his house. *Defense of the Royal Society* (London, 1678), pp. 11–12. For the effect of the fire on the progress of his universal character, see p. 213. For Baxter's comment see Baxter, *Reliquiae Baxterianae*, Part III, 16.

P. 166, l. 16

On scarcity of livings see Worthington, *Diary and Correspondence*, II, Pt. II, 285. On salary see Guildhall Library, MSS St. Lawrence Jewry, Vestry Minutes, 2590, I, 592, 593, 594.

P. 166, l. 31

Wilkins, *Sermons upon Several Occasions*, pp. 350, 351.

P. 167, l. 12

Ibid., pp. 330–333, 337–338, 342, 345, 348. Many conforming city magistrates were not very sympathetic to the establishment.

*P. 167, l. 28

On Wadham relations see Wadham College, MSS Garsington Oxon, 73/6A–6D. On Cromwell relationship see Pope, *Life of Seth Ward*, p. 56. Despite danger to himself, Wilkins was willing to aid Richard Cromwell in 1666. Richard had asked Wilkins to intervene with Clarendon to have his name removed from a recently issued proclamation recalling Englishmen, particularly those with republican associations, to their homeland. Cromwell's servant testified that Richard held "no correspondence with fanatics, nor with the King of France nor States of Holland" and indicated that, "to avoid suspicion," his master was "going by Dr. Wilkins' advice into Italy or Spain." *C.S.P.D., 1665–1666*, p. 299. See also James Waylen, *The House of Cromwell* (London, 1891), pp. 15–17. It was feared that English exiles abroad might conspire with the Dutch. Cromwell did not wish to return because his debts "would ruin him." Cromwell was considered dangerous by the government as late as 1671. David Ogg, *England in the Reign of Charles II* (2nd ed., Oxford, 1955–56), I, 210. On Sheldon see Pope, *Life of Seth Ward*, p. 56.

*P. 168, l. 4

On Ward's concern see Pope, *Life of Seth Ward*, p. 56. On Polebrooke see Wood, *Athenae*, II, 961. The benefice, which was in the gift of the bishop of Peterborough, had already been promised to a relative of the bishop of London, however, and it was necessary for Ward to convince him that the post should go to Wilkins. The bishops then requested that Archbishop Sheldon ask the bishop of Peterborough to present the place to Wilkins instead. The archbishop wrote, "I find [the bishop of London] is rather willing to provide a Distressed London Minister with one Living than furnish a relation of his own with a Plurality." He therefore added that it was his request as well as that of the bishops of London and Exeter "that yr. Ld would be pleased to bestow that Living upon Dr. Wilkins, the Dean of Rippon, whose worth and . . . condition as I doubt but they will plead. . . ." Bodleian Library, Additional MSS, C, 308, f. 69. Sheldon apparently was not ready to plead Wilkins's "worth" himself but was willing to comply with Ward's desire. The Polebrooke living made Wilkins a pluralist, and he had to petition the archbishop for dispensation to hold both St. Lawrence and Polebrooke. Lambeth Palace, MSS Act Book, Archbishop of Canterbury, II, 29. On Wilkins's attitude see Worthington, *Diary and Correspondence*, II, Pt. II, 227.

P. 168, l. 15

Thomas Birch, *History of the Royal Society*, (London, 1756), III, 128. November 27, 1666.

P. 168, l. 28

C.S.P.D., 1668–1669, p. 54; Le Neve, *Fasti ecclesiae Anglicanae* (London, 1716), p. 88. *Book of the Valuations of all the Ecclesiastical Preferments in England and Wales* (n.p., 1680), p. 45. Despite the fact that Wilkins was entitled to the canonry by ancient statute, it was initially given to someone else. C.S.P.D., 1667, p. 258. See also C.S.P.D., 1668, pp. 54, 76. On visits see Kennet, *Register and Chronicle*, p. 314; Birch, *Royal Society*, II, 192. It is unlikely that Wilkins returned to London before the end of October.

P. 168, l. 30

Lambeth Palace, MSS 6394, f. 644. He held the preferment from March 26, 1667, to January 12, 1669.

P. 169, l. 23

Walter Simon, "The Crown and the Episcopacy," *Colorado Studies in History*, (1961), pp. 124; Burnet, *History*, I, 464.

*P. 170, l. 9

On Buckingham and Ashley see Baxter, *Reliquiae Baxterianae*, Pt. III, 22–23; W. C. Abbot, "English Conspiracy and Dissent 1660–74," *American Historical Review*, XIV (1909), 712; Keith Feiling, *History of the Tory Party, 1640–1714* (Oxford, 1924), p. 136. It has been suggested that Buckingham had tried to obtain Wilkins's elevation to the episcopal bench from 1662. Simon, *Restoration Episcopate*, p. 21.

P. 170, l. 31

On Sheldon see Bodleian Library, Additional MSS, C. 308, f. 98v. See also fols. 77, 101. On Buckingham see Baxter, *Reliquiae Baxterianae*, Pt. III, 22; James Ralph, *The History of England* (London, 1744), I, 170. The terms of the bill are to be found in H. Thorndike, *Theological Works* (Oxford, 1854), V, 301–308.

P. 171, l. 29

Baxter, *Reliquiae Baxterianae*, Pt. III, 23. Simon, *Restoration Episcopate*, pp. 162 (citing from Barlow MSS), 163, 164. The terms are to be found in Bodleian Library, Linc. 14, 15, or in a slightly abbreviated form in Thorndike, *Works*, V, 304–306. See also Baxter, *Reliquiae Baxterianae*, Pt. III, 23–25. Wood, *Church Unity Without Uniformity;* J. W. H. Nankivell, "A Survey of the Attempts at Religious Comprehension in the Church of England, with Special Reference to the Period from the Restoration to the Revolution" (B. Litt. thesis, Oxford, n.d.) deposited at Hurd Castle.

P. 172, l. 11

On Parliament see Baxter, *Reliquiae Baxterianae*, Pt. III, 34–35. Baxter preferred Ussher's plan to one based on the King's Declaration, p. 23. On Baxter see Simon, *Restoration Episcopate,* p. 163, citing Edmund Calamy, *A Defense of Moderate Nonconformity* (London, 1704), II, 57.

P. 172, l. 21

Baxter, *Reliquiae Baxterianae,* Pt. III, 37. Roger Thomas, "Comprehension and Indulgence," *From Uniformity to Unity,* ed. G. F. Nuttall and O. Chadwick (London, 1962), p. 199.

P. 172, l. 29

Bodleian Library, MSS Linc. B. 14, 15. The indulgence scheme was worked out by Wilkins and modified by Barlow. Simon, *Restoration Episcopate,* p. 166.

P. 173, l. 8

Walter Simon, "Comprehension in the Age of Charles II," *Church History,* XXXI (1962), 443, citing Barlow MSS, xxii. Letter, Barlow to Reynolds, p. 444 citing Barlow MSS, xxv. On Hale see Burnet, *Hale,* p. 32. In 1660 Hale had introduced a bill transforming the Declaration of Breda into law.

*P. 173, l. 28

On pushing bill through see Baxter, *Reliquiae Baxterianae,* Pt. III, 34. On canvassing see Bodleian Library, Tanner MSS, 45, fols. 278, 288, 295. On party organization see John Oldmixon, *History of England During the Reigns of the Royal House of Stuart* (London, 1730), p. 544. When Sheldon found the Presbyterians had been "conspiring" with "Treacherous divines in the English church, men that liked nothing in the Church but its preferments," and had "found out their strategems," he personally reproved them for their attempt to revise ecclesiastical legislation without the consent of Convocation or their metropolitan. Sykes, *From Sheldon to Secker,* p. 81, citing Samuel Parker, *History of His Own Times* (1727), pp. 36-37. Tillotson and Wilkins were admonished by the bishop of London and the archbishop. Wood, *Athenae,* IV, 512-513. On the opposition see Burnet, *Hale,* p. 33. On the Roman Catholic issue see Baxter, *Reliquiae Baxterianae,* Pt. III, 35. Thomas has suggested that, while Owen's proposals explicitly excluded Roman Catholics, the lack of doctrinal requirements in Wilkins's proposals would have permitted their inclusion. *From Uniformity to Unity,* p. 200. For Wilkins's view see Smith, *Woodcock Extracts,* p. 67.

P. 174, l. 19

For the Commons view see Pepys, *Diary,* VII, 292. On Nicholas see Simon, *Church History,* XXXI, 445. On the bill's failure see Stoughton, *History of Religion,* III, 380; John Milward, *Diary,* ed. C. Robbins (Cambridge, 1938), p. 215.

P. 174, l. 23
Thomas, *From Uniformity to Unity,* p. 203.

P. 175, l. 15
Burnet, *Hale,* p. 33. Wood, *Athenae,* IV, 512–513. An anonymous writer noted that Wilkins "might as soon get to the Moon in one of his own Chariots as accomplish the less probable Project of union with the Dissenters." "A True and Impartial Relation," *Somers Tracts,* III, 57, 58; Lloyd, *Funeral Sermon,* p. 50; Simon, *Church History,* XXXI, 443. See also Bodleian Library, Tanner MSS, 44, f. 196.

P. 175, l. 28
On discouragement see A. G. Mathews, *Calamy Revised* (Oxford, 1934), p. 129. On healing endeavors see Edward Pearse, *Conformist's Plea* (London, 1681), p. 36. On later efforts see Baxter, *Reliquiae Baxterianae,* Pt. III, 78, 93; Nankivell, "Comprehension," pp. 167–257; Thomas, *From Uniformity to Unity,* pp. 189–253.

P. 176, l. 13
Burnet, *Hale,* pp. 31, 32, 34, 37, 38, 54, 96, 98, 101.

P. 177, l. 6
On Buckingham's character see Burnet, *History,* I, 454–455. Nevertheless, although Richard Baxter recognized that "the man was of no Religion" and "notoriously and professedly lustful," he also thought the duke was a man "of great wit and parts, and sounder Principles as the Interest of Human, and the Common good, than most Lords of the Court." Baxter, *Reliquiae Baxterianae,* Pt. III, 31. As proponent of toleration see *Ibid.,* p. 21. For Wilkins and Buckingham see *Ibid.,* p. 22; Edmund Ludlow, *Memoirs,* ed. C. H. Firth (Oxford, 1894), II, 503. For Buckingham's tract see *Short Discourse of the Reasonableness of Men's Having a Religion* (London, 1685). For "a pocky peer . . ." see *Poems on the Affairs of State: Augustan and Satirical Verse,* ed. George de F. Lord, I, 182. For Buckingham's assistance see Bodleian Library, Aubrey MSS, 13, f. 39v.

P. 177, l. 18
Pope, *Life of Seth Ward,* p. 29.

*P. 177, l. 36
On rumors see British Museum, Sloan MSS, 4278, f. 336. See also *C.S.P.D.,* 1667, p. 258. On Wilkins's selection see *C.S.P.D.,* 1667–1668, p. 603; Bodleian Library, Tanner MSS, 14, f. 37; Pope, *Life of Seth Ward,* p. 54; Burnet, *History,* I, 454–455. His competitors were said to be William Sancroft, Dean of St. Paul's and William Thomas, Dean of Worcester, Sloan MSS, f. 342; *C.S.P.D.,* 1667–

1668, p. 360; *Historical Manuscripts Commission, Twelfth Report,* Appendix, Part VII, p. 59. Although there is some indication that Sancroft may have refused the post, other sources suggested that the archbishop of Canterbury and the bishop of Hereford had tried to get the post for him but had failed. British Museum, Additional MSS, 39616, f. 119. On Buckingham aid see Burnet, *History,* I, 454-455. "Wilkins had a courage in him that could stand against a current, and against all the reproaches with which ill-natured clergymen studied to lead him. He said he was called for by the king, without any motion of his own, to be in a public station, in which he would endeavour to do all the good he could, without considerating the ill effects that it might have on himself." Lloyd, *Funeral Sermon,* p. 50.

*P. 178, l. 11

For Sancroft's view see Bodleian Library, Tanner MSS, 44, f. 37. Sancroft suggested that Sheldon was unable to prevent Wilkins's appointment. Sheldon told Wilkins, "if I could have hindered it [the Chester appointment], I would have hindered." When Wilkins wished to know the "grounds" of his opposition, Sheldon replied, "1. I look upon you as a man not well affected to the church of England. 2. You maried too near unto you know who. 3. Your parts are such that I hold Chester to bee a place to mean for your merit. Whereunto the L. elect of Chester replied thus. The first I deny & renounce, for that it was an intire mistake. As to the second, I never sought the match . . . : As for the third pretended Reason, I look upon it as a near intire perfect complement." *Ibid.,* 134 f. 50. Michael Roberts to Sheldon, July 11, 1678. Roberts was reporting a conversation with Wilkins in which Wilkins had told him about the circumstances of his elevation. Pope also indicates that Wilkins was made Bishop "not only without, but against the consent" of the archbishop. *Life of Seth Ward,* p. 57. For the administrative problems see Bodleian Library, Additional MSS, C. 308, f. 121; Lambeth Palace, MSS Act Book, Archbishop of Canterbury, II, f. 148.

*P. 179, l. 6

London Gazette, November 15, 1668; Evelyn, *Diary,* III, 517. There seems to have been some difficulty in finding someone willing to consecrate Wilkins. On displeasure of Sheldon see British Museum, Additional MSS, 39616, f. 119. On the dinner see Evelyn, *Diary,* III, 517-518. On Cosin conversation see Thomas Jackson, ed., *Life of John Howe* (London, 1839), p. 32-33. A similar story is told in connection with Morley. Morley was said to have told Wilkins that he "did not rejoice at his being a Bishop, because he was not for the Church. To which Wilkins replied, that he believed he was as much for the Church as his Lordship. He confessed indeed his opinion was for it having a larger foundation, because he apprehended the larger the foundation was the more secure the building would be that was raised on it. Whereas if the Church stood on the top of a Steeple, as some seem'd inclined to have it stand, for the sake of height, it might possibly so stand but, like a top, not without scourging." John Lewis, "Life of John Wallis," Bodleian Library, Rawlinson, C. 978, f. 47. Yet still another source indicates it was "A Saying of Dr. Wilkins" that "they had set up as a Topp on the Toe, which would not spinn or stand no longer than it was whipt by penal laws; but he would have it stand on the broad Basis, and it would stand without whipping." Smith, *Woodcock Extracts,* pp. 54–55. For Wilkins's conciliatory gestures see Lloyd, *Funeral Sermon,* p. 43.

P. 179, l. 18
These sermons were first published separately. In 1677 they were printed together as *Sermons Preached upon Several Occasions Before the King.* I have cited from the second (1680) edition. See British Museum, Harleian MSS, 5317, fols. 1–5.

P. 180, l. 4
Wilkins, *Sermons upon Several Occasions,* pp. 36, 68, 86.

P. 180, l. 26
Ibid., p. 53. For Hacket see Bodleian Library, Tanner MSS, 44, f. 196.

*P. 181, l. 8
Hill, *Society and Puritanism,* p. 327; E. H. W. Dunking, ed., *Index to the Act Books of the Archbishops of Canterbury, 1663–1850* (London, 1929), II, 152. The arrangements made concerning payment of the customary first fruits and tenths also suggest he was given special consideration. *Calendar of Treasury Books, 1600–   ,* ed. William A. Shaw (London, 1904–   ), III, Pt. I, 2, 5, 21, 33; *C.S.P.D.,* 1668–1669, pp. 74, 154–155, 190; Public Record Office State Papers, 29/254, fols. 56, 94–97. Thirty-two of the 77 Restoration bishops were permitted to retain earlier clerical livings. Simon, *Restoration Episcopacy,* p. 35. At his death Wilkins left about £700 to his widow, £200 to Wadham College and £400 to the Royal Society. Bodleian Library, Lister MSS, 34, f. 76; Somerset House, Wills, Pye 1673, f. 2.

P. 181, l. 19
On his soft interpretation see A. G. Mathews, *Calamy Revised* (Oxford, 1934), p. 129; See also W. Urwick, ed., *Historical Sketches of Nonconformity in Chester* (n.p., 1864), pp. 10, 50, 51, 64, 65, 74;

Lloyd, *Funeral Sermon*, pp. 50–51. On Presbyterians see *C.S.P.D.*, 1670, p. 335.

*P. 181, l. 26

Kennet, *Register and Chronicle*, p. 918; Dr. Williams Library, MSS Baxter Letters, III, f. 122. Rawlet told Richard Baxter, "I have had much Discourse both with the Bp & Dr. Tillotson about Conformity . . . they are both very earnest for it, that it may without any violence to the words or any evacuating the end of the law, bee interpreted such endeavours as tend to Disturb the Peace of the Church or State. . . ." Rawlet objected to their "terms" of conformity but said, "but if this might indeed bee so interpreted, one of my greatest objections agt. subscribing were removed. This I remember the Bp added in his discourse with mee, that as all peaceable endeavours after such alterations as might tend to the interest of religion, hee lookt upon himself so little disobliged from them by subscription or declaration, that hee both already had, and should still use them as hee had opportunity." *Ibid.*

P. 182, l. 6

Adam Martindale, *The Life of Adam Martindale*, ed. Richard Parkinson (Manchester, Chetham Society, 1845), p. 196.

P. 182, l. 27

On the lecturer see Samuel Palmer, ed., *Nonconformist Memorials* (London, 1802–1803), II, 90. On Tilsley see Oliver Heywood, *Autobiography, Diaries, Anecdotes and Event Books,* ed. J. H. Turner (Brighouse, England, 1881–1885), I, 87; *C.S.P.D.*, 1670, p. 335; *H.M.C., Report Fourteen*, Pt. IV, p. 93; Dr. Williams Library, MSS Baxter Letters, III, f. 122. On evasions see Kennet, *Register and Chronicle*, pp. 818–819; C. E. Whiting, *Studies in English Puritanism* (London, 1931), pp. 34, 35, 36.

P. 183, l. 4

John Lowe, "The Case of Hindley Chapel, 1641–1698," *Trans. Lancashire and Cheshire Antiquarian Society*, L (1957), 69; W. B. Shaw, *The Story of Presbyterianism in Wigan* (London, 1912), pp. 38–39, 41; Dr. Williams Library, MSS Baxter Letters, III, f. 121; Cheshire Record Office, MSS Bishop of Chester, Register, III, 57, 58; A. J. Hawkes, *Sir Roger Bradshaugh 1628–1684* (Manchester, 1945), p. 19.

P. 183, l. 21

On Chester dissent see F. Bate, *The Declaration of Indulgence 1672* (London, 1908), p. 103. On the Wilkins appointment see Simon, *Restoration Episcopacy*, p. 152, citing D. Neal, *History of the Puritans* (London, 1754), II, 123. On relations with Wilkins see Heywood, *Autobiography*, pp. 258, 268, 286; R. Parkinson, ed., *The*

Autobiography of Henry Newcombe (Manchester, Chetham Society, 1852), I, 179, II, 202; A. H. Drysdale, *History of the Presbyterians in England* (London, 1889), p. 333; R. Halley, *Lancashire, Its Puritanism and Nonconformity* (Manchester, 1899), I, 151; Angier, *Life*, p. 102. On hostility see Dr. Williams Library, MSS Baxter Letters, III, f. 122. See also Lloyd, *Funeral Sermon*, p. 46.

P. 183, l. 31
Dr. Williams Library, MSS Baxter Letters III, f. 279; J. Booker, *A History of the Ancient Chapels in Manchester Parish* (Manchester, Chetham Society, 1857), p. 88; F. R. Raines, *Rectors of Manchester* (Manchester, 1885), pp. 139–143; Bridgeman, *Wigan*, III, 580.

P. 184, l. 4
Bodleian Library, Additional MSS, C. 308, fols. 126v, 127v; British Museum, 7377, f. 42v.

P. 184, l. 14
Dr. Williams Library, MSS Baxter Letters, I, 68; C. E. Raven, *John Ray, Naturalist* (Cambridge, 1942), pp. 149, 164, 166; Palmer, *Nonconformist Memorials*, I, 214.

*P. 184, l. 26
On Tillotson see Dr. Williams Library, MSS Baxter Letters, I, 68, 69. Tillotson was acting in some official capacity in 1670 and 1671. He instituted several clergymen to benefices. Cheshire Record Office, Diocese of Chester, Act Book, *passim*. On Pope see Cheshire Record Office, Bishop of Chester, Register, III, 61–62, 88. On Bury see Anon., *History of the Cathedral Church at Chester* (London, 1793), p. 92.

P. 184, l. 34
Worthington, *Diary and Correspondence*, II, Pt. II, 132, 134, 305, 305–306, 307, 309–310, 317.

P. 185, l. 12
A Sermon Preached at the Funeral of Benjamin Whichcote (London, 1683), p. 25; Hughes, *St. Lawrence Jewry, Register*, I, 102; W. C. De Pauley, *The Candle of the Lord* (London, 1937), pp. 5–36.

P. 185, l. 28
Pepys, *Diary*, VII, 243; Historical Manuscript Commission, *Eleventh Report*, p. 531.

P. 186, l. 4
Dr. Williams Library, MSS Baxter Letters, I, 68; III, 121; N. Crew, *Memoirs*, ed. A. Clark (Camden Miscellany, LX, 1893), pp. 11–12; John Macgrath, ed., *Flemings in Oxford—Being Select Documents of Oxford Men, 1650–1700* (Oxford, 1904–24), I, 188–189.

P. 187, l. 9
Andrew Marvell, *Poems and Letters,* ed. H. M. Margoliouth (Oxford, 1927), II, 301, 307.

P. 187, l. 22
F. R. Harris, *Life of Edward Montague, Earl of Sandwich* (London, 1912), II, 324, 325. See also Marvell, *Poems and Letters,* II, 301, 302.

*P. 188, l. 6
Marvell, *Poems and Letters,* II, 301; Harris, *Life of Montague,* II, 318–319. Cosin and Wilkins each spoke twice. They were the only bishops on the committee to study the bill. *Lords Journal,* XII, 316. Ludlow thought that Wilkins was the only bishop who was seriously in favor of the bill. *Memoirs,* II, 503. See also P. H. Osmond, *A Life of John Cosin* (London, 1913), p. 293. For Wilkins's arguments see Burnet, *History,* I, 471n; Harris *Life of Montague,* II, 302.

*P. 188, l. 17
Bishop Hacket writing to Archbishop Sheldon, while excusing Cosin's performance, condemned Wilkins and said, "For his brother in evil, Chester, I make no reckoning of him and never look for any good from him." Bodleian Library, Tanner MSS, 44, f. 196. Another critic excused Cosin who was "doted through age," but Wilkins was branded for his efforts as a "reputed Socinian." J. S. Clarke, *The Life of James II* (London, 1816), I, 439. Morley indicated to Sheldon that he had no hope that Wilkins "will ever do any good at all in the Church." Quoted in E. Cardwell, *A History of Conferences Connected with the Revision of the Book of Common Prayer* (Oxford, 1849), p. 395n.

*P. 189, l. 1
Burnet, *History,* I, 493–495. Wilkins, however, replied to the king, "he thought it an ill thing both in conscience and policy: therefore, both as he was an Englishman and a bishop, he was bound to oppose it." When Charles tried to convince Wilkins that he should at least stay away from the House while the bill was pending, Wilkins replied "by the law and constitution of England, and by his majesty's favour, he had a right to debate and vote: and he was neither afraid nor ashamed to own his opinion in that matter, and to act pursuant to it." *Ibid.,* p. 494.

P. 189, l. 11
Philip Henry, *Diaries and Letters,* ed. M. H. Lee (London, 1882), p. 220; *Lords Journal,* XII, 334, 335, 338.

P. 191, l. 11
John Wallis, *A Defense of the Royal Society* (London, 1678), p. 8.

P. 192, l. 25

The Record of the Royal Society (London, 1940), p. 7. Scientific organization was a topic of general discussion. In March 1660 there were rumors of a scientific society sponsored by members of nobility. British Museum, Stowe MSS, f. 101v. On Moray see John Aubrey, *Brief Lives*, ed. O. L. Dick (Ann Arbor, Michigan, 1957), p. 212. On organization see Charles R. Weld, *A History of the Royal Society* (London, 1848), I, 68–70; Thomas Birch, *The History of the Royal Society* (London, 1756), I, 7.

P. 193, l. 11

Thomas Sprat, *History of the Royal Society of London*, ed. J. I. Cope and H. W. Jones (St. Louis, Missouri, 1958), pp. 34, 91. See also pp. 33, 82, 104–106, 347. Weld, *Royal Society*, I, 218. See also H. G. Lyons, *The Royal Society, 1660–1940* (Cambridge, 1944), pp. 41–42.

P. 193, l. 18

Sprat, *History of the Royal Society*, pp. 57, 63, 64. Oldenburg noted in May 1666, "In time, I hope, all nations, however little civilized, will join hands as loving friends, and combine both their intellectual and their economic resources in order to banish ignorance and inaugurate the rule of the true and useful philosophy." Oldenburg, *Correspondence*, III, 129–130.

P. 193, l. 29

Samuel Pepys, *Diary*, ed. Henry B. Wheatley (London, 1893), VII, 193–196. John Evelyn, *Diary*, ed. E. S. De Beer (London, 1955), III, 369–370, 526.

*P. 194, l. 5

Dorothy Stimson, "Dr. Wilkins and the Royal Society," *Journal of Modern History*, III (1931), p. 551. Miss Stimson has also shown that during the time Wilkins attended meetings, he proposed a majority of the candidates for membership. Actually he may not have been quite so influential in determining membership as she indicates, for the secretary was required "to give notice of the Candidates propounded in order to Election." Sprat, *History of the Royal Society*, p. 146. He may thus have been performing a purely formal function.

P. 194, l. 29

Birch, *Royal Society*, I, 373, 445, 496; II, 206.

P. 195, l. 2

Ibid., II, 65–66. See also I, 391, 408; II, 76; Boyle, *Works*, V, 332.

P. 195, l. 8
Birch, *Royal Society*, II, 194, 194n. Lyons, *Royal Society*, p. 66; Boyle, *Works*, V, 381. Oldenburg indicated that he and Wilkins were among the "principal beggars."

P. 195, l. 29
On Chelsea see Birch, *Royal Society*, II, 234, 238, 239, 275, 282, 289–291, 301, 302; Weld, *Royal Society*, p. 211. On Wilkins's bequest see Somerset House MSS, Wills, 1673 Pye, f. 2; H. G. Lyons, "The Society's First Bequest," *Royal Society Notes and Records*, II (1939), 43–46.

P. 196, l. 19
On breadth of interests see Stimson, *Journal of Modern History*, III, 539–564. On astronomy see British Museum, Sloane MSS, 1326, f. 41. On comets see Birch, *Royal Society*, II, 47. On weather prediction see *Ibid.*, I, 300, 305, 310; Royal Society MSS, Early Letters, W. III, 4. On microscopic studies see Birch, *Royal Society*, I, 342, 348.

P. 196, l. 31
Birch, *Royal Society*, I, 36, 82, 132, 272; Evelyn, *Diary*, III, 292. Wilkins also attempted to raise weights with explosives. Birch, *Royal Society*, I, 292–293, 295, 299.

P. 197, l. 10
Boyle, *Works*, V, 307; Birch, *Royal Society*, I, 31, 41, 46, 50, 70, 114, 118, 153, 172, 213, 384, 424, 425; John Wilkins, *Essay Towards a Real Character and a Philosophical Language* (London, 1668), pp. 191–192.

P. 197, l. 29
Birch, *Royal Society*, I, 67, 68, 84, 117, 173, 207, 213, 425; Nehemiah Grew, *Musaeum regalis societatis* (London, 1681), p. 359.

P. 198, l. 7
Birch, *Royal Society*, I, 22, 84, 213, 237, 267, 270; II, 90.

P. 198, l. 13
Ibid., I, 292, 303, 304, 320, 328, 445.

P. 198, l. 32
Ibid., I, 48, 50, 53; II, 186. Pepys, *Diary*, VII, 192–193. Weld, *Royal Society*, p. 221. See also Boyle, *Works*, V, 372.

P. 199, l. 9
Birch, *Royal Society*, I, 394, 425, 462, 475, 478, 483; II, 143. Royal Society, MSS Early Letters, P. I, 44, 45.

P. 199, l. 21
Birch, *Royal Society*, I, 126, 131, 216, 324, 327, 332, 334, 343, 406; Grew, *Musaeum, passim*.

P. 200, l. 9
Pepys, *Diary*, IV, 379, 380. Birch, *Royal Society*, II, 60. Boyle, *Works*, V, 543, 544, 545. Evelyn, *Diary*, III, 416.

P. 200, l. 13
Royal Society, MSS Early Letters, I, 11, 14.

P. 201, l. 4
R. W. T. Gunther, *Early Science in Oxford* (London, 1920–1945), I, 231. Robert Hooke, *Micrographia*, Vol. 13 in Gunther, *Early Science in Oxford*, unpaged preface.

P. 201, l. 25
Birch, *Royal Society*, II, 99, 166; Pepys *Diary*, V, 183–184, 190. See also Robert K. Merton, "Science, Technology and Society in Seventeenth Century England," *Osiris*, IV (1938), 542, 543.

P. 202, l. 11
Birch, *Royal Society*, II, 355, 398, 413, 470; III, 16–17, 42, 47, 48–49; Royal Society, MSS Early Letters, O. 2, 43; QR. 13; Bodleian Library, Lister MSS, 34, f. 59.

P. 202, l. 17
British Museum, Sloane MSS, 1008, f. 194.

P. 202, l. 35
Anthony Wood, *Athenae Oxoniensis*, ed. Phillip Bliss (London, 1813–1820), III, 967. Christian Huygens, *Oeuvres complètes*, publ. par la Société Hollandaise des Sciences (La Haye, 1888–1950), II, 295; VII, 12.

P. 203, l. 9
Birch, *Royal Society*, I, 403, 421; II, 65, 350; III, 16, 17. British Museum, Sloane MSS, 1326, f. 39–39v. Evelyn, *Diary*, III, 340.

P. 203, l. 21
Birch, *Royal Society*, I, 85.

P. 203, l. 30
C. L. Sonnichsen, "The Life and Works of Thomas Sprat" (unpubl. Ph.D. diss., Harvard, 1931), p. 64. See also p. 95.

*P. 204, l. 10
Sprat, *History of the Royal Society* (London, 1667), p. 94. Birch, *Royal Society*, I, 507; II, 161, 163, 171; III, 2, 6, 7, 47, 138, 161, 171, 197. That Sprat wrote under Wilkins's supervision is now widely recognized. See Sonnichsen, "Sprat," *passim;* F. R. Johnson, "Gresham College; Precurser of the Royal Society," *Journal of the History of Ideas*, I (1940), 416; Francis Christianson, "John Wilkins and the Royal Society Reform of Prose Style," *Modern Language Quarterly*, VII (1946), 179–187. Purver has emphasized that ultimate supervision and control remained in the hands of the Society, especially its

Council. See *Royal Society,* pp. 1–19. She also substantiates Wilkins's role. See also Oldenburg, *Correspondence,* II, 560.

P. 204, l. 22
Birch, *Royal Society,* II, 249.

P. 205, l. 1
Purver, *Royal Society, passim.*

P. 206, l. 28
Sprat, *History of the Royal Society,* pp. 62, 112, 113; Wilkins, *Real Character,* pp. 17, 18; On Sprat's style see Sonnichsen, "Sprat," pp. 65, 203, 205, 209, 267.

P. 207, l. 3
Christianson, *Modern Language Quarterly,* VII, 280. Birch, *Royal Society,* I, 499; II, 7.

P. 207, l. 31
Jonathan Cohen, "On the Project of a Universal Character," *Mind,* LXIII (1954), 49–63; Benjamin De Mott, "Comenius and the Real Character in England," *P.M.L.A.,* LXX (1955), 1068–1081.

*P. 208, l. 4
See Wood, *Athenae,* III, 372; "An Abstract of Dr. Wilkins' Essay Towards a Real Character and a Philosophical Language," in Wilkins, *Mathematical and Philosophical Works* (London, 1708), pp. 171–174; Otto Funke, "On the Sources of John Wilkins' Philosophical Language," *English Studies,* XL (1959), 208–214; Otto Funke, *Zum Weltsprachenproblem in England um 17. Jahrhundert* (Heidelberg, 1929), pp. 5–54; George Dalgarno, *Ars signorum* (London, 1661).

*P. 208, l. 18
William Petty, *Advice of W. P. to Mr. Samuel Hartlib* (London, 1647), p. 5; Thomas Birch, *Life of the Honourable Robert Boyle* (London, 1744), p. 73; John Amos Comenius, *The Way of Light,* trans. E. T. Campagnac (London, 1938). Comenius, like Descartes, insisted that the creation of such a language must await the true philosophy (pp. 192, 219, 220). Unlike Wilkins or Dalgarno, he wanted the language to be the "richest and most copious" of all languages (pp. 183, 192).

P. 208, l. 34
Benjamin De Mott, "The Sources and Development of John Wilkins' Philosophical Language," *Journal of English and Germanic Philology,* VII (1958), 8–9; Wallis, *Defense of the Royal Society,* p. 46; Walter Charleton, *The Immortality of the Humane Soul* (London, 1657), p. 46.

P. 209, l. 24
Wilkins, *Real Character,* To the Reader; [Joh]N. [Wilkin]S. and

[Set]H. [War]D., *Vindiciae academiarum* (London, 1654), pp. 21, 22, 24–25.

*P. 210, l. 28

Charleton, *Immortality of the Soul*, pp. 45–46; Wilkins, *Real Character*, To the Reader; Wallis, *Defense of the Royal Society*, p. 17. About the origins of the efforts we know less. In 1654 Ward noted, "I know one in this University, who hath attempted something this way and undertakes as farre as the tradition of reall Learning, by which I understand the Mathematicks, and Naturall Philosophy, and the grounds of Physick" (*Vindiciae academiarum*, p. 22). It is not clear whom he meant. Wilkins had not yet become seriously involved. Nor had Dalgarno, who in any event would not have been considered a member of the university. He may have referred to Petty or perhaps even himself.

*P. 211, l. 13

Robert Plot suggests that Dalgarno first showed his work to Wilkins about 1656. *The Natural History of Oxfordshire* (Oxford, 1677), p. 283. Cave Beck, *The Universal Character* (London, 1657). British Museum, Sloane MSS, 4377, f. 148. April, 1657.

P. 211, l. 30

Boyle, *Works*, V, 269; Wilkins, *Real Character*, To the Reader.

P. 212, l. 12

Robert Vaughan, *The Protectorate of Oliver Cromwell* (London, 1838), II, 435; G. S. Turnbull, "Samuel Hartlib's Influence on the Early History of the Royal Society," *Royal Society Notes and Records*, X (1953), 119; Boyle, *Works*, V, 269, 271.

P. 212, l. 23

"News to the Whole World of the Discovery of an Universal Language," Sloane MSS, 4377, f. 143. This was composed at Hartlib's house. "A New Discovery of the Universal Character," Sloane MSS, 4377, fols. 146v, 166v.

P. 212, l. 31

Wallis, *Defense of the Royal Society*, p. 16; John Owen, *Of the Divine Original* (London, 1659), p. 277; Turnbull, *R. S. Notes and Records*, X, 119.

P. 213, l. 10

For letter to Hartlib see Turnbull, *R. S. Notes and Records*, X, 119n. For Wilkins's encouragement see Plot, *Oxfordshire*, p. 283; Dalgarno, *Ars signorum*, Introductory Letter by William Morrice and Preface.

P. 213, l. 20

Wallis, *Defense of the Royal Society*, pp. 16, 17. Wilkins's efforts were widely known by 1663 when a doggerel verse was circulated:

A Doctor counted very able
Designs that all Mankind shall,
Spite o' th' confusion made att Babell
By Character call'd Universall.
How long this Character will be learning
That truly passeth my discerning.

Cited in Stimson, *Isis,* XVIII (1932), 103–117.

*P. *214, l. 4*

On assistance see Pepys, *Diary,* V, 183–184; Wilkins, *Real Character,*
Dedicatory Letter. Wilkins indicated that only one copy of Book I
survived and that the manuscript copy and Book II, as well as the
Dictionary from the letter *R* on, also in the hands of the printer,
were destroyed. *Philosophical Letters . . . Between John Ray and
Several Correspondents,* ed. W. Derham (London, 1718), p. 367. On
improvements see Derham, *Philosophical Letters,* p. 367. On indefati-
gability see William Lloyd, *A Sermon Preached at the Funeral of
John Wilkins,* (London, 1675), p. 37.

P. *216, l. 32*

On the universal language see Wilkins, *Real Character,* pp. 20–21.
For the categories see Clark Emery, "John Wilkins' Universal Language," *Isis,* XXXVIII (1948), 177, 178. For a detailed description
see *Ibid., passim.;* E. N. da C. Andrade, "The Real Character of
Bishop Wilkins," *Annals of Science,* I (1936), 4–12.

*P. *217, l. 5*

Wilkins, *Real Character,* p. 194. He recognized that alterations might
be necessary. See also p. 69.

P. *217, l. 32*

Ibid., p. 414.

P. *218, l. 11*

Ibid., Dedicatory Letter; Birch, *Royal Society,* II, 283, 315; Sprat,
History of the Royal Society, p. 251. The Society often did not receive the reports it ordered or follow up its proposed discussions and
experiments. Several members appointed to the committee were
favorably inclined toward Wilkins's scheme.

P. *218, l. 26*

Benjamin De Mott, "Science versus Mnemonics. Notes on John Ray
and on John Wilkins' 'Essay Towards a Real Character and a
Philosophical Language,'" *Isis,* XLVIII (1957), 3–12; Charles E.
Raven, *John Ray, Naturalist* (Cambridge, 1942), pp. 183, 192ff,
323–325.

P. *219, l. 9*

Pepys, *Diary,* V, 292; Wallis, *Defense of the Royal Society,* p. 17–19;
Wilkins, *Real Character,* p. 357. For Holder and Lodowyck see Wil-

kins, *Real Character,* Preface to the Reader. For Buckingham see Bodleian Library, Aubrey MSS, 13, f. 39v.

P. *219, l. 27*
Wilkins, *Real Character,* Dedicatory Letter.

*P. *220, l. 14*
Ibid. Wilkins was fully aware of the problems of adoption. Wallis, *Defense of the Royal Society,* p. 17. Huygens, *Oeuvres,* VI, 397, 425. It was thought that Wilkins's Real Character "so well pleased the King that his Majestie is resolved to make him a Bishop upon the next opportunity. . . ." Sloane MSS, 4278. Letter John Collins to John Pell, May 28, 1668. Wallis, *Defense of the Royal Society,* pp. 16, 17; Royal Society, MSS Early Letters, W. 1, 49. Wallis later told Boyle that while he did not dispute the "practical possibility" of introducing the character, which he found "very Feasible if not very Facile," but he would have preferred using traditional characters rather than Wilkins's. *Philosophical Transactions,* V (July 18, 1670), 1091-1092. For Hooke see Gunther, *Early Science in Oxford,* VIII, 150-151; Robert Hooke, *A Description of Helioscopes* (London, 1676).

P. *220, l. 22*
De Mott, *Isis,* LXIII, 3-12; Emery, *Isis,* XXVIII, 184.

*P. *220, l. 30*
Aubrey, *Brief Lives,* p. 320. Ray was expected to continue work, but he did not wish to cooperate further. The progress of Aubrey and Hooke, who were the "chiefest patrons" of Wilkins's scheme, was slow because the group could not agree on whether to improve, change, or even scrap Wilkins's work and start over. Alternative plans, such as those of Lodowyck and Dalgarno, were again bruited about, and some wished to pursue Ward's scheme based on the *Vindiciae academiarum* and his more recent ideas. Ward himself did not become very actively involved although he discussed his ideas with some of Aubrey's group. They attempted to recruit Buckingham, who had also worked on the Dictionary earlier and William Lloyd. See Royal Society, MSS Early Letters, P.I. 57; Bodleian Library, Aubrey MSS 12 and 13, *passim;* Boyle, *Works,* V, 506; Ray, *Correspondence,* 128-129; John Ray, *Further Correspondence,* ed. R. W. T. Gunther (London, 1928), pp. 90, 160-166.

P. *221, l. 3*
Ray, *Correspondence,* p. 129; Ray, *Further Correspondence,* pp. 164-165; Pepys, *Diary,* VIII, 16, 18, 30, 57, 159; *Letters and the Second Diary of Samuel Pepys,* ed. R. G. Howarth (London, 1932), p. 249; Anon., *Propositions for the Carrying a Philosophical Correspondence* (London, 1670), p. 3.

P. 221, l. 13
Isaac Newton, *The Correspondence,* ed. H. W. Turnbull (Cambridge, 1959), II, 296. See also R. W. V. Elliott, "Isaac Newton's 'Of an Universal Language'," *Modern Language Review,* LII (1957), 1–18; John Locke, *Lettres inédities,* ed. Henry Ollion and T. J. de Boer (La Haye, 1912), pp. 106–107; J. E. Spingarn, *Critical Essays of the Seventeenth Century* (Bloomington, Indiana, 1957), III, 226; Emery, *Isis,* XXXVIII, 184n.

P. 221, l. 27
On symbolic logic see Cohen, *Mind,* LXIII, 49–63. On Borelli see Stephen J. Rigaud, *Correspondence of Scientific Men of the Seventeenth Century* (Oxford, 1841), II, 518. On the Elector see Bodleian Library, Aubrey MSS, 12, unpaged. Pigot to Aubrey May 24, 1677. On translations see Ray, *Further Correspondence,* p. 163.

P. 222, l. 5
For Wotton see Spingarn, *Critical Essays,* III, 226. For Walpole see Emery, *Isis,* XXXVIII, 183n, 184n.

P. 222, l. 23
Ibid., pp. 183, 183n, 184, 184n; Andrade, *Annals of Science,* I, 7; Cohen, *Mind,* LXIII, 49–63; B. C. Vickery, "The Significance of John Wilkins in the History of Bibliographical Classification," *Libre,* II (1953), 326–343; Lancelot T. Hogben, *Dangerous Thoughts* (New York, 1940), pp. 41–43.

P. 222, l. 34
Cohen, *Mind,* LXIII, 62–63.

P. 224, l. 35
For Stevin see Lewis S. Feuer, *The Scientific Intellectual* (New York, 1963), p. 202. For Bacon see Christopher Hill, *Intellectual Origins of the English Revolution* (Oxford, 1965), p. 93 quoting letter from Bacon to Tobie Mathew, October 10, 1609.

P. 225, l. 4
Even Hill, who offers Raleigh in support of the tie between Puritanism and science (*Ibid.,* p. 22), at the same time concludes that "Ralegh . . . seems to have had the sort of tolerance born of indifference which finally triumphed in 1689" (*ibid.,* pp. 171, 172).

P. 225, l. 25
Richard S. Westfall, *Science and Religion in Seventeenth Century England* (New Haven, 1958), p. 132; C. E. Whiting, *Studies in English Puritanism from the Restoration to the Revolution, 1660–1688* (London, 1931), p. 495; Boyle, *Works,* I, 20; Erich Strauss, *Sir William Petty* (London, 1954), p. 26; William Petty, *Reflections upon some Persons and Things in Ireland* (London, 1660), p. 137;

Thomas Warton, *Life and Literary Remains of Ralph Bathurst* (London, 1761), p. 181; Anthony Wood, *Life and Times*, ed. Andrew Clark (Oxford, 1891–1900), I, 365; Mitchell S. Fisher, *Robert Boyle, Devout Naturalist* (Philadelphia, 1945), pp. 127, 140; J. P. Wood, ed., *Funeral Sermons by Eminent English Divines, 1650–1760* (London, 1831), pp. 290–292; J. C. Crowther, *Founders of British Science* (London, 1960), p. 79; M. B. Rex, *University Representation in England 1604–1690* (London, 1954), p. 187.

P. 225, l. 36

John Wallis, *The Necessity of Regeneration* (London, 1682), Preface; John Wallis, *Theological Discourses* (London, 1692), p. 6; John Wallis, "Account of Some Passages of His Own Life," *The Works of Thomas Hearne* (Oxford, 1725), III, clxix.

P. 226, l. 7

John Ray, ed., *The Ornithology of Francis Willoughby* (London, 1678), Preface; Isaac Barrow, *Works,* ed. John Tillotson (London, 1687), I, 273–274, 278; Westfall, *Science and Religion,* pp. 154, 158; P. H. Osmond, *Isaac Barrow: His Life and Times* (London, 1944), pp. 76, 78.

P. 226, l. 34

Robert Boyle, *Works,* ed. Thomas Birch (London, 1744), V, 516; S.[imon] P.[atrick], *A Brief Account of the New Sect of Latitude Men,* in *Phoenix* (London, 1707–08), II, 500, 508. T. E. S. Clarke and H. C. Foxcroft, *Life of Gilbert Burnet, Bishop of Salisbury* (Cambridge, 1907), p. 477; Richard B. Schlatter, *The Social Ideas of Religious Leaders, 1660–1688* (Oxford, 1940), pp. 52–53. Moray too was widely known for his latitudinarian sympathies. A. J. Robertson, *The Life of Sir Robert Moray* (London, 1922), p. 173; Mathew Hale, *The Works, Moral and Religious,* ed. T. Thirlwall (London, 1805), pp. 98, 136, 243. Maurice Cranston, *John Locke* (New York, 1957), p. 40. H. R. Foxbourne, *The Life of John Locke* (New York, 1876), I, 309.

P. 227, l. 16

Thomas Sprat, *The History of the Royal Society,* ed. J. I. Cope and H. W. Jones (St. Louis, 1958), pp. 33–34 .

*P. 227, l. 32

Joseph Glanvill, *Plus Ultra* (London, 1668), pp. 127–128, 147; John Wilkins, *The Principles and Duties of Natural Religion,* ed. John Tillotson (London, 1675), pp. 35–36; *The Discovery of a New World: Or, A Discourse Tending to Prove, That ('tis Probable) There May Be Another Habitable World in the Moon,* in *Mathe-*

matical and Philosophical Works (London, 1708), Preface to the Reader; Sprat, *History of the Royal Society,* pp. 54, 427. The earliest description of the latitudinarians indicated that the latitude men were "followers for the most part of the new Philosophy. . . ." S. P., *Brief Account,* pp. 500, 508.

P. 228, l. 12

Joseph Glanvill, *Essays on Several Important Subjects* (London, 1671), pp. 14, 27. See also Glanvill, *Philosophia pia* (London, 1671), pp. 89, 92; Glanvill, *Essays,* pp. 24. See B. J. Shapiro, "Latitudinarianism and Science in Seventeenth Century England," *Past and Present,* XXXIX (1968).

*P. 229, l. 12

Henry G. Van Leeuwen, *The Problem of Certainty in English Thought 1630–1690* (The Hague, 1963). Although Wilkins's most extended treatment appeared in 1675, similar arguments appeared in a sermon preached in 1660 or 1662. His views were undoubtedly known to the close circle of associates which included Tillotson, Boyle, Glanvill, and Stillingfleet who all contributed to the development and dissemination of these views. Priority thus cannot be determined solely by date of publication.

*P. 229, l. 28

Wilkins, *Natural Religion,* pp. 3–4. See also, Wilkins, *Real Character,* pp. 195–196. For Wilkins the senses were

those *faculties* whereby we are enabled to discern and know such *particular* objects as are *present.* These are either
   1. *Outward,* by which we can apprehend external *objects,* as when we see, or hear, or touch anything presented to us.
   2. *Inward,* by which we can discern *internal* objects, and are conscious to ourselves, or sensible both of the impressions that are made upon our outward *senses,* and of the inward motivations of our *minds;* namely our apprehensions, inclinations, and the power of determining ourselves, as to our own Actions; and by which we can any time be assured of what we think, or what we desire, or purpose.

(Wilkins, *Natural Religion,* pp. 3–4.) When referring to the inward sense, he refused to indicate whether these were "real faculties" and contented himself with describing common sense, memory, and appetite along the lines of common usage (John Wilkins, *Essay Towards a Real Character and a Philosophical Language* [London, 1668], p. 196). There were two aspects to understanding. "Apprehension" was the capacity to distinguish between the truth and falsehood of both general and particular propositions, to compare and elaborate propositions, and to apply general propositions to particular cases (*Ibid.*, p. 195). "Motivation," which was related to the will, enabled men to rationally approve and follow the good and reject evil. On sense and understanding see Wilkins, *Natural Religion*, p. 82. Aside from this systematic categorization of "evidence," Wilkins also sometimes lapses into the traditional categories of knowledge and wisdom. Science or knowledge "furnished the mind with the due Notions and conceptions concerning the Nature of things, their Causes, Differences, Relations and Dependencies" (Wilkins, *Real Character*, p. 205). See also John Wilkins, *Sermons Preached upon Several Occasions*, ed. John Tillotson (London, 1682), p. 171. His conception of wisdom followed the definition of Aquinas. "Not only skill in books and things, and notions, but the art of business, directing a man to what is fit and convenient in several cases and circumstances, the knowledge of human nature, of the various inclinations, tempers, interests of *men* and *times*" (*Ibid.*, p. 151). Wilkins does not explain the interrelation of knowledge and wisdom nor how either fit into his categorization of evidence. One suspects that here Wilkins simply took over traditional categories without combining them into a meaningful system.

P. 229, l. 34
Wilkins, *Natural Religion*, pp. 5, 6.

P. 230, l. 12
Ibid., pp. 7-8.

P. 231, l. 15
Ibid., pp. 9-10.

P. 231, l. 20
Ibid., pp. 10, 11.

*P. 232, l. 6
Ibid., pp. 23, 25, 27-29, 34, 37. Van Leeuwen suggests that Wilkins was not citing Aristotle directly but was quoting from Grotius, *Truth of the Christian Religion*, (*Problem of Certainty*, p. 67).

P. 232, l. 20
Ibid., pp. 30, 31.

P. 232, l. 30
Ibid., p. 31. *Natural Religion* was printed in 1675, 1678, 1683, 1699, 1704, 1710, 1715 (twice), 1722, and 1734. H. M. Lord, "A Bibliography of John Wilkins, 1612-1672" (unpubl. Library School thesis, University of London), p. 32. For influence on liberal Dutch theologians, see Phillipus van Limborch, *A Complete System or Body of Divinity . . . with Improvements from Bishop Wilkins*, ed. William Jones, 2nd ed. (London, 1713).

P. 233, l. 6
Westfall, *Science and Religion*, pp. 106-145.

P. 233, l. 27

Wilkins, *Natural Religion*, p. 40. Twelve chapters were complete at the time of his death. The remainder were edited and completed from his notes by Tillotson.

P. 234, l. 3

Ibid.

P. 234, l. 19

Ibid., pp. 41, 46, 50-51. The Hobbesian view that belief was based on fear or was merely a "device of the Statists" was rejected (p. 53).

P. 235, l. 4

Ibid., pp. 56, 57, 58.

P. 235, l. 25

Ibid., pp. 58, 60, 61, 157, 158.

P. 236, l. 5

Ibid., p. 70. He began with the proposition that the world either had a beginning or existed from eternity. If the world had begun at some given point in time, it was either created by chance or a "wise agent." A series of conventional arguments then disposes of chance creation and leaves the action, and thus the existence, of God as the only basis for a created world. Wilkins, like most advocates of natural religion, rejected the Aristotelian teachings on the eternal nature of the universe which had provided a straw man for generations.

P. 236, l. 8

Ibid., p. 78. In his early astronomical works he noted that a study of the heavens would lead men to acknowledge God and religion. Nature exhibited such "excellent contrivance" that a creating deity had to be acknowledged. The human body, animal life, even minerals and vegetables were all obviously the "contrivance of some wise Agent." The "visible things of the world" were "Witnesses of a Deity" and "plainly declared his Power and Glory" (pp. 82, 84). See also Westfall, *Science and Religion*, pp. 26-48.

P. 236, l. 24

Ibid., p. 80. See also pp. 205-206.

P. 236, l. 32

Wilkins, *Natural Religion*, p. 83.

P. 237, l. 30

John Wilkins, *Discourse Concerning a New Planet*, p. 248; Wilkins, *Discovery*, pp. 98-99. See also Wilkins, *Sermons Preached upon Several Occasions*, p. 72. Limiting miracles to Biblical times was encouraged by the joint Anglican and Puritan campaign against Roman Catholic claims to present day miracles. Paul H. Kocher,

Science and Religion in Elizabethan England (San Marino, California), pp. 104, 107. See also Wilkins, *Mercury,* p. 60.

P. 238, l. 5
  Westfall, *Science and Religion,* pp. 78–79; see also pp. 70–105.
  Kocher, *Science and Religion,* pp. 93–118.

P. 238, l. 35
  Wilkins, *Natural Religion,* pp. 133–134, 84.

P. 239, l. 29
  Ibid., pp. 138–139, 203–204.

*P. 240, l. 2
  Ibid., p. 139. He wouldn't, however, be expected to deal with the subject of grace in a work on natural theology.

P. 240, l. 17
  Ibid., pp. 82, 83, 135.

P. 240, l. 35
  Ibid., pp. 179–180, 181, 184–185.

P. 241, l. 13
  Ibid., pp. 212, 267, 268, 270, 271, 283. See also Edward Fowler, *Principles and Practices of Certain Moderate Divines* (London, 1670), pp. 11–12.

P. 241, l. 34
  Wilkins, *Natural Religion,* p. 213, 289–293; Wilkins *Sermons Preached Before the King,* 2nd ed. (London, 1680), pp. 43–44.

*P. 242, l. 20
  Wilkins, *Natural Religion,* pp. 306, 314, 330–332, 383, 384, 385; Wilkins, *Sermons Preached Before the King,* pp. 1–34. Barrow also preached on the theme that "Both temporal prosperity and eternal felicity are the wages" of piety (*Works,* I 37). See also Cranston, *Locke,* pp. 123–125. The most direct adaptation of Wilkins's is John Ray's, *Persuasive to a Holy Life* (London, 1700). Ray acknowledged that he had borrowed a good part of his "Matter" from Wilkins's *Natural Religion.*

P. 243, l. 5
  Wilkins, *Natural Religion,* pp. 394, 231, 232–233, 392.

*P. 243, l. 23
  Ibid., pp. 374, 406, 299, 407; Wilkins, *Sermons Preached upon Several Occasions,* pp. 208–209. Revelation provided "a clearer light to discover" our duties "with greater certainty, and to put beyond all doubt and dispute what is good and acceptable to the Will of God . . ." (*Natural Religion,* p. 395). See also *Ibid.,* p. 199.

P. 244, l. 5
Ibid., pp. 397, 398. Wilkins, *Sermons Preached upon Several Occasions,* pp. 209–210.

P. 245, l. 6
Bishop Wilkins' Character of the Best Christian (2nd ed., Dublin, 1759), p. 5.

P. 245, l. 28
Wilkins, *Sermons Preached upon Several Occasions,* p. 414.

P. 246, l. 17
Quoted in William Haller, *The Rise of Puritanism,* (New York, 1957), pp. 330, 198.

P. 246, l. 24
Douglas Bush, "Two Roads to Truth: Science and Religion in the Early Seventeenth Century," *E.L.H.,* VII (1941), 92.

P. 247, l. 14
Bishop Wilkins' Character of the Best Christian, p. 6.

P. 247, l. 30
For Luther's criticism see Herschel Baker, *The Dignity of Man: Studies in the Resistance of an Idea* (Cambridge, Mass., 1947), p. 269. For Erasmus see E. G. Winter, trans. and ed., *Erasmus–Luther, Discourse on Free Will* (New York, 1961), pp. 7, 101.

P. 248, l. 4
See Baker, *The Wars of Truth;* Bush, *E.L.H.,* VIII, 81–102; Bush, *Science and English Poetry* (New York, 1950); Basil Willey, *The Seventeenth Century Background* (London, 1954); B. Willey, "The Touch of the Cold Philosophy," in R. F. Jones, ed., *The Seventeenth Century: From Bacon to Pope* (Stanford, California, 1951), pp. 367–376.

P. 248, l. 18
Baker, *The Wars of Truth,* pp. 312, 317, 366.

P. 249, l. 6
Wilkins, *Natural Religion,* p. 156.

Bibliographical Note

Unfortunately for the biographer of John Wilkins, there does not appear to be any major collection of his personal papers. The Great Fire of London probably destroyed a great many. Those extant at the time of his death were left in the care of his son-in-law John Tillotson, later archbishop of Canterbury. Neither these nor Tillotson's own papers have come to light. This has meant that any assessment of Wilkins is to some extent dependent on the views of his contemporaries; and as we have noted elsewhere, his contemporaries were sharply divided as to his talent, character, and accomplishments. See p. 251, note *P. 5, l. 1.*

Wilkins's published works help to compensate for the absense of personal papers. These works cover many of the subjects that interested him, and he is rarely reticent about his personal views. His scientific writings are most conveniently found in *The Mathematical and Philosophical Works* (London, 1708). This collection includes *The Discovery of a New World; or, A Discourse Tending to Prove, That ('tis Probable) There May Be Another Habitable World in the Moon* (1638); *Discourse Concerning the Possibility of a Passage to the World in the Moon* (chapter added in 1640 to *The Discovery*); *Discourse Concerning a New Planet; Tending to Prove, that ('tis Probable) Our Earth Is One of the Planets* (1640); *Mercury; or, The Secret Messenger: Showing How a Man with Privacy and Speed Can Communicate His Thoughts to His Friend at any Distance* (1641); *Mathematical Magick: or, The Wonders that May Be Performed by Mechanical Geometry* (1648).

Those works concerned with religion include *Discourse Concerning the Beauty of Providence* (London, 1649); *Ecclesiastes: or, A Discourse of the Gift of Preaching* (London, 1646); *Discourse Concerning the Gift of Prayer* (London, 1651); *Sermons Preached upon Several Occasions* (London, 1682); *Sermons Preached upon Several Occasions Before the King* (London, 1680); *Of the Principles and Duties of Natural*

321

Religion (London, 1675). Tillotson completed the later chapters of this volume from Wilkins's manuscript notes. Wilkins was also the author of *An Essay Towards a Real Character and a Philosophical Language* (London, 1668). An Abstract is contained in *Mathematical and Philosophical Works*. Wilkins was the co-author of *Vindiciae academiarum* (Oxford, 1654). Seth Ward was the principal author of the volume, which appeared under the authorship of "N.S." and "H.D." For the various editions of Wilkins's work, see H. M. Lord, "A Bibliography of John Wilkins, 1614–1672" (unpublished Library School thesis, University of London, 1957).

Wilkins's life and activities must be reconstructed from a large variety of sources, none of which alone is of overwhelming importance. The most useful diaries and collections of letters and comment proved to be John Aubrey, *Brief Lives* (ed. Andrew Clark, Oxford, 1898); John Evelyn, *Diary* (ed. E. S. de Beer, 6 vols., Oxford, 1955); John Evelyn, *Diary and Correspondence* (ed. William Bray, 4 vols., London, 1875); Samuel Pepys, *The Diary* (ed. H. B. Wheatley, 9 vols., New York, 1893); Thomas Barlow, *The Genuine Remains* (London, 1693); Richard Baxter, *Reliquiae Baxterianae* (London, 1696); Anon., *Bishop Wilkins's Character of the Best Christian* (2nd ed., Dublin, 1759); Robert Boyle, *The Works of Robert Boyle* (ed. Thomas Birch, 5 vols., London, 1744); Gilbert Burnet, *History of My Own Time* (ed. Osmond Airy, 2 vols., Oxford, 1897–1900); Edward Fowler, *Principles and Practices of Certain Moderate Divines* (London, 1670); William Lloyd, *A Sermon Preached at the Funeral of John Wilkins* (London, 1675); *The Moderate Man, the Best Subject in Church and State, Proved from the Argument of Wilkins* (London, 1712); Walter Pope, *Life of Seth Ward, Bishop of Salisbury* (ed. J. B. Banborough, Oxford, 1961). Grant McColley's numerous articles on Wilkins are cited where the topics they deal with are discussed. The most valuable source materials for the period at Oxford were Anthony Wood, *History and Antiquities of the University of Oxford* (ed. J. Gutch, 4 vols., Oxford, 1672–1796); *The Life and Times of Anthony Wood* (ed. A. Clark, 5 vols., Oxford, 1891–1900); Montagu Burrows, ed., *The Registers of the Visitors of the University of Oxford from A.D. 1647 to A.D. 1658* (Camden Society, 1881); Walter Charleton, *The Immortality of the Humane Soul* (London, 1657). The most valuable materials on the Royal Society were Thomas Birch, *History of the Royal Society of London* (4 vols., London, 1756). Thomas Sprat's *History of the Royal*

Society of London (London, 1667), of which Wilkins was something less than co-author and something more than supervising editor, reflects both the events and the personalities connected with the founding of the society and Wilkins's attitude toward them. Earlier biographical accounts of Wilkins are to be found in the *D.N.B.;* Aubrey, *Brief Lives;* Anthony Wood, *Athenae Oxoniensis* (ed. P. Bliss, 4 vols., London, 1813–1820); P. A. Wright-Henderson, *The Life and Times of John Wilkins* (Edinburgh, 1910); Dorothy Stimson, "Dr. Wilkins and the Royal Society," *Journal of Modern History,* III (1931), 539–564; and the life included in Wilkins's *Mathematical and Philosophical Works,* which may have been the work of Thomas Sprat.

Among the more useful surveys or interpretations of the changing intellectual environment of the seventeenth century are Herschel Baker, *The Wars of Truth* (Cambridge, Mass., 1947); Basil Willey, *The Seventeenth Century Background* (London, 1954); R. F. Jones, *Ancients and Moderns: A Study in the Background of the "Battle of the Books"* (rev. ed., St. Louis, 1961); R. F. Jones (ed.), *The Seventeenth Century: Studies in the History of English Thought and Literature from Bacon to Pope* (Stanford, Calif, 1951); Christopher Hill, *Intellectual Origins of the English Revolution* (Oxford, 1965); Robert K. Merton, "Science Technology and Society in Seventeenth Century England," *Osiris,* IV (1938), 360–632; Henry G. Van Leeuwen, *The Problem of Certainty in English Thought, 1630–1690* (The Hague, 1963); W. K. Jordan, *The Development of Religious Toleration in England* (4 vols., Cambridge, Mass., 1932–40); R. S. Westfall, *Science and Religion in Seventeenth Century England* (New Haven, 1958); Alexander Koyré, *From the Closed World to the Infinite Universe* (Baltimore, 1957); Walter Simon, *The Restoration Episcopate* (New York, 1965); Dorothy Stimson, *The Gradual Acceptance of the Copernican Theory of the Universe* (New York, 1917); Norman Sykes, *From Sheldon to Secker: Aspects of English Church History 1660–1768* (Cambridge, 1959); F. R. Johnson, *Astronomical Thought in Renaissance England* (Baltimore, 1937); Jackson Cope, *Joseph Glanvill, Anglican Apologist* (St. Louis, 1956).

For special problems such as the relationship of Puritanism to the development of science or the creation of a universal language the reader should consult the notes to chapters where such topics are discussed.

Index